A thrilling and suspenseful novel
in the tradition of
Dinner at Antoine's

Lady Laura Whitford—Her elegant façade concealed secrets too brittle to be touched.

Jacques de Valcourt—The suave aristocrat dabbled in love, libation . . . and poison.

Baldwin Castle—The Ambassador's roving youth had planted seeds of hate at home and abroad, and on both sides of the footlights lurked relics from his past.

Janice Lester—The brilliant actress had a long memory, a short temper, and a fatal allure.

Another distinguished best seller in the company of such outstanding Keyes successes as *Came a Cavalier*, *Steamboat Gothic*, and *Blue Camellia*, THE ROYAL BOX is rated among her best by readers and reviewers alike. To date the ever-growing number of Keyes fans have bought over one and a half million copies of THE ROYAL BOX.

THE ROYAL BOX
was originally published by
Julian Messner, Inc.

Books by Frances Parkinson Keyes

Fiction

All That Glitters*
Also the Hills
Blue Camellia*
Came a Cavalier*
The Career of David Noble
Crescent Carnival*
Dinner at Antoine's*
Fielding's Folly
The Great Tradition*
Honor Bright*
Joy Street*
Lady Blanche Farm
The Old Gray Homestead
Parts Unknown
Queen Anne's Lace
The River Road
The Royal Box*
The Safe Bridge
Senator Marlowe's Daughter

Nonfiction

Along a Little Way
Capital Kaleidoscope
The Grace of Guadalupe
Letters from a Senator's Wife
Silver Seas and Golden Cities
The Sublime Shepherdess: The Life of St. Bernadette of Lourdes
Written in Heaven: The Life of the Little Flower of Lisieux

Poetry

The Happy Wanderer

Juvenile

Once on Esplanade

*Published by POCKET BOOKS

Frances Parkinson Keyes

THE ROYAL BOX

PUBLISHED BY POCKET BOOKS NEW YORK

THE ROYAL BOX

Julian Messner edition published 1954

POCKET BOOK edition published May, 1975

L

This POCKET BOOK edition includes every word contained in the original, higher-priced edition. It is printed from brand-new plates made from completely reset, clear, easy-to-read type. POCKET BOOK editions are published by POCKET BOOKS, a division of Simon & Schuster, Inc., 630 Fifth Avenue, New York, N.Y. 10020. Trademarks registered in the United States and other countries.

Standard Book Number: 671-78897-3.
Library of Congress Catalog Card Number: 54-6770.
This POCKET BOOK edition is published by arrangement with Julian Messner, Inc.
Front cover illustration by Bob Berran.

Printed in the U.S.A.

To Jack Mitford

Whose careful comments helped me greatly
while I was writing
THE ROYAL BOX
and
Whose good companionship helped even more.

Author's Note

I have often remarked that books come into being in many and various ways; also that sometimes circumstances suggest a title and that other times a title suggests a plot. The present novel was written as the result of both these suggestions.

While in London during the summer of 1952, I was invited to a theater party which I found in every respect enjoyable; but I was even more intrigued with my immediate surroundings than I was with the spectacle on the stage. After being guided down a long flight of steps, I was ushered into an imposing apartment which had all the attributes of an elegant Victorian parlor. At one end, opposite the door by which we had entered, was another door which led backstage. On one side of the room, beside an ornate chimney piece, a third door opened into an outmoded but monumental lavatory. Facing this, at the end of a short flight of steps, was the box itself, where the decor was characterized by the same crimson and gold magnificence as the parlor. During the entr'actes–or to use the English term, the intervals–refreshments were placed by an attendant on the marble-topped center table. I was so impressed with all this grandeur, that the following day I started to describe it to a British acquaintance. Before I had progressed very far, he interrupted me.

"Don't you know where you were?" he inquired.

"Why, no!" I answered in some bewilderment.

"In the Royal Box," he replied almost casually.

He then went on to explain that many theaters in England are similarly equipped,* but, with the exception of the Royal Box at the Covent Garden Opera House, which is never available to anyone except members of the Royal Family and their personal guests, such regal accommodations may be secured by anyone who desires them, provided the management has been assured that they are not required by Royalty. Such an arrangement, my informer went on to explain, not infrequently means that someone who has been unable to make bookings in advance, ends up with a last minute prize!

I listened to this gentleman with avid attention and, before he had finished his explanation, I thought I knew what both the title and the setting of my next novel would have to be. When I took up the question successively with my British, my French and my American publishers, they all heartily agreed with me. Bowing to the inevitability of the project which had been so unexpectedly–I may say so accidentally–thrust upon me, I changed my plans for a long quiet sojourn in Spain and a still longer, but equally quiet one in Louisiana, and went to work on *The Royal Box.*

As usual, I must place Hermann B. Deutsch, Associate Editor of the New Orleans *Item,* at the head of those who have assisted me. Though not a collaborator in as complete a sense as in the case of *Dinner at Antoine's,* his sphere of helpfulness has extended beyond that of an editorial adviser. His familiarity with the technique of the suspense story has been invaluable to me; so has his acquaintance with certain types of characters and colloquialisms with which I have had few personal contacts. He has taken several trips to New England and one to Old England in the interests of the story, and has

* Lest some reader, his curiosity aroused, endeavors to locate the exact setting which inspired the above description, I feel compelled to state that when I returned to London in '53, and decided to give a theater party myself, I found, to my great disappointment, that this particular suite had been demolished, in order to make way for more stalls, and that the theater in question—the name of which is of course not the Terry—is one which no longer has a Royal Box.

gone to infinite trouble with research in several different fields. I am extremely grateful to him.

Lady Jean Spender, the wife of Sir Percy Spender, the distinguished Australian Ambassador to the United States, is another author whose familiarity with the technique of the suspense story has been very helpful to me. Lady Spender is herself the author of several highly successful suspense stories and her suggestions, especially in regard to the treatment of my fictional character of Lady Laura, opened up many new avenues of thought.

I am also indebted to my friend, the Hon. Cornelius Van H. Engert, for many helpful suggestions, not only in response to questions asked in connection with this book, but to those made over a long period of years. Nearly thirty years ago, he was the first person to interest me in Persia, as it was then called, where he had been Second Secretary of Legation early in his diplomatic career. Later, he and his charming wife were responsible for most of the success of my first visit to Venezuela, where he was then Chargé d'Affaires. Afterward, among many other important posts, he was the first American Minister to reside in Afghanistan. His thorough knowledge of conditions in many distant parts of the world, but especially in Latin America and the Near and Middle East, has long been invaluable to me.

It is a pleasure to record my appreciation of the assistance given by President J. W. Hoover of the Chevron Oil Company, now residing in Houston, Texas. As exploration chief of the California Company, he placed at my disposal not merely some invaluable textbooks from its library on the history and development of petroleum exploration there, but a wealth of personal material from his diaries about his experience in locating the first producing oil field along the Persian Gulf.

Data about Oklahoma's system of awarding collegiate scholarships was put at my disposal by W. T. Doyel, Secretary of the Oklahoma State Board of Education.

I am extremely grateful to all the departments of the Savoy Hotel, which facilitated the work I did there myself and supplied me with the necessary source material for the fictional and historical references which appear in the novel.

The form taken by the legal proceedings leading to a trial and the form of the trial itself differ very greatly in England and in the United States; and while resolving these I have been greatly helped by my eldest son, Henry W. Keyes, who is also my personal attorney. He had already spent some time in studying English Law and in visiting English law courts, before I called on him for such assistance; and he supplemented these studies and these visits by current consultation with Dudley B. Bonsal, Esq., a New York attorney with international sources of information, and through him with a British firm which modestly declines public credit, and with Dr. Beatrice Kershaw, a psychiatrist of Belmont, Mass. In like measure, methods of English police procedure, which also differ from those in the United States, have been authenticated.

Two eminent physicians of New Orleans—Dr. Nicholas Chetta, one of the South's foremost authorities on forensic medicine, and Dr. Robert M. Willoughby—and Dr. Matthew White Perry, an outstanding diagnostician of Washington, D. C., were consulted in regard to the plausibility of the form, administration and results of poison, as introduced into the plot. They have been unanimous in their opinion that its presentation was authentic and, indeed, made helpful supplementary suggestions, besides replying to the questions asked on the author's initiative.

I have already mentioned my indebtedness to Mr. Deutsch as regards certain types of colloquialisms and characters with which I have had few contacts. I am similarly indebted to my valued English friend, Captain the Hon. John Mitford, though of course in this case the colloquialisms and characters were not the same. I could not help having some qualms lest my faithful British public—which, as I shall always gratefully remember, raised me to the rank of a best-selling author before my own countryfolk did so—might feel that my English characters slipped into Americanisms here and there in their speech or behavior. If this danger has been averted, as I hope and believe it has, the credit is due largely to Captain Mitford.

Sven Nielsen, Director of *Les Presses de la Cité,* the Paris firm which publishes the French editions of my books, presented me with a copy of Roger Delpey's *Soldats de la Boue,* thinking I might find it useful as source material relative to Indo-China. I did indeed; and the following passage gave me a key phrase:

"A lire certains ouvrages de guerre, on est tenté-parfois de croire que la guerre en dentelles *de nos aieux fait encore partie intégrante de notre patrimoine—ce vaste magazin à accessoires. Le Français aime le rêve et y croit—mais il admet aussi le cauchemar, s'il est bien présenté.*

*"La présentation! Tout est là!"**

In discussing with Mr. Deutsch how the term "lace-trimmed war" could be used to best advantage, he called my attention to the illustrated articles which had appeared in the December 12, 1953 issue of the Boston *Herald,* the December 14, 1953 issues of *Newsweek* and *Life,* and the December 19, 1953 issue of the New York *Times.* These excellent articles, supplementing what I had already learned from *Soldats de la Boue,* supplied the basic facts for the *fictional* episode about De Valcourt in the Epilogue—an episode, incidentally, among those with which Mr. Deutsch was most helpful.

I myself visited Broadmoor on a beautiful autumn day, making the trip to and from London by car, in the company of two English friends; and my own impressions of the countryside through which we passed, together with the helpful information given me by these

* "In reading certain works on war, one is sometimes tempted to believe that the *lace-trimmed war* of our ancestors is part of our patrimony—that vast store of accessories. The Frenchman loves a dream and believes in it—but he also admits the existence of a nightmare, if it is graphically presented to him.

"The manner of presentation—that is everything!"

friends, forms the basis of the descriptions in the final episode of the Epilogue. However, I doubt if I could have worded these so aptly or so authentically, if I had not chanced on the short article entitled, "Autumn Color Effects"–one of a series with the general title, "The Course of Nature"–which appeared in the London *Times* on October 20, 1953. As this series carries no signature, only the caption, "From a Correspondent," I am unable to make as complete an acknowledgment as I should like for the pleasure and profit of his charming contributions. I hope, however, that this incomplete acknowledgment will somehow and sometime fall within his range of vision and that he will recognize the sincerity and gratitude with which it is offered.

The historic house and its beautiful garden associated in this story with De Valcourt are not imaginary. They are actually located in Chiswick and their present owner is Lady Violet Benson. Though she was absent at the time of my stay in London, her son, Jeremy Benson, and his delightful wife–both rising young architects–were in residence and I had the pleasure of visiting them, thanks to the good offices of a mutual friend. This is a privilege for which I am profoundly grateful, and which I hope will be enjoyed, vicariously, by my readers, as much as it was enjoyed by me in reality.

–FPK.

Beauregard House, New Orleans and Compensation, Crowley, La.–December, 1952–April, 1953.
The Oxbow, Newbury, Vt.–May, 1953.
Hotel Miramar, Malaga, Spain–June, 1953.
Old St. James' House, London, England–August 17–November 17, 1953.
SS America–November 17–November 23, 1953.
The Oxbow, Newbury, Vt.–December, 1953–January, 1954.
Sulgrave Club, Washington, D. C.–February, 1954.
Compensation, Crowley, La.–March, 1954.

Cast of Characters

In Order of Their Appearance

Police Constable Fergus Gilpin of Scotland Yard.

Lady Laura Whitford, an impoverished lady of noble birth.

Althea, her daughter.

Hilary Thorpe, Counselor of the American Embassy in London and Althea's suitor.

Celestino, Thorpe's Mexican houseboy and chauffeur.

Jevad Ahani, Ambassador of Aristan to the Court of St. James.

Joe Racina, an American journalist.

Judith, Joe's wife.

Colonel Jacques de Valcourt, Military Attaché at the French Embassy in London; also Althea's suitor.

Cornelia Castle.

Baldwin Castle, Cornelia's husband, newly appointed American Ambassador to Aristan.

Lalisse, Thorpe's West Indian cook.

Zeina, wife of Ahani.

Ahani's mother-in-law.

Janice Lester, star in Gold of Pleasure.

Hugo Alban, her husband and manager.

Evan Neville, leading man in Gold of Pleasure.

Luigi, maître d'hôtel at the Savoy Hotel, London.

Pelosi, his assistant.

Manager of the Savoy.

Gradie Kirtland, Chief Inspector of Scotland Yard.

Sergeant Griffin, his assistant.

Barney Martin, Cornelia's son by her first marriage.
Abby Blaker, old friend and former neighbor of Cornelia's.
Major Jeannot, fellow officer of Colonel de Valcourt's.
Antoine Magniard, fellow officer of Colonel de Valcourt's.
Don Augustín de Piedras Negras, friend of Lady Laura's.
Abner Thorpe, Hilary's father.
Bertha Randall, Abner's housekeeper.
Undersecretary of State.
Edson, member of the Department of State.
Dr. Goring, member of the staff at Broadmoor.

The main action of the book takes place between 5 P.M. on an October afternoon in 1951 and 5 A.M. the following morning.

The flashbacks go back twenty-five years.

The Epilogue takes us straight up to the present day.

PROLOGUE

POLICE CONSTABLE FERGUS GILPIN, one of several P.C.'s taking incoming calls in the underground "nerve center" of New Scotland Yard, leaned forward and spoke pleasantly into the telephone of his individual headset. A metallic loop, passing under and behind the collar of his two-tone uniform of blue, held the mouthpiece so suspended that a slight inclination of the head would bring it into range of his lips. In obedience to an injunction by Mrs. Gilpin, a meticulous housekeeper, he had wrapped two sheets of white foolscap about the metal bands to keep them from direct contact with the cloth of his tunic.

As he addressed an occasional phrase to the mouthpiece, he scribbled hasty notations on the ruled form clipped to a piece of fiberboard on the shelf-desk before him.

"There'll be a wireless car there almost at once, sir," he assured the person at the other end of the telephone. Then he rose without haste, withdrew the jack of his headset from its socket and walked to the four huge map tables representing the four quarters of London's Metropolitan Police District. Each bore a large magnifying lens, mounted in a brass standard, and a number of varicolored checkerlike discs and triangles, some plain, some with rings of colored plastic about them.

Picking a red ring from the shelf at one end of a table, Constable Gilpin glanced thoughtfully at the map before dropping his circlet about a red disc stamped with the characters "5-C." Then he continued his walk to the far end of the room, while removing the top copy from the pad clipped to his fiberboard. It bore the words: "Savoy Grill entrance. Man ill or injured in car." He added the symbol "5-C," and handed the slip to one of two elderly constables seated at a smaller desk from whose surface rose two metal stalks, each with a nickeled microphone at its tip, like a pair of fabulous Machine Age flowers.

One of the constables took the paper and, holding it before him, flicked a switch and intoned in a measured singsong:

"Hello, 5-C! Hello, 5-C! I have a message for you from M-2-GW. Savoy Grill entrance. Man ill or injured in motorcar. Message ends. Time of origin 23:19."

Almost without perceptible interval, words—faintly distorted by electronic amplification—came from a loudspeaker:

"Hello, M-2-GW! Hello, M-2-GW! Message received by 5-C."

The transmitting constable flicked switches and was ready for the next call. A rum thing, wasn't it now, the way the calls multiplied as soon as the pubs closed for the night, he reflected, as he docketed the "5-C" slip on the rapidly mounting pile before him.

Constable Gilpin stepped to a near-by doorway beyond which, on a low table, stood a teapot, a jug of hot water, milk, sugar and some white stoneware cups. Thoughtfully, he poured out a measure of strong black tea, added hot water, milk and two pieces of sugar. He sipped this appreciatively, meanwhile letting his eyes rest on the now-disconnected panel, where five of the varicolored switches which, in wartime, had sounded the air raid alarm sirens in divers sections of London, were still kept as souvenirs of a grim time when Londoners could be made to suffer and to die, but not to cry for quarter.

He rinsed his cup, replaced it on the tray and returned quietly to his place at the shelflike desk he shared with his colleagues in taking the calls of those Londoners who dial "999"–the New Scotland Yard emergency number. A bit of prime luck, now, he reminded himself gleefully, having one of the night shifts; tomorrow he'd be watching the soccer match at Chelsea.

By the time he had plugged the jack of his telephone back into its socket, a small wireless car had already scuttled out of the Strand into the Savoy's driveway, drawing to a halt beside a shiny black limousine with a large coat of arms.

Part I

CHAPTER I

"It's no use, Althea. I've tried and tried to figure out some way of keeping it. But we'll have to give up the telephone."

"Oh, Mother, *please!* There must be something else we could do without instead!"

"There isn't. I tell you I've tried to find one—for your sake. But we've already given up everything else we could possibly do without."

"I could go to work. I could—"

"Althea, don't make it any harder for me than it is already. It's gall and wormwood to know that I can hardly afford to live in the basement of my own house! It was bad enough to divide it up into flats—and then to move from the best one to the next best one and finally down here. When we were on the first floor, the drawing room still gave an illusion of elegance, even if we couldn't entertain in it any more. And we could look out on the square, and see grass and flowers and trees, even if we couldn't go out to the country. But here, we're isolated, we're trapped, we might as well be in prison!"

"Mother, it isn't as bad as all that."

"It is, it is! Never to have people in, never to go anywhere! Not even to see anything green—just a bit of pavement and the feet and legs of passers-by, who look as if they'd been cut off above the knees! Sometimes I feel as if I couldn't stand the sight of those truncated figures another minute."

Involuntarily, Althea followed her mother's glance toward the small barred windows of their little sitting room, which had once been the servants'. In the murky light of a rainy afternoon, the wet street, the clumsy galoshes and the damp flapping hems of mackintoshes were certainly not a cheering sight, and they were all that was visible.

"You don't know what it's done to me," Lady Laura went on. "Parting with almost every possession I had in the world—first Shepherd's Haven and then Helston Abbey and then gradually everything else—the paintings and the tapestries and the furniture, the plate and the jewelry, and finally even your father's butterfly collection. And now, being here, in the only semblance of a home I have left."

She turned from the desk where her checkbook lay open before her and looked appealingly at her daughter, who was leafing through a magazine that she had stopped pretending to read. Althea was stretched out on a shabby chaise longue, which once must have been very handsome, and which was not far from the desk, but still nearer the instrument under dispute. Her suit, which might have been a rather good one in its day, was now so outmoded that it had lost any distinctive style it could originally have possessed; moreover, it had obviously been designed for a younger girl, both because of its type and because it was too short and too tight. In flinging herself down, she had made no effort to dispose it neatly about her and its present disarray revealed more clearly than she realized a length of shapely leg and a youthful bosom which showed promise of great beauty. Her hair, which was also in a state of disarray, showed more than a promise; it was beautiful already, magnificently golden, and falling in rich, loose waves around her rosy face. Her lovely color was so fresh, her blue eyes so clear and everything about her so suggestive of abundant vitality, that it would have been impossible to attribute even momentary inactivity on her part to physical lassitude. Almost any casual observer could have drawn the same rapid conclusion as her mother: that she was apparently idle only because she was actually alert and that this alertness was closely connected with the telephone.

"It might be a blessing in disguise, after all," Lady Laura remarked. "I don't like this habit you've acquired,

Althea, of lounging about, waiting for the telephone to ring. And it's growing on you."

"I haven't neglected anything you've asked me to do, have I, Mother? I did go out to get the groceries, and I did remember to get the change in shillings, so that we'd have them to put in the meter. I've already put one in, so it ought to be warmer here presently. I felt terribly because I forgot yesterday and you were so cold. I've put everything I bought neatly away; the kitchen is in perfect order. And the rest of the flat was in perfect order before I left. Wasn't it?"

Althea spoke pleadingly, in much the same way that her mother had spoken to her, when Lady Laura begged her daughter not to make things harder than they were already. Indeed, there was an exceedingly strong resemblance between the two; not only were their voices alike; their coloring, their features and their figures were likewise strikingly similar. In fact, it was only through her voice that Lady Laura betrayed her lack of well-being; she was not a faded or bitter-looking woman. Like her daughter, she had beautiful golden hair; like her daughter, she had an exquisite complexion; like her daughter, she had an almost faultless figure. But she was by far the more soignée of the two. Her hair was carefully, even elaborately and becomingly, arranged; her skin had the almost petallike quality that comes not only from natural softness but from constant care; her lavender dress was as distinctive in style as it was delicate in color, and the tiny fluted lace ruffles with which it was trimmed gave it the final touch of daintiness. Seated at her desk, with two neat bundles–the larger one labeled "Unpaid Bills" and the other, much smaller, marked "Paid Bills" flanking her open checkbook–she looked far less like a harassed housewife than like a fragile lady of quality, who, through some unforeseen force of circumstances, had been obliged to engage in an inappropriate occupation. As a matter of fact, there was nothing misleading about this impression.

"No, you haven't neglected anything I've asked you to do, Althea," she said slowly. The slight interval that had elapsed between the question and the answer, and the almost inaudible sigh which accompanied her words, heightened their hopeless quality. "But when you've finished that much, you don't do anything–except lounge around in unbecoming attitudes, and wait for the telephone to ring."

Althea sat up, pulling down her skirt, tucking in her blouse and shaking back her unruly hair. "I'm sorry," she said contritely. "I must look rather a mess. And I must seem frightfully lazy, too. I'll go and tidy up and get my needle point–I know how much the chairs need recovering. But you see, I've kept expecting every minute . . . . And I thought that, until I did, I wouldn't change or start anything because I wasn't sure–"

"You've kept expecting! That's just it! And someday you'll be terribly disappointed. Either the call won't come through at all, or when it does–"

"Mother, I don't see why you say that! If Hilary doesn't ring exactly when I expect him to, there's always a good reason."

"He's always *given* some good reason, so far. But suppose someday he doesn't? That's what I'm trying to prepare you for, Althea, so that it won't be too much of a shock to you when it does happen."

"But why are you so certain it's going to happen? Why should you be? There's not a single thing Hilary's ever done . . . . Oh, Mother, why do you dislike him so?"

The girl rose, precipitately, and, crossing over to the desk, flung her strong young arms around her mother's shoulders and pressed her glowing cheek against Lady Laura's soft face. But though there was no actual withdrawal from this embrace, there was no return of it, either, and no spoken response. Althea tried again.

"It can't be just because he's a foreigner. You like Jacques."

"Yes, I like him very much. I'd be perfectly satisfied, Althea, if you'd marry Jacques de Valcourt–in fact, such a marriage would make me very happy. I've told you *that,* over and over again."

"But I've told *you* over and over again that I don't love him. I can't marry him just for his title and his châteaux and his fortune."

"He has a great deal more than that to offer you. From your tone of voice anyone would think that he was a disreputable old roué, and that his rank and his money didn't make up for his moral and physical decadence. He has charm and sophistication and character. He's very good looking, much better looking than Hilary Thorpe. He's an outstanding sportsman. Of course his landscape gardening's just a hobby with him—a rather strange one, if you ask me, for a military man—but he has a genius for it. He could have made a fortune out of it, if he'd wanted or needed to. He—"

"Oh, Mother, won't you stop! I've admitted all that before and I'll admit it again. He is charming and sophisticated and, as far as I know, there isn't a single flaw in his character. He's about the best-looking man I ever saw and in a nice outdoorsy way, too—somehow, he doesn't seem a bit like the so-called 'typical Frenchman.' It's no wonder he's become Jack instead of Jacques to almost everyone who knows him." Althea paused, seeing Jacques de Valcourt as her mother saw him—as she admittedly saw him herself: his fine build, his well-shaped head, his blue eyes and white teeth that were so startlingly bright in contrast to his healthy tan. "He's the best tennis player and the best polo player I've ever seen," she went on ungrudgingly. "And his Chiswick gardens are something fabulous. I suppose the ones in France are, too—All the same . . . . Well, it wouldn't be honest—it wouldn't be even decent for me to marry him. I don't see, Mother, how you can keep on urging me to accept Jacques when you know—"

Althea herself had now withdrawn from the embrace. She faced her mother defiantly and went on.

"When you know I love Hilary. Of course he hasn't a title, of course he hasn't a château—Americans don't have titles or châteaux. And I can see why you don't find him as charming or as sophisticated as Jacques, but he's got lots of personality, too. And I like his looks.

There's nothing the matter with his character, either. And he may not have an immense fortune, like Jacques, but he's no pauper, either. If he were, he couldn't afford to have a sweet little house in Devonshire Mews and a Cadillac car. He couldn't afford to give elaborate parties all the time and take nice week-end trips everytime he can get away from the Chancery. A man simply can't do such things on a counselor's salary–you know that as well as I do! He's never talked to me much about money, but he's certainly got enough to support a wife–I know that much. He's got everything I want and need to make me happy. It can't be that you object to him just because he's an American!"

The telephone rang. Althea bounded toward it and snatched up the receiver.

"Yes–yes!" she said rapidly. "Oh, Hilary, please don't say 'No, no!' when I've just said, 'Yes, yes!' Won't you ever learn that when an English operator asks you if you're 'through,' she doesn't mean have you *finished*, she means have you got your connection all right? Of course you've only just begun–she knows that. Now tell me–" For the next few minutes Althea listened intently, without interrupting. "Hilary, that is annoying, isn't it?" she said at last. Then, after another long interval, "No, I'm not doing anything special. I can perfectly well wait until you ring back. I wish there were something I could do to help, but naturally . . . . Yes–yes. Any time. Good-by, good-by–dear."

She replaced the receiver on its cradle and turned to her mother, almost triumphantly.

"I knew there was some good reason," she said excitedly. "Poor Hilary's in the most awful jam. It seems that the new American Ambassador to Aristan, who was expected to arrive at Southampton on the *Queen Mary* last week, changed his plans with practically no notice and took the *Franconia* to Liverpool, instead. A very important journalist, Joe Somebody-or-other, was assigned to write a series of feature articles about him for a national magazine with an immense circulation and great deal of prestige, and they both decided that the best way to get this done would be in the course of a long ocean voyage—the Ambassador likes the sea anyway. Then he decided he wanted to do some motoring through the English countryside before he came on to London. The American Embassy here was informed about this change of plan, and Trevor Greene, one of the second secretaries, went over to Liverpool to meet the *Franconia.* Of course the Consul-General at Liverpool met it, too, and the whole consular staff went into action. All the proper arrangements were made for the motoring trip, with the first stop, at Chester, and seemed to be completely satisfactory. The Ambassador wasn't expected in London until next week. And then what does he do but turn up here this afternoon and telephone the Chancery, perfectly furious because he couldn't get the kind of suite he wanted at Claridge's, just like that, without any notice at all!"

"The new *American* Ambassador to Aristan you say?" Lady Laura inquired quietly.

"Oh, Mother, don't say 'American' like that, as if all Americans were unreliable and temperamental and everything else! It isn't the Ambassador's fault anyway, from what Hilary says—it's his wife's. He's recently married for the second time, a woman a lot younger than he is, and he wants her to be pleased with everything. And she isn't pleased with *anything.* She was looking forward to the trip on the *Queen,* she didn't want to cross on a smaller, slower ship, she got seasick, she thought it was an outrage to have this Joe—Joe Racina, I've remembered now, that's his name—tagging along on what was practically a honeymoon trip."

"You can't blame her for that. Any woman would resent it."

"This isn't *exactly* a honeymoon. The wedding took place several months ago and there's already been a marvelous trip to Hawaii and quite a long stay in New York for shopping and theaters and so on, and an official visit to Washington. Besides, it seems the Racina articles are very important to the Ambassador—there's been a good deal of opposition to the appointment and he felt they'd do a lot toward changing public feeling. But I gather his wife's the sort who wouldn't take that into consideration and who wants more and more, the more she gets. Of course Hilary tried to be tactful. He said she was very striking looking—handsome, really—but he did speak of her as being 'bejeweled and befurred' in a way that sounded as if she were *over* bejeweled and befurred. And she's furious about the appointment to Aristan herself. Hilary says this Mr. Castle—"

"Mr. *who?*"

"Mr. Castle, the newly appointed ambassador," Althea answered, almost impatiently. "Didn't I mention his name before? Well, it's Castle, Baldwin Castle. He made a very substantial contribution to the presidential campaign, with the understanding that, in return, he was to get anything he wanted in the way of a diplomatic post—that is, anything in reason. Only he and the President didn't quite agree as to what was reasonable. Apparently, Mr. Castle expected it would be Paris or London—Rome or Madrid anyway. And instead, it's Kirfahan! His wife claims she never even heard of Kirfahan before and she's mad as a hornet. Mr. Castle doesn't mind so much, because he spent quite a little time in Aristan as an engineer, when he was a young man, and he rather likes it. But naturally, he's sorry about his bride's disappointment and wants to do everything he can to make up to her for it."

"And she didn't care for the English countryside? She'd never heard of Chester, either?"

"That's just what happened, Mother. She insisted on coming straight through to London."

"A typical rich American, I'd say."

"Oh, Mother, *please!* Well, Hilary finally got them some kind of a suite, and thought that would be all for tonight, that he and I could go dancing, just as we'd planned. It never occurred to him that the next thing these Castles would take for granted would be an official entertainment given in their honor–immediately! The Ambassador's just gone to Edinburgh and–"

"I thought you said he'd just come from Chester."

"I'm talking about the American Ambassador to the Court of St. James now, not the Ambassador to Aristan! And the American Minister's sick in bed with the flu. Hilary's next in line when it comes to entertaining V.I.P.s."

"I'm afraid you'll have to translate for me, Althea. You know I'm not clever about understanding Americans at any time. And when they indulge in their passion for using initials instead of words–"

"V.I.P. stands for Very Important Person. I thought you'd heard that used. Almost everyone does it–Well, while Hilary was trying to think whom he could possibly find free, at a moment's notice, that the Castles would consider as important as themselves, Mrs. Castle sprang another surprise on him. She's in the mood for only one kind of a party–a theater party. And there's only one play she wants to see–*Gold of Pleasure,* starring Janice Lester! *Gold of Pleasure*–why, the entire house is sold out weeks in advance!"

While Althea was talking, Lady Laura had taken the two neat piles of bills and put them in a desk drawer, closing it carefully upon them. Next she shut the checkbook and put that in another drawer. Then she rose.

"So I suppose the matter is now left that Hilary Thorpe will telephone you again when he can arrange some substitute entertainment for these Castles, in which you are to be included, since he knows you at least are free?"

"Yes. But not just because he knows I'm free, Mother. Because he wants to see me as much as I want to see him. He's very disappointed that we can't have the sort of evening we planned. But at least we can be together. He said he hoped you'd join the party, too. He feels sure he can get hold of an extra man somewhere."

"I suppose it wouldn't occur to him to try Jacques de Valcourt?"

"Why it might! They're very good friends, as you know, even if they are—well, rivals. I'll suggest it to Hilary, if you'd like to have me. I don't in the least mind spending an evening in Jacques's company, as long as he understands I'm Hilary's guest, not his. I like him very much. I don't see why the Castles shouldn't like him, too. The Castles and Hilary and Jacques and you and I—why, that would make a very nice little group, Mother!"

"I agree with you. Very nice. And suppose, instead of calling Hilary Thorpe immediately, to suggest Jacques de Valcourt as the extra man, you let me use the telephone first." There was no sadness in Lady Laura's voice as she spoke this time. "I should like to see Janice Lester myself; and it might be interesting to meet the new American Ambassador to Aristan and his bejeweled and befurred wife. Moreover, I should not be sorry to show that self-important suitor of yours that his connections do not amount to much after all, compared to ours, and I believe that I may be in a position to do so. After all, I still have relations at Court, even if I am a pauper. It so happens that while you were out, Cousin Julia dropped in and told me, confidentially, that Queen Mary would probably change her plans for going to the theater tonight, because of a slight indisposition. Julia wouldn't have notified the management of the Terry, however, until the probability became a certainty; so she may not have done it yet. If it does become a certainty, we might manage *Gold of Pleasure* after all. Even if the house is reportedly sold out, there is still the Royal Box."

CHAPTER II

"Lady Lauŕa, I don't know how to thank you! My diplomatic stock had sunk almost out of sight when you came to the rescue. Now it's up to the Coca-Cola—American Tel & Tel bracket."

Celestino, Hilary Thorpe's Mexican houseboy, beaming and bowing according to his habit, had opened the front door for his master's guests. But Hilary himself had come forward in Celestino's wake and, for the first time in the course of their fairly long acquaintance, had taken Lady Laura's hands quickly in his and pressed them warmly, which was a far more significant gesture than if Jacques de Valcourt had kissed them deferentially. Lady Laura was obliged to confess to herself that she could see why Althea considered Hilary good looking, in his own way, and why the girl said he actually had as much personality as the far handsomer Frenchman. He had a pleasant and open countenance; but it did not reveal the lack of perception and will power sometimes betrayed by obvious amiability and candor. On the contrary, his gray eyes were keen as well as kindly, and though he was smiling at the moment, the lower part of his face suggested determination rather than deference. As he turned from Lady Laura to her daughter, a look of affectionate understanding passed between them; and while he did not take her hands, her mother did not fail to observe that there was something suggestive of a caress in the way he removed her wrap, without waiting for Celestino to take it from her.

"I'm so glad you came early," Hilary went on, addressing himself to Lady Laura rather than to Althea. "I'm providing for all the usual drinks, of course, including Dubonnet for Jack, who claims anything stronger before dinner spoils the taste of his soup—as if dinnertime weren't so far off, thanks to the awful theater hours, that no matter what you drink, it's died on you long before you get to your soup!" He motioned toward an antique butler's-tray, glittering with ice and tall glasses, which were flanked by numerous well-filled bottles. "What I started to say was, I'm also having tea, and I want you to pour for me. Come and have a look at the setup."

He led the way through the entrance hall which, in the tiny house that had once been a stable, also served as the living room, toward the small dining room at the rear. A coal fire glowed cosily in the grate and, before it, a table, covered with a fine embroidered cloth, was lavishly spread. At one end of the table stood a silver teakettle which was singing invitingly, with a silver caddy, teapot, sugar bowl and cream jug and delicate Dresden cups grouped companionably around it.

"Hot biscuits are coming in a minute, too," he said. "Lalisse doesn't think any party's complete without those."

"Lalisse?"

"Yes. My cook. I acquired her at Martinique—my first post after I entered the Foreign Service. She's been with me ever since. Her costume and her cooking are both rather on the spectacular side—not that there's anything spectacular about biscuits though, incidentally, I was using the word the way we Americans do—what you call biscuits, we call crackers—I wasn't talking about crackers! But aside from such excrescences as American biscuit made by a West Indian, I've tried to do everything in the English manner. Is there anything I've forgotten that you'd like to suggest?"

"No, I don't think you need any suggestions," Lady Laura said slowly. This was the type of ménage to which she had been accustomed in her youth and early married life, but which she had not seen in many a long day—even her most prosperous English friends could have nothing like this, under rationing. Americans, it appeared, still had everything they wanted, not only enough on which to gorge themselves, but enough to waste. Her sense of resentment against them, which had temporarily been engulfed in her sense of triumph because she had secured the Royal Box, emerged again.

"But I thought there were to be only six of us," she went on, after a short silence which neither Hilary nor Althea sought to break, though again they looked at each other with affectionate understanding. "You realized, didn't you, that the Royal Box doesn't hold more than that? And I see you have nine teacups set out."

"Oh, yes, I understood about the capacity of the box and I wasn't trying to stretch it. But Joe Racina telephoned me almost immediately after I got your good news—you know, the writer who's doing the series of articles on Castle—and I invited him to drop in here before the theater. He and I are old friends—or rather, we're very good friends. Actually, I've known Judith, his wife, much longer than I've known him. Dexter Abbott, a neighbor of hers, was a classmate of mine at the University of Vermont. I used to visit him quite often on Farman Hill, where they both grew up. In those days, it looked as if Dexter and Judith were going to make a match of it, so she was a good deal in evidence and I liked her from the first. But Joe Racina came along and got in his way, and Dexter consoled himself very happily with a beautiful young southern widow. Apparently, it all turned out for the best, just as everything is always supposed to and so seldom does. Anyhow, none of this interfered with my admiration of Judith. Incidentally, she deserted her father's farm and did a grand job as a nurse, during the war, but was badly burned by the explosion of a hand grenade in Africa. She got some pretty deep scars—not that they show much any more, because she's learned to dress and do her hair in a way so that they won't. But perhaps I ought to warn you."

"And she's with her husband? Mr. and Mrs. Racina—is that the name—both came over on the *Franconia?*"

"Yes, didn't Althea tell you? Well, come to think of it, I forgot to tell *her*. But Joe and Judith are practically inseparable. You never saw such a devoted couple." For the third time, Hilary looked at Althea in an affectionate and understanding way, this time as if to suggest that it would be easy enough for anyone to see another such couple, if only he and Althea could be married. Again, the look was not lost on Lady Laura, but she appeared to disregard it.

"That still makes only eight," she said, straightening the spoon on one of the saucers, and then checking herself from making any further movement connected with the tea table. She was not at all interested in the Racinas, and her desire to sit down and devour everything in sight was growing on her. She wished the other guests, whoever they were, would come and put an end to this futile delay which, she tried to tell herself, was annoying only because she was afraid they would be late for the play. Still, she was fearful lest her growing greed would betray itself.

"That's for Jevad Ahani."

"You mean the Ambassador from Aristan?"

"Yes. He heard that Castle was in town almost as soon as we did. I don't know whether Castle got in touch with the Embassy himself or whether this was another case of the good old grapevine—fantastic how that works, especially among those Eastern people! It's hardly safe to think; they can pick your mind before you've had time to act . . . . Well, Ahani wanted to see Castle right away for a very important conference."

"But there won't be time for that here! Especially if your other guests are much later!"

"Well, if there isn't time here, perhaps there will be between the acts."

"But I explained—"

"Oh, Ahani's not expecting to sit with us. But he *is* going to *Gold of Pleasure,* too! I don't mean he pulled wires at the last moment, with miraculous success, like you, Lady Laura! But of course everyone wants to see Janice Lester these days and Ahani's no exception to the rule. After trying for a long while, he finally got tickets, and it just happens they were for tonight. He has a small box, quite close to ours. So, as I said, it'll be a simple matter for him to join us between the acts. And I know he'd like to, whether or not it was necessary from the viewpoint of some dispatches. Well, speaking of angels—"

A small dark man, wearing numerous orders and decorations on his well-cut tail coat, and a broad ribbon, from which still another medal was suspended, across his immaculate shirt bosom, had handed his silk hat and opera cape to Celestino and was already halfway across the living room before Hilary caught up with him. In response to his host's cordial but hasty greeting, he murmured that he was delighted, explained his dress on the grounds of a later official reception, and bowed rather unconcernedly in the direction of Lady Laura and Althea. He then glanced rapidly around, under heavy-lidded eyes, searching, without any attempt at subterfuge, for something or someone he did not find.

"The Castles aren't here yet," Hilary informed him, interpreting the roving glance correctly. "But that's all right—we've plenty of time. And look who *is* here!" he went on, abandoning the Ambassador to Lady Laura and Althea, and again advancing, with even more speed than before. "Got a kiss for me, Judith? Well, I'm going to have one anyway. Great to see you, Joe! How's everything?"

"Couldn't be better."

"That's all I need to know at the moment. Details can wait. Come on and meet the others."

While the indicated presentations were taking place, the new arrivals underwent a swift scrutiny, delicately veiled on the part of Lady Laura, searching under the heavy-lidded eyes of the Ambassador, and candidly astonished on the part of Althea. Joe Racina was immensely tall and correspondingly stoop shouldered; he was wearing a soft shirt, a black bow tie which had obviously been secured without the aid of a mirror, a dinner jacket which looked as if he had slept in it, and trousers which had long since lost their original crease and which gave no indication of having been pressed since. This casual costume appeared all the more careless in comparison to the Ambassador's faultless and formal apparel and to Hilary's less-ostentatious, but equally well-tailored and well-kept clothes; and the contrast to the attire of Joe's wife was even more startling. Her dress of gold and black brocade, made with long sleeves finished with frills of gold lace, and a high neck, encircled about with a heavy gold necklace, looked as if it had been copied from a Renaissance portrait—as indeed it had. Her hair was banded around her head and low over her ears and neck with golden ribbon. This was not the way either Lady Laura or Althea, who had so recently been given a brief outline of Judith's background, expected a girl to look who had been brought up on a farm and who had later become a trained nurse. True, her husband was now evidently a writer of some standing and therefore probably in comfortable circumstances; but there was nothing about his appearance to suggest prosperity or even much regard for the amenities. The Ambassador, still less informed than the others, was also puzzled and took immediate steps to put an end to his bewilderment.

"You have just arrived in London" he inquired of Joe, coming straight to the point.

"Yesterday. We took the boat train direct to London."

"Ah, now I understand! You came on the *Franconia* with the Castles."

"Well, I don't know that they'd put it just that way. We had passage on the same ship and I'm doing some articles on Mr. Castle, but I don't think he and his wife considered us members of their party. They do have a maid and valet along though—not to mention eighty-seven pieces of baggage."

Joe grinned, and the smile suddenly lighted a face which, in repose, had seemed almost somber. Thus illumined, its lines and its sallowness were somehow almost obliterated. Simultaneously, Lady Laura and Althea decided that though, by no stretch of the imagination, could he have been called good looking, he, too, had considerable personality. Both would have been glad to engage him in small talk, but found themselves compelled, instead, to take a minor part in the conversation between Judith and Hilary, who were reviewing old times with evident enjoyment. The Ambassador now had Joe Racina firmly in his clutches.

"Ah—I did not catch your name at first! Of course, of course! I have read a number of your articles, all with great pleasure and admiration. So now you are turning your attention to the Middle East. I'm delighted to hear it."

"Well, not to the Middle East, exactly. I've never been there, and, unfortunately, I'm not one of those writers who can burst successfully into print about one of the places he's never seen, or where he's been for only two or three days—spent mostly at the bar of the best hotel. But as I said, I'm writing now about Mr. Castle and, naturally, the subject of the Aristanian oil fields enters into the picture. Of course you know that he spent a good deal of time in them, when he was a young engineer."

"Of course, of course!" echoed the Ambassador. "In my country we are delighted with his appointment. Such long experience, such thorough knowledge as Mr. Castle possesses are very rare in an outsider. We should also be delighted to have you visit us. I would be only too pleased to offer you every facility."

"It's very kind of you. But this is just a flying trip—literally, as far as our return is concerned. We've left the kids behind with my wife's parents and they'll be such spoiled brats by the time we get back that there'll be no living with them, if we're gone too long. Besides, Judith worries when she's away from them."

Joe's gaze shifted from the diplomat to Judith, who was still pleasantly engaged in reminiscences with their host, while Lady Laura and Althea, still feeling rather at sea, made occasional comments and asked occasional questions. Judith flashed an answering glance in her husband's direction and went on talking with Hilary. The Ambassador persisted.

"Then I hope you will give me the opportunity of conferring with you here, not only about oil, but on many kindred subjects. I should be delighted to have you and your wife dine with me at the Embassy. Or perhaps, as a starter, we could talk a little tonight. I'm going to the play, like the others. In fact, I have the box next to theirs. It seats only three, but that would be just large enough."

"It's very kind of you. However, I'm sure you must have invited other guests and–"

"My wife was planning to join me," the Ambassador interrupted. "My wife and my mother-in-law. The latter is quite of the old school, and my wife, as a dutiful daughter, defers to her wishes; so they do not go to parties like this. But occasionally they do go to a play, sitting in the rear of a box. It would be very simple for me to telephone and say I have made other plans. Really, I should be de–"

"I hadn't quite finished," Joe said imperturbably. "I started to say that we're all fixed for the play anyhow. I sent Janice a radio from the ship–I thought as long as I was going to be here for a few days, I might as well do a piece on her, too. She started calling me before the boat train got in and after we finally made connections, she offered me her house seats for tonight. I knew her when–she knew me when, too, as far as that goes. We were both supes in the same play when I was working my way through a graduate course at the University of Chicago and she was trying to help her mother pay for the groceries. The money came in handy for both of us and we didn't know at the time she was going to be a real actress, so it didn't occur to her to high-hat me. I gave her as much of a rush as my very limited finances would allow and she's never held it against me that I didn't follow through. No reason why she should –she's had plenty of other interests. But we've kept in touch with each other, more or less, and apparently she feels–well, delighted is the word, isn't it?–at the prospect of a piece. Excuse me–I think Hilary's trying to catch our eye and call our attention to another arrival."

Jacques de Valcourt, suave, elegant and self-assured, and obviously in the best of health and spirits, came gaily forward. He was wearing the uniform of a French Colonel of Cavalry, and its row of multicolored ribbons bore witness to a distinguished military career. He needed no introduction, except to the Racinas, and he was soon chatting with them as easily as if he had known them all his life. He had been playing polo that afternoon and it had looked like a good game; then they had been obliged to call off the match because of the weather. This English climate! But it was wonderful for gardens. He was really proud of his roses and a good many were still in bloom. The Lancaster and York? No, he did not have that one, though he had heard of it. They *did?* Well, it would be worth a trip to the United States just to come to Farman Hill, in that case. He would have to see if he could not get sent on some mission to Washington. The Foreign Office was always dreaming up missions. Meanwhile, the Racinas must come out to Chiswick and see such flowers as he did have . . . . He had given a party there for the principals in *Gold of Pleasure* the previous Sunday and they had apparently enjoyed it —the water lilies, both crimson and white, were still lovely, as well as the roses, and the acers and peony foliage were really gorgeous in their autumn coloring. Perhaps the next day, at teatime? And of course they were to be his guests, with the others, for dinner at the Savoy, after the play. He was delighted at the prospect of seeing it again—he had been to the first night and twice since then. Janice Lester was certainly a charmer . . . .

The Ambassador from Aristan, inwardly acknowledging temporary defeat at the hands of the French Military Attaché, as far as the Racinas were concerned, turned, not without reluctance, to Lady Laura and Althea. The former had never been one of his favorites and he considered the latter entirely negligible. He did not see how she possibly could have captured the fancy of two such eligible bachelors as Jacques de Valcourt and Hilary Thorpe, though he was well aware that she had. While his expert eye took in all the defects of her homemade clothes, he did not fail to observe the beauty of the form which these covered; but even this did not stimulate him. It was rather too slim for his taste and, besides, any number of girls whom he met in society—not to mention girls whom he met under less circumscribed conditions—had fine figures and knew how to reveal them to good advantage, either with the help of first-class dressmakers or in settings appropriate for greater revelation. Judith Racina, covered as she was to the very ears, had more appeal for him. Unless all his experience counted for nothing, that woman had potentialities. He would find a way of breaking in on Jacques de Valcourt, who seemed to think, merely because he was French, that he was irresistible . . . .

Before the Ambassador could put his plan into execution, however, Celestino opened the door for the final guests. The appearance of the first one proved so overpowering to him that an expression of wide-eyed astonishment supplanted his customary beaming smile and he forgot to bow. Mrs. Castle was as tall as her husband, and she wore an immense glittering tiara which gave her added height. Moreover, she was enveloped from head to foot in white fox furs so bushy that, momentarily, they concealed her husband from view; Mae West, in her most effulgent days, had never presented so dazzling a spectacle. The furs parted, as Cornelia Castle surrendered her wrap to the stunned servant, and disclosed neck, arms and a generous expanse of bosom, bare except for glittering gems; a strapless dress of magenta velvet made this white expanse seem all the greater because of the violent color contrast. The make-up of the new Ambassadress was extreme, her fair hair obviously retouched, her face, like her figure, too full; indeed, its amplitude bore little resemblance to that pleasing plumpness which Ahani admired, when this was an accessory to the freshness of extreme youth and to an expression of sweet docility. As Cornelia swept forward, not even waiting for her husband, Ahani knew that the feeling she roused in him was not one of mild contempt, such as he felt for Lady Laura, nor one of male disparagement, like that with which he regarded Althea. He realized that at sight he hated this creature, and that her presence in his country would be a constant cause of affront to the women of his land, where the veil still remained a symbol, even though it ceased to be a garment.

CHAPTER III

"MY GOODNESS, are we late?" Mrs. Castle exclaimed, accepting her host's hand and belatedly glancing back at her husband. "Baldy, your watch must be slow."

In view of Baldwin Castle's thatch of iron-gray hair, the *petit nom* sounded almost ludicrously inappropriate. When his wife shed her fluffy cocoon he was disclosed as ruddy and rather thickset; but he carried himself well, and the solidity of his build gave an impression of strength rather than overweight. At the moment, his expression betrayed so much annoyance that it was not hard to guess he had a temper and that he had never learned, perhaps never tried, to control it. But his forceful face was not unpleasant and everything about him bespoke vitality and the general well-being engendered by success.

"There's nothing the matter with my watch, *Cornelia,*" he said shortly, stressing the pompous name in such a way that the use of it in its entirety plainly indicated that he did not care to be addressed in public as Baldy. "I told you you weren't allowing enough time to dress, if you were going to put on all those gimcracks. And then, there's this damn fog closing in. It took us twice as long to get here as that tall-hatted doorman told us it would. How are you, Thorpe? Nice little place you've got here. Doesn't have that empty look so many people are going in for nowadays, either. You've collected quite a lot of knickknacks in the course of your travels, haven't you? Old pictures, too. Not that I care for them, but of course for people who like that sort of thing, that is the sort of thing they like—as Lincoln, or maybe it was Barnum, used to say. Peruvian, are they?"

"No, sir, Mexican. May I present you to—"

"What's this I hear about the University of Vermont?" Castle interrupted. "Went to a state university myself, of course—Oklahoma. But I thought there was an unwritten law all *career* diplomats had to be Harvard men."

"I'm the exception that proves the rule. My father—"

"Oh, I've heard about him! Wanted you to get the practical training that would teach you to run his nurseries, eh? Or was it the talc mines? And then you fooled him by running off."

"I'd be pleased to tell you about those conflicting family interests later, sir, if they really interest you. But meanwhile everyone here is so anxious—"

"Pleased to meet you, Mrs.—" Castle said, turning belatedly from his host to face his fellow guests. Then he stopped abruptly.

"Lady Laura Whitford," Thorpe prompted. "Her daughter Althea. His Excellency, the Ambassador from Aristan. The Marquis de Valcourt. Mr. and Mrs. Joseph Racina—well, of course you know them already. The American Ambassador to Aristan and Mrs. Castle."

"That's quite a mouthful of titles, isn't it, Mr. Thorpe?" the new Ambassadress inquired. "Pleased to meet you all, I'm sure." Her husband continued to stare straight ahead of him, while mumbling a general acknowledgment of the introduction, but she immediately extended a jeweled hand. Her expression of pleasure was quite sincere. This was the sort of society in which she had been hoping to move, and now she was having at least a glimpse of it, after that long dreary ocean voyage and those dull provincial towns, before she was dragged off to some unspeakable place in the Middle East, where she foresaw nothing but dirt and discomfort. As a matter of fact, the appearance of the bemedaled Ambassador from Aristan was a source of sudden, if slight, reassurance. He was the most elegant man in the room, more elegant even than the French marquis. If Aristan could produce one such specimen, it might conceivably produce others and this was an agreeable surprise . . . . "Hello, Judith. How are you, Joe?" she remarked, coming eventually to them in her gracious rounds. "I didn't know you were in on this party."

"Oh, we're not! That is, not actually—don't worry about it for a minute. It's just that Hilary, being an old friend and incurably kind-hearted, suggested that we might get hungry if we didn't have a sandwich or something before the evening was over. As it happens, we're going to *Gold of Pleasure,* too. But we're sitting in the pit with the rest of the *hoi polloi*—not in the Royal Box with you."

"Shut up, Joe!" Hilary muttered under his breath. "And if you must talk, say 'stalls' instead of 'pit,' will you?" Mrs. Castle had glanced at the journalist suspiciously, as if vaguely conscious that he was ridiculing her; but the uneasy suspicion passed, leaving her mind untroubled. She was far too excited by the sound of the great names Hilary had pronounced to be concerned by the tone of a man named Joe Racina. "You're *the* Lady Laura, aren't you?" she inquired of the fellow guest to whom she had first been presented. "I mean, the one whose photograph was in last week's *Tatler*. I saw it in the hotel at Chester. There wasn't much of anything to do there, so while Baldy was in the bar I picked up a magazine that was lying on the table in the lounge and there was a picture in it labeled, 'Latest Portrait Study of Lady Laura Whitford, Eldest Daughter of the Late Duke of Haverford and Widow of Sir Guy Whitford.' "

"Yes, I saw it, too," Hilary said quickly. "It *was* lovely, wasn't it . . . . And it's entirely due to Lady Laura's swift and efficient action that we're able to go to the theater tonight. And now, I think we ought to ask her to start pouring tea. Will you come with me to the dining room, Lady Laura? We haven't too much time. The people who have such perverted tastes that they prefer strong drinks can help themselves, with a little assistance from Celestino," Hilary went on, nodding toward the Mexican, to indicate that he could leave the door now, and waving a welcoming hand in the direction of the butler's-tray. "Just the same, I'm sure you'll have some immediate customers, Lady Laura."

"Myself among them, of course," Ahani said, following them quickly and standing expectantly beside Lady Laura's chair, watching her as she poured boiling water from the purring teakettle and rinsed a small earthernware pot which had been placed inconspicuously in the midst of the gleaming silver.

"And me," Baldwin Castle said unexpectedly, detaching himself from the little group already forming around the butler's-tray and following almost as quickly. "My wife calls me a sissy for wanting my tea every afternoon. But I've never forgotten how good it used to seem, coming in, after a hard day's work, to hear the samovar singing. And then, to draw a chair close beside it and get a good hot cup of fresh-made tea." He drew up a chair now, disregarding the fact that Ahani was still standing. "The custom's habit forming. You know how it is, don't you, *Lady* Laura?"

He stressed the word "lady" as a few minutes earlier he had stressed the name "Cornelia." Ahani, who had not failed to observe the emphasis on both occasions, and had correctly interpreted the reason for it the first time, swiftly decided that Castle misprized titles to the same degree that his wife gloated over them.

"*I* know how it is," he said. "And the fact that you do, Mr. Ambassador, is another welcome sign of your familiarity with our small customs as well as our great ones—a familiarity that bodes well for better understanding between our two countries. But I believe Lady Laura has never visited the Middle East."

"Perhaps not. Just the same, I'm sure she's almost as familiar with its customs, great *and* small, as I am. Aren't you, *Lady* Laura?"

"Hardly. I've heard a few references to them, from returning travelers and educators and diplomats, but that's all," she said, measuring tea leaves carefully into the earthenware pot she had rinsed.

"You never had any long letters about them, written on the scene, from someone who lived there?"

"No, never. And the Ambassador is right in believing I've never visited the Middle East myself, so I must confess that the subject of its customs isn't one that's ever concerned me closely or, to be truthful, intrigued me very greatly . . . . I hope you will find this to your taste, Excellency."

In the course of conversation, she again poured boiling water from the purring kettle, this time over the carefully measured tea leaves in the crockery pot, and allowed them to steep for a matter of minutes. Then, with equal care, she had poured the brew from the crockery pot to the silver one, separating it from the leaves. The cup which she handed Ahani was filled with fragrant undiluted liquid.

"Perfect," he assured her, savoring it slowly. "It could not be better if you had learned to make it under the expert tutelage of someone thoroughly conversant with our ways."

"I insist that she must have," Castle said positively.

"No. We English pride ourselves on our téamaking, too, you know. And our host has provided me with every facility–somewhat to my surprise, I must confess. I had been led to believe that all Americans were addicts of teabags . . . . How shall I fix yours, Mr. Ambassador? Two slices of lemon, three lumps of sugar, a small portion of tea and the cup filled up with cognac?"

"You're just pulling my leg. Of course I take it exactly like Ahani here."

"Oh–I should have remembered those years Mr. Thorpe told me you have spent in his colleague's country instead of thinking of you as another unenlightened American. Do forgive me."

She put down the silver tongs which she already held poised over the sugar bowl and, filling another delicate Dresden cup with clear tea, handed it to Castle with a gracious smile. She was looking her loveliest and she knew it; her dress of soft gray chiffon, made with floating panels, was extremely becoming and the chain of moonstones, which she wore with it, set it off to perfection. The moonstones had escaped the sale of her more precious jewels because they did not have enough value to attract a cautious buyer; but they suited her far better than her costlier gems had ever done. In fact, they enhanced the general effect of quiet elegance which she always produced, and at the moment the gaudy trappings of Mrs. Castle suffered conspicuously in comparison. The new Ambassadress was now well into a second glass of bourbon on the rocks, having tossed off the contents of one in record time; she had managed to corral Jacques de Valcourt, who was slowly sipping a light Dubonnet and soda, and her remarks to him, delivered in a high strident voice, were clearly audible in the dining room.

"I was an actress myself before matrimony got in the way of my career," she was informing the Frenchman. "Oh, I don't mean my recent plunge with Baldy! I had two other husbands before him. But I've always kept up my interest in the stage. I want to go to the theater every night we're in London—and I mean to drag out our stay here just as long as I can and then have another like it in Paris. Lord knows there won't be any plays, or much of anything else, in that godforsaken place we're headed for. And of course I wanted to see Janice Lester more than anyone. I want to find out what she's got I didn't have. The chorus was my limit; the top spots always went to somebody else's girl friend. I'll admit I never had much of a voice; but then she's not a singer, either; and her figure's not a bit better than mine was. I've been putting on a little weight this last year, but I've found a wonderful new diet and I'm planning to take off the extra poundage just as soon as we get to Kirfahan. Probably I won't have much trouble. I doubt if there's anything fit to eat there . . . . Well, as I was saying, I'm really tickled we're going to *Gold of Pleasure* tonight. The title has me buffaloed though. What do you make of it?"

De Valcourt's reply, being lower pitched than Mrs. Castle's question, was inaudible in the dining room. Her husband, who of course realized that she had been overheard, and who looked visibly annoyed again, though not in the least embarrassed, repeated the query as he handed his cup to Lady Laura for a refill.

"Gold-of-pleasure is the name of quite an ordinary weed," she explained. "At least, it's considered quite an ordinary weed in Europe—I believe in the States it's been cultivated and raised to the rank of an herb—anyhow, that's what Jacques de Valcourt, who knows a great deal more about plant life than we do, told Althea. Be that as it may, gold-of-pleasure has a very pretty bright yellow flower. I believe the plot of the play centers around this flower, as personified by a very beautiful girl. Especially about its—shall we say elevation?—under advantageous circumstances. Naturally, I don't know the details, as I haven't seen the play myself yet. But I understand that Janice Lester's excellent in the main part . . . . May I give you a second cup, too, Excellency? Oh—in just a minute perhaps! Apparently we are about to have an addition to our fare, which seemed to me very copious already."

While Lady Laura was defining gold-of-pleasure, the door leading from the pantry into the dining room had opened slowly, and Hilary's olive-complexioned West Indian cook had majestically emerged. She was wearing a gaily striped sateen dress with the full skirt looped up on one side, a filmy lace fichu and apron, and a *tignon* which matched the brightest stripe in her dress, a rich crimson. Golden hoops hung from her ears and the fichu was fastened at her breast with an immense gold brooch. Her general appearance was so striking that the covered dish she was carrying, almost tenderly, in both shapely hands, and even the proud expression on her oval face, escaped the immediate observation of the astonished guests. Hilary had taken adventage of Mrs. Castle's monopoly of De Valcourt to give Althea a chance of becoming better acquainted with Joe and Judith and to enjoy her company himself, without interruption from his rival; now he excused himself and guided his astonishing domestic in an encouraging manner toward the tea table.

"This is Lalisse," he said, smiling first at her and then at the others. "I told you about her before the rest of the company came, Lady Laura, so I'll let you help me pass on the information. Lalisse likes to serve her specialities herself and I like to have her. Celestino's a good boy, but I think you'll agree he doesn't add as much to the *décor* as she does. Offer your biscuits to Lady Laura first, Lalisse, and then to the others in the dining room. Afterward, take them into the living room and pass them around. When you've done that twice, perhaps you'd better go back to the kitchen for a fresh supply."

Lalisse advanced, lifting the cover of the silver dish she was carrying. As Lady Laura accepted a biscuit and bit into it, exclaiming, "Delicious!" the cook's expression, which had become increasingly grave while Hilary was talking, lightened visibly again; when Castle, after the first taste, exclaimed, "Hold on a minute! I want two of those the first go round!" it changed to one of actual joy. Her eventual disappearance took on the attributes of a triumphant departure after a regal progress.

"Look here, Hilary, unless I miss my guess, there's another story for me!" Joe exclaimed. He was still chewing as he spoke, and when he had swallowed the last morsel in his mouth, he immediately started on the first of two more choice tidbits which he was holding in his hand. "Judith can make damn fine biscuits—so can her mother. And in case you've forgotten, my father's a retired baker. I was raised in a place that smelled of good bread, and if there's any better smell. I haven't sniffed it yet. But these products of Lalisse's are something else again. What's her background? Where did she learn to cook? How does she manage to do any work, all dolled up like that? Yeah, I heard about Martinique, somewhere along the line, and me for the French West Indies on my next trip, if she's a sample of what they've got there. But meanwhile, I want to know a lot more."

"All right, stop talking nonsense about flying home next week and I'll see what I can do to help you out,"

Hilary responded cordially. "Perhaps you might ask De Valcourt about her, too—he knew her before I did and he doesn't think quite as highly of her as I do. In fact, he's always urging me to get rid of her before I find she's been up to mischief. Not that I ever would, no matter what tall tales he tells about her past. You might like to hear his version though—it certainly would add drama to your story. But I'm afraid we can't go into all that now. In fact—" he glanced at his wrist watch—"we ought to be out of this place inside of ten minutes, unless we're going to be late for the curtain. Not that I want to speed the parting guest."

"I get you. And I'll be back tomorrow to see Lalisse. Have I time for one cup of tea before we start? Of course, I've already had two Martinis, but I think tea makes a good chaser."

"Change places with me then. I've had two cups of tea and I think whisky would make a good chaser."

Castle put down his empty cup and moved away. Ahani, also putting down an empty cup, hurried after him.

"I'd like very much to have a few words with you—in private," he said in a low voice. "I've already mentioned the matter to Mr. Thorpe, and he told me, in an aside, that we were welcome to go up to his study. Suppose that, while the others are finishing their drinks—"

"I want a drink myself—I mean a real one. I need it. I haven't had anything except tea so far."

"But I understood that was your preference. I assure you this matter is urgent. If it weren't—"

" 'If it's urgent today, just think how much more urgent it will be tomorrow'—that's what a French general my dad knew during World War I used to say and I think he had the right idea. Don't you agree with your distinguished compatriot, Colonel?"

De Valcourt, still in the clutches of Mrs. Castle, who had now embarked on her third drink, had not heard the first part of the new Ambassador's speech. Castle repeated it, obligingly, as he poured a stiff Scotch and helped himself to a caviar *canapé*. Any idea of a private discussion about dispatches was futile, at least for the time being–Ahani saw that only too well. He was not amused by the jest that emanated from a distinguished compatriot of De Valcourt's; he could only hope that an entr'acte would afford him a better opportunity. Probably the sooner they could all reach the theater and get settled in their respective places, the better it would be.

"May I offer anyone a lift?" he inquired of Hilary, who had just reappeared after a brief absence. "I have my Rolls and my chauffeur here, of course." Ahani had observed that while Lady Laura was engrossed with Joe and Judith, who had asked for tea almost simultaneously, Hilary had followed Lalisse into the pantry. That was natural enough; with a household staff of only two, a host had to keep on the alert himself, in the matter of directions and supervision. What seemed less natural or, at any rate, less fitting, was that Althea, after a glance at her preoccupied mother, had also disappeared. Now the girl was standing beside Hilary, her cheeks, which were always pink, rosier than ever, her hair, which was never noticeable for its tidiness, actually disheveled. It was not hard for Ahani to draw certain conclusions; and, in spite of their disparaging nature, he admitted to himself that the girl was extraordinarily pretty; in fact, that she was very close to being beautiful, and that when she had filled out a little and learned how to dress . . . . Meanwhile, since the curious customs of Occidentals saw nothing actually immoral about a swift, stolen embrace, probably Hilary should not be considered too blameworthy or, for that matter, Althea, either.

"It's very kind of you," Hilary said politely. His hair was slightly ruffled, too, and he put up his hand and smoothed it. Then, catching Ahani's understanding eye, he returned the look without embarrassment, while straightening his tie. "I usually drive my car myself, but when I want him to do so for any reason, my houseboy Celestino doubles as chauffeur. I meant to have him do it tonight, so that I wouldn't be bothered with a parking problem. And I think perhaps I ought to take the Castles myself, as they're primarily my guests. I meant to take

Lady Laura and Althea, too. But it seems Jack got ahead of me there. He slipped in his bid to Lady Laura while I was—er—out of earshot and she accepted it. After all, I can't blame her. I've got nothing to compare in elegance with his Daimler, and we would have been a little crowded if both the Castles and the Whitfords had come with me—not that I'd have minded." He looked down at Althea and again they exchanged glances, as Lady Laura had seen them do earlier in the evening; but this time there was ardor, as well as affection and understanding, in the look. "So, if you'd take the Racinas," he concluded. "You said something about wanting to talk to Joe."

"Yes, yes, of course. I shall be delighted to take the Racinas. I will ask them, immediately, if such an arrangement would be agreeable to them."

It was Castle I really wanted to talk with. You know that, Thorpe, Ahani said to himself. Then, with commendable justice, he added, *but of course you're right. You are their host, you have to take them with you. And in any case, what could I say to Castle, in the presence of that unspeakable wife of his? She was bad enough, when she was sober. And now that she's two-thirds drunk, anything can happen. Who knows what a low-born woman like that may say or do when she's in her cups and the few inhibitions and restraints she has managed to acquire are sloughed off? . . . that alone would be reason enough why I must get Castle away from the others. I'll manage that later somehow. I must. Meanwhile . . . .*

Meanwhile, it would be very agreeable to him to talk with Judith. He had not had a chance so far. And he remembered now he had thought, when she first came in, that she had great potentialities. He looked at her again—at the dress which was so modest and at the same time so distinctive, at the lovely banded hair, at the earnest, intelligent face. He approached her with unfeigned pleasure.

"I understand from our host that you and your husband will come in my car to the theater," he said. "I shall be delighted."

"So shall we," Judith answered. And Ahani saw that her face, like her husband's, was transfigured by a smile.

When her master and all his guests had gone, Lalisse came in from the kitchen and gathered up the dishes. She had taken off her beautiful striped dress and put on a nondescript gray garment, but she still wore her bright *tignon* and her hooped earrings. While she was tidying up she dripped some coffee, and after everything was in order she helped herself to brandy and made a *brûlot,* too, setting fire to the liquor after she had mixed it in a spoon with sugar. She did not eat anything, but she sat for a long time, drinking her *brûlot* and singing to herself about the green hills of Martinique and the blue waters around the island. As she sang, she seemed to see them again, and she felt thankful that she did not have to go out in the London fog, like Celestino. By and by she cradled her head in her arms, putting them down on the kitchen table, and went to sleep, feeling sure that the lover she had lost through her own act would come back to her in her dreams.

CHAPTER IV

THE DISTANCE BETWEEN Devonshire Mews and the Terry Theater was not sufficiently great to permit prolonged conversation on any subject. However, each of the groups which left Hilary's house, more or less simultaneously, created an opportunity for the discussion of those matters which most interested them at the moment.

"You did mighty well to get a crowd like that together,

on such short notice. Thorpe," Castle told him. "This Ahani–you know him fairly well, do you?"

"Yes, fairly well. Not nearly as well as I know Jacques de Valcourt, but still–"

"But still you'd say he was probably on the level, wouldn't you?" inquired Castle, who habitually interrupted. This was partly because his alert mind usually kept him one jump ahead of anyone with whom he was talking; and partly because, though unconscious of his rudeness, he would have been indifferent to it in any case. "Ahani seems damned anxious to have a private talk with me," he continued, before Hilary could answer, "and I don't know of any reason why we should have one in such a rush, if at all. I can't help wondering whether he's got something up his sleeve."

"Of course I wouldn't know, for sure," Hilary answered cautiously. "I really haven't any reason to suppose he wasn't telling the complete truth when he laid his haste to some dispatches that came in just this morning. Still, I think Kipling was right."

"What about?" inquired Mrs. Castle, pushing her fluffy fur collar away from her mouth in order to speak audibly.

"Why, when he said that East was East and West was West and that the twain would never meet," Hilary said, his voice betraying no more surprise at her question than at her husband's. "Orientals and Occidentals just don't speak the same language."

"Well, of course I know that. Whoever would expect a good American to talk any of those outlandish dialects they have over in Asia?"

"Good God, Cornelia, that's not what Thorpe meant! And look here! I thought you didn't drink, and I just saw you gulp down one bourbon on the rocks after another. What's the idea? If you suddenly start going in for that sort of thing, one of these days you'll come out of a fog wondering whether what you vaguely recall doing after four highballs was or was not a murder. . . . And speaking of fogs, we're sure groping our way through one now . . . . Well, as for Ahani, it's your idea, isn't it, that for the present at least I'd better accept him at par? Right. I'll give him a chance to spit out whatever he's got on his chest besides ribbons and decorations. That brings us to the Frenchman. He also seems to have a chestful of ribbons, but I expect they mean a lot more than Ahani's. Can you brief me on where he's been and what he's done there?"

"He served in LeClerc's armored division—I think all the way from Lake Chad to Tripoli. After that, he didn't even wait to be sent to England and join the Continental Invasion from there. He parachuted into France, helped to organize the FFI, and did more than any other one man I know of to demoralize the Nazis. He's not just a daredevil, either; he's smart, too. Gets the credit for working out the use of coated cyanide."

"Coated?"

"Yes. I forget the exact name for it. There is one, though. In Holland, the girls had a little routine of carrying a tiny cyanide crystal under a fingernail, and releasing it in Nazi officers' drinks. Trouble was, cyanide acts so quickly it was always simple to identify the girl who had done it and then of course she got hers. Well, De Valcourt had learned from a maternal uncle of his who's a doctor about a coating that's sometimes put around aspirin tablets. You know, there are some people who can't take it in its usual form and—"

"That's me," Cornelia interrupted, unmuffling herself as before. "The headaches I get, you wouldn't believe, and Baldy says that—"

"If you start sopping up bourbon by the quart, you'll have more headaches than ever. Keep quiet, can't you? I want to hear what Thorpe's trying to tell me. It might be important."

"Seems some persons get a bad reaction from aspirin," Thorpe went on hastily, "so medics or druggists or somebody developed a coating that's very slow to dissolve. When it's used, the tablet's no longer in the stomach when the aspirin's liberated. De Valcourt managed to get cyanide crystals coated like that, and when one of these Dutch girls I mentioned slipped it into some Nazi's food or drink, he didn't feel any discomfort. Then about four hours later, bingo! He keeled over dead before he knew what had hit him. And by that time, the girl would have disappeared completely."

"Smart trick, all right! Chief Cloudy Day, one of our Ponca braves back home, would find only one fault with the system. The guy'd die without suffering."

"Well, I don't know that De Valcourt especially wanted him to suffer. He's not essentially cruel. He just wanted to get rid of as many Nazis as possible–and he got rid of plenty. And was decorated for it. That's what some of those ribbons you saw are for. Since then, he's picked up one or two more in Indo-China, where he's been most of the time. He got a bad head wound in some guerrilla fighting, but he's made a fine recovery–you can see that he's the picture of health now. However, he had it pretty rough for quite a while and did well all along the line. I take it he was sent to London partly by way of respite and partly by way of reward. The post of military attaché can be pretty pleasant here–at least, in peacetime–under almost any circumstances; and Jack's so popular that he's in on practically everything that's going on. Besides, he has plenty of leisure for his gardening, which is what he really loves. He's done wonders with the fine old place in Chiswick that he's taken on a long lease–the garden, like most English gardens, had gone to wrack and ruin during the war and he's restored it and developed it. As a matter of fact, that was our first common bond of interest. You see–"

"Oh, yes, the elder Thorpe's nurseries! You did take an interest in them then? I gathered you didn't, or you wouldn't have left them."

"It was because I *was* interested in them that I left them in the beginning. Dad wanted me to experiment with trees and shrubs that aren't indigenous with us, so that he could find out whether they'd thrive and become comercially profitable in our climate. He sent me scouting about from place to place and I got to like living abroad. So then I entered the Foreign Service School at Georgetown and–"

"Yes, yes, I know how one thing can lead to another, that way . . . . De Valcourt's sweet on the Whitford girl, isn't he?"

"That dowdy little thing!" Mrs. Castle protested, again emerging from her furs, despite her husband's admonition. "Baldy, you're crazy! He hardly went near her, all the time we were at the party!"

"Because you didn't give him the chance. You latched onto him the minute we got there and it would have taken a crowbar to pry you loose. That girl's not bad looking at all. At least, I don't think so. What about you, Thorpe?"

"I think she's very beautiful," Hilary said; and this time, instead of speaking cautiously, he spoke coldly.

"Oh, you do, do you? Well, she may be at that—one of these days. Her mother certainly is—still. I mean, she must be fortyish, at least, to have a daughter that old, and still she's a knockout, in her way. Not that I'd call her showy . . . . You know the Whitfords pretty well, too, don't you?"

"Yes, pretty well. I met them at the first Garden Party I went to after I came here, and that was over two years ago . . . . Why, here we are at the Terry. I'll get out first, if you'll excuse me . . . . Be back at ten, Celestino. We're going on to the Savoy and I'll need you to take us there . . . ."

"I hope you're comfortable, Lady Laura—you, too, Althea."

"Very comfortable, thank you." Lady Laura leaned back in the luxurious rear seat of Jacques de Valcourt's smart Daimler and gave a sigh of mingled satisfaction and relief. This was the sort of transportation and the kind of company she really craved. "Even if I weren't, I should be thankful for my escape. Those dreadful people! If I had dreamed—"

Jacques de Valcourt did not have Baldwin Castle's habit of interruption; therefore, though Lady Laura left her sentence unfinished, this was because she was permitted to give it greater dramatic effect. Jacques understood her perfectly: if she had dreamed that the Castles, especially Mrs. Castle, could be so thoroughly offensive, she would not have consented to spend an evening in their company, much less would she have exerted herself to secure the Royal Box as the vantage point for their entertainment. Jacques strove to speak soothingly.

"I believe that the new Ambassador is really a very able man—rather a rough diamond, perhaps, but American presidents seem to have a way of choosing gems in that category for their representatives; and sometimes these do surprisingly well in foreign posts. As to the Ambassadress—well, she may be overstimulated by her new experiences. It is obvious that they *are* new to her. And probably she did not realize that, owing to the early openings, ladies do not as a rule attend the theater in London quite so elaborately dressed."

"She is certainly overstimulated. But I do not believe this is entirely due to her new experiences, as you so charitably express it. I believe the amount of whisky she consumed also has something to do with this. As to her indecent frock and her ostentatious display of jewelry, I do not believe they can be excused on the ground of unfamiliarity with our customs. I believe they are an indication of inborn vulgarity. And to think she is going to a country where the consumption of alcohol, in any form, is contrary to the religious beliefs of its people, and where the veil has so recently been discarded! Even if her husband is as able as you seem to think, she will certainly ruin his career."

Slightly to his surprise, De Valcourt thought he detected satisfaction, rather than regret, in Lady Laura's final statement. He decided that it would probably be wiser not to pursue that phase of the subject.

"Perhaps you heard me inviting them to Chiswick tomorrow," he said. "I had hoped you and Althea would come, also, Lady Laura—in fact, while you were occupied at the tea table, Althea told me she would be glad to."

"Hilary's going, too," Althea interposed quickly.

"Yes, Hilary is going, too," De Valcourt corroborated, a trifle dryly. "Is the company of the Castles so distasteful to you, Lady Laura, that you would prefer not to come at the same time? I would suggest another day—in fact, I shall, an additional one! But the chrysanthemums are so beautiful just now that I do want you to see them in all their glory."

"Oh, Mother, please!"

"Well—" Lady Laura said hesitantly. "Of course, Althea should not have accepted without consulting me. But since she has . . . . If it would be convenient for you to send for us. Our car is out of commission just now and—"

This time Jacques did interrupt. "*Send* for you! Of course I shall *come* for you! And on our way to Chiswick we will talk about that little trip to France I want to have you make. My mother always remains in the country until after Toussaint and she is so eager to welcome you at Château Vaujours. The chrysanthemums there are even much finer than they are at Chiswick—that is, the gardens are, of course, much more extensive. My mother will be writing you herself in the very near future. And I find I can get off for a long week end, almost any time now."

Again Lady Laura sighed softly, and this time there was no possibility of mistaking the sound for any except one of satisfaction. If the Marquise de Valcourt was actually on the point of inviting Lady Laura Whitford and her daughter to pay a visit at Château Vaujours this could mean only one thing: that Jacques de Valcourt was about to ask for Althea's hand in marriage, after the most approved French fashion. She would then become the Marquise de Valcourt; not only exalted rank but immense wealth would be assured her and her mother would share in the benefits and pleasures of them. After years of penny-pinching and pretense, of humiliation and hurts, she would be lapped in luxury, treated with deference, able to condescend or to avenge as best suited her mood and her purpose. With all this in view, she could well afford to tolerate the Castles on one more occasion at least. Of course, there was still the troublesome question of expense–even reduced to its minimum, the cost of that trip to France would be something. And then there would be the inevitable tips to the servants at the château, of whom there were doubtless a great many. But she would manage somehow. In spite of what she had told Althea, only a few hours earlier, there must be something else they could do without.

"If your mother is so kind as to invite us, we shall be very pleased to visit her at Château Vaujours," she told Jacques graciously.

"Provided Hilary can get away the same week end as Jacques and make the trip with us," Althea said suddenly and stubbornly. And, as Lady Laura started to reply, she realized with dismay that the car had stopped in front of the Terry Theater, and that Raoul, Jacques de Valcourt's chauffeur, was opening the door for them.

Ahani, like Castle, was bent on securing information. He had a good deal already, but he wanted more.

"In the course of preparing these articles you are writing, Mr. Racina," he said, as soon as he and Joe and Judith were settled in the Rolls-Royce, "you must have learned a great deal about the new American Ambassador to our country."

"Well, yes. Of course I had to, or I couldn't write the articles. After all, I was supposed to come up with more than you'd find in *Who's Who*."

Ahani leaned forward. "Naturally," he said. "That is what I meant. I can look up where he was born, when he graduated from the University of Oklahoma and when he secured the first foreign oil concession from Aristan. In fact, of course I've already done so. But certain other–"

"Please forgive me for interrupting," Judith said suddenly, "but I've never been to London before and I'm wondering whether this wretched fog keeps me from hearing as well as from seeing. Am I just imagining that it seems to muffle all sound?"

"Anything special you're yearning to hear?" Joe inquired. His tone was one of raillery. But the glance he cast in his wife's direction was one of mingled love and pride. With her usual swift intuition, she had guessed that he did not want to discuss Castle with Ahani and was purposely creating a diversion.

"Superspecial," Judith replied promptly. "Bow Bells. I've read that you're not a Cockney unless you were born within sound of Bow Bells, but we never get to hear anything Londonish back home except the department store versions of Westminster Chimes. So I want to hear Bow Bells, too."

"I deeply regret so charming a visitor must be disappointed, for the moment," Ahani said suavely. "Bow is in the East End, which is a poor neighborhood—a slum I believe you would call it. We are now in the West End, the fashionable quarter of London, and St. Mary-Le-Bow, the City Church which was the home of Bow Bells, was destroyed during an air raid—otherwise, if Madame had been interested, I should have been delighted to put my car at her disposal any day, with instructions to the chauffeur that he should drive up and down Bow and Bromley and Hackney, where she could see and hear to her heart's content."

"That's very kind of you. But in any case our plans depend on what the Castles decide to do. I believe Mrs. Castle wants to stay here for a week or so and then go on to Paris. But Mr. Castle wants to be on his way to Aristan as soon as possible."

"We are no less eager to welcome him there," Ahani assured her.

"Doesn't that depend on just whom you mean by 'we'?" Joe asked casually.

"I beg pardon?" The rising inflection of Ahani's voice did nothing to modify the abrupt sharpening of its timbre.

"I'm not much good at double talk, Excellency," Joe said, speaking more emphatically. "I've always got my dope by telling who I was and what I wanted, not by disguising myself as a bellhop, or something. I mean everyone knows a three-way disagreement's taking shape in Aristan. At one corner of that triangle's the Ameristan Oil Company. At another, Sultan Izzet ibn Hamis. At the third, the Premier. Are all of them equally eager to welcome Baldwin Castle as U.S. Ambassador?"

"Now really, Mr. Racina," Ahani said, still suavely. "I know something of the privileged position journalists occupy in your country. But even so, you would hardly ask that sort of a question of one of your own officials. I mean not with the serious hope of being answered."

"You'd be surprised. But never mind the answer. Shall I go on?"

"As you wish."

"What can I lose? Young Baldwin Castle, newly graduated from Oklahoma U in petroleum engineering, was scheduled to be one of the American technicians the Bolos imported into Holy Russia by droves in the middle twenties: business administrators, agricultural experts, factory managers, petroleum wizards, electronics engineers. The idea was that they were to teach the newly liberated proletariat the difference between a tractor and an abscessed tooth. But he got only as far as London, when a wire from Perisphere Petroleum, back in Tulsa, switched his route to read, 'Destination Aristan.' You can check me any time you wish, sir."

"I have no comment at this point, Mr. Racina," Ahani murmured politely.

"I'll go right ahead, then. In Aristan, Sultan Suleiman ibn Hamis, father of the present ruler, is shaky on his throne, but very, on account of no money in the kitty despite heavy taxes. After all, what's a sultan or a sheik or a shah? He's a boss. And a boss with no fleshpots to set before the faithful isn't long for this world, whether he's in Hackensack, Argentina or Aristan."

"Did Mr. Castle tell you all this himself?"

"Enough so I could fill in the gaps without trouble. I already knew something about the Red Line Compact; after all, I live in Louisiana, which is a major oil center. A big global syndicate, controlled pretty much by British members, once drew a red line about a map of the Middle East; they had agreed cosily among themselves that within that line they wouldn't bid against one another. So Suleiman ibn Hamis, left to dangle, was about as sure of his immediate future as a tipsy tightrope walker with the hiccups. All of a sudden, an upstart nobody named Castle grabs the concession by handing ibn Hamis enough folding money, so that all Suleiman's chillun will be sitting pretty from then on, especially after they find a young ocean of oil before the sands of the desert grew cold."

"Interesting. Most interesting."

"One moment more, Excellency. The syndicate wasn't the only outfit whose nose was put out of joint when brash young Castle took ibn Hamis off the hook. Some Nationalists, as they called themselves, though they were really as red as three gallons of borsch, had counted on moving into the vacuum Hamis' fall would create. Those babies haven't forgotten who cooked up that mess of crow they had to eat. I don't know whose side Castle will be on; but whichever of your three push-pulls wins, it's up to Castle to see the U.S. doesn't lose . . . . How come we've stopped? Oh, we're at the Terry. Sorry I monopolized the rostrum. You should have shushed me, Ju. Aren't you supposed to provide terminal facilities for my rampages?"

Though all three cars took approximately the same route, Celestino was the first to deliver his passengers at the Terry Theater. He had begun his driving in Mexico City and, in consequence, had never entirely suppressed his instinct for dashing headlong through the densest traffic. Having dismissed the chauffeur, Hilary said that perhaps it would simplify matters if he went ahead and guided the Castles through the crowded vestibule, whose walls were covered with striking pictures of Janice Lester taken during the most compelling scenes in *Gold of Pleasure.* Then he led them toward a long flight of steps which skirted the stalls. At this point, an attendant came forward, respectfully asked to see their tickets and then, still more respectfully, preceded them onward.

"Where on earth are we going? Down a shaft?" Mrs.

Castle inquired. The edge of her pleased excitement had worn off in the course of the drive, and she was not happily impressed with the steep, narrow and dimly lighted stairway which they were now descending. In fact, she was a little frightened by it, for it was not only utterly unlike anything she had pictured as the approach to a Royal Box, but unlike anything she had seen in an American theater. No one had thought of warning her about the difference in construction between these and their English counterparts; so she had expected to go up and not down. Once she stumbled a little and swore under her breath as she clutched for support. But when the attendant threw open a door and then stood back, bobbing her head, Cornelia Castle stopped on the threshold with an exclamation of enchanted amazement.

The door led into the Royal Retiring Room, a circular apartment quite as large as Hilary's living room, if not actually larger, furnished in a manner which had represented the height of elegance when the theater was built, and which still embodied this, in Mrs. Castle's fascinated gaze. The walls were covered with crimson brocade, and from the high ceiling was suspended a many-branched crystal chandelier. Ponderous chairs, framed in carved and gilded wood and upholstered in crimson velvet, were grouped around a marble-topped center table. A marble mantel, which surmounted a glowing grate, was, in turn, surmounted by a heavy, gilt-framed mirror. On one side of this fireplace was a closed door; on the other, one had been left discreetly ajar to reveal a basin with large glittering faucets, which was set in a huge slab of chocolate-colored marble. Beyond and above this basin loomed the unmistakable outlines of a large overhead tank and a pull chain. Opposite the entrance where they had paused was another doorway, draped to match the upholstery of the velvet chairs and leading, by means of a short flight of crimson-covered steps, down to a large semicircular box. This was likewise brocade lined, and in it six chairs, similar in design to those in the Royal Retiring Room, were placed three abreast.

"Programs, sir? Sixpence each," the attendant said to

Hilary. "And could you tell me now whether you'll be wanting coffee in the first or the second interval?"

Hilary accepted the programs, adding largesse to their cost, and said he would have to let her know later about the coffee. The attendant, greatly pleased with her tip, made another suggestion.

"May I take Madam's coat?" she inquired deferentially. Cornelia Castle turned on her.

"When I want to get rid of this coat, I'll say so," she snapped. "I suppose you want money for taking that, too. Paying for programs! I never heard of such a thing. Besides, it's probably warm enough by the fire, but I bet out there in the box it's as cold as it is almost everywhere else in England. Just the same–" she added, advancing far enough to permit her husband and Hilary to follow her into the Retiring Room, "this is *it*, isn't it? Why even the john–" She threw open the door which had been left so discreetly ajar and laughed aloud. "Say, I haven't seen one of those, I mean one of *that kind*, since I was a kid. Talk about antiques! Just the same, it sort of adds to the Victorian atmosphere, doesn't it? And all this gilt and marble and velvet are certainly the cat's whiskers. Look at the amount of space we have, too! We could give a party right here."

"The attendants pass coffee and ices between every act," Hilary told her.

"My God, I'm not interested in coffee and ices! I mean lobster salad and caviar sandwiches–that sort of thing. And champagne, lots and lots of champagne! I was sick as a pup aboard ship until the stewardess recommended that and it fixed me up in a jiffy. Now I've decided it's pretty good for whatever ails you." She broke off, laughing at her own feeble witticism. Then she went on. "Look, Baldy, you were dead set against my sending a note to Janice Lester and asking her if we couldn't go backstage. I bet she'd have said yes just like that. But now I've got a better idea. Let's ask her to come *here*–her and her manager and her leading man and anyone else she'd like to bring along."

"Listen, Cornelia, we've just had one big feed and

we're going to have another after the theater. That's enough. Besides, maybe you've forgotten, but this is Thorpe's party, not ours."

"Of course, I want to do everything I can to add to Mrs. Castle's pleasure," Hilary said hastily. "I'm sure if I send out right away, I could get the champagne. I'm not so sure about the lobster salad, but I can always try."

"All right, you try. And while you're doing that, I'll dash off a few lines to the fair Janice."

"Cornelia, I've told you before and I'm telling you again that I don't give a damn about seeing Janice Lester. I didn't even care much about seeing her on the stage, though I was willing to humor you about that. But when it comes to dragging her in here—"

His wife paid no attention to him. She had already seated herself at the marble-topped table and was scribbling on a small pad which she had extracted from her jeweled evening bag. At that moment, the attendant again opened the door of the Royal Retiring Room to admit Lady Laura, Althea and Jacques de Valcourt. Cornelia ripped off the sheet of paper and handed it to her.

"Here," she said, "you take this backstage and give it to Janice Lester—put it right into her hand, you understand. When you come back and tell me you've done it, I'll give you a tip myself, after all—a pound. And I'll have another note ready for you then, too. I want you to take it to that small box just back of this one, where that dark-complexioned man with all the medals on is just sitting down. See?" She began to scribble again and, when she looked up, Lady Laura and Althea were already seated in the front of the box, and De Valcourt was sitting in the center chair of the rear row, leaning forward and talking to them. Hilary had stepped out, presumably to order champagne and lobster salad, but Castle was still standing close to his wife and still arguing furiously. She continued to disregard his protests as she tore a second sheet from the pad and replaced it in her evening bag. When the attendant returned, Cornelia had already wrapped the second message she had written in a pound note; but she unfolded the slip of paper which had been brought to her before she handed over the one she had prepared.

"Listen to this! she read aloud, at last looking up at her husband.

Dear Mrs. Castle:

How very kind of you to invite us to have champagne with you in the Royal Retiring Room! We shall be delighted to come during the first entr'acte, which is the longer of the two; and since you are good enough to make your invitation so inclusive, by "we" I mean my husband Hugo, who is also my manager, and my cousin Evan Neville, who is our *jeune premier*. As you will see for yourself in a few minutes, the male lead in the play calls for a very young man, and I think you'll agree that Evan plays the part to perfection. But I mustn't say more than that, for I don't want to give the plot away–I do so hope no one else has done that already.

A bientôt, dear Mrs. Castle,

Cordially yours,
JANICE LESTER

P.S. *En attendant,* give Win my love.

Cornelia Castle pronounced the French words hesitantly, Anglicizing them almost past recognition. But though there was bewilderment, there was no hesitancy in her voice when she read the final part of the postscript. She looked up from the slip of paper and met her husband's angry eyes with a look that was angrier still.

"Give Win my love! she repeated. "So you were Win to Janice Lester, were you, before you were Baldy to me? Well, I might have known there was some reason why you were fighting shy of her!"

"Did Madam wish me to deliver another note?" the attendant inquired from the doorway.

"There goes the curtain," said Hilary, coming hurriedly back into the room.

CHAPTER V

THE ADJECTIVE MOST frequently used to describe the effect of Janice Lester's acting was "magical" and none could have been more apt. This magic began its spell as soon as she appeared on the stage, and before the end of the first act her enchanted audience was oblivious to everything else. Judith stopped worrying about the effect which the chilly blasts sweeping over Farman Hill might have on young children not yet acclimated to October in New England. Joe stopped wondering how he was to present Baldwin Castle truthfully and at the same time tactfully to the readers of *This Month*–not that he was unduly concerned about Castle's personal feelings; but he knew that the international situation was already precarious and he shrank from putting it still further out of balance through an injudicious choice of words. Ahani had also been troubled by the possibility of this augmented unbalance, not only through Joe Racina's potential approach to an immense number of readers, but also on account of the dispatches just received and the way in which Castle might conceivably react to them. Then there was Castle's wife, who would certainly complicate the situation still further. Ahani had come to the theater a harassed and angry man and had taken no notice of his own wife Zeina, who arrived shortly after he did and sat silent and shadowy in the rear of their small box; with her mother, still more wrapped in obscurity, beside her. But when the curtain fell, and Zeina leaned forward to whisper in his ear, the abstraction with which he answered her was caused neither by his normal condescending indifference to her nor by his recent abnormal upheaval from calm, but by the difficulty he experienced in returning to reality from the realms to which Janice had transported him.

The spectators in the Royal Box were no less bedazzled and beguiled. Hilary, sitting directly behind Althea, had managed to capture her hand in his and to hold it throughout the act; how much of their mutual rapture was caused by this handclasp, and by the sense of reassurance it gave their own romance, and how much by the enactment of ripening romance on the stage, they neither knew nor cared; but they were aware that except for the benignant darkness of the theater, no such prolonged caress would have been possible, and their mood became more and more ecstatic as it continued. Lady Laura and Jacques de Valcourt both found themselves reliving past pleasures of the world, the flesh and the devil, with emphasis on the world as far as the former was concerned, and on the flesh and the devil when it came to the latter. Lady Laura was no longer the bitter, impoverished, middle-aged woman, striving to make both ends meet in the basement flat of the once proud house which had been all her own; she was the debutante curtsying to the King and Queen at Buckingham Palace, the lace-veiled bride at St. George's, Hanover Square, the young wife traveling with her husband to exotic lands where he added to his magnificent collection of butterflies; the serene chatelaine of Helston Abbey, where tea was served on the terrace by footmen in livery and white swans glided over the glassy surface of the lake beyond. Jacques de Valcourt was no longer the elegant dilettante, dabbling in horticulture because there was no war to test his valor, and courting a virtuous, rosy-cheeked English girl, because there was no dark-eyed, seductive Provençale to rush with joyous abandon into his arms; he was once more the daredevil who stole by night into a certain house on the Cannebière, to alert the FFI for the landing of an airborne invasion from the south, and having delivered the message, to go dancing with his mistress under the very noses of the Nazis.

Even the Castles, who had both been seething with rage when they took their seats, had gradually become calmer, had next regained a measure of good humor, and eventually had begun to find enjoyment in spite of themselves. *Baldy might have told me he knew Janice Lester already,* Cornelia reflected; *after all, I told him everything of that sort—or nearly everything. But then, I never supposed Minnie Brown, that sickly first wife of his, was the only other female in his life. I was always pretty sure Minnie got him on the rebound, but it didn't matter anyway. Come to think of it, Janice Lester doesn't matter, either. She was just the Other Woman—and I'm an ambassador's wife, and now I've got sables and diamonds, and a big life insurance policy made out in my favor. So that, whatever might happen to Baldy, I could go right on having sables and diamonds, or anything else I wanted to have. I could do anything I wanted, too—the policy isn't tied up with a lot of red tape. Not that I really want Baldy to pass out of the picture—at least, I don't when I'm sober. And I'm sober now—practically sober. And having a damned fine time. This show we're seeing right now, for instance—I never would have got to it if it hadn't been for the kind of people Baldy knows, like Lady Laura and Hilary Thorpe. And Janice Lester is certainly a knockout in it. There isn't anyone on the stage who can touch her. Of course, she makes the show—*Gold of Pleasure *isn't much of a play if you pick it to pieces: all about a girl who lives on the wrong side of the tracks, and a man a lot older, a rich, highbrow widower, who lives on the right side of them, and who takes a liking to her and marries her. It's easy enough to see what is going to happen next. She and his playboy son are going to fall for each other and then there will be unshirted hell. Not that I blame the girl in the play. Why, if Baldy had a handsome son like that . . . but of course he didn't. Women like Minnie Brown never have any children, no matter what sort of he-men they marry . . . I wish I could have hung on to* *my own kid, he sure was cute. But I guess he was better off on the farm with his old man, at first. And now it's too late to get him away—at least, I suppose it is . . . .*

As Baldwin Castle's rage subsided, his reflections became equally satisfactory. *Of course Cornelia had made a damned fool of herself, and he would question her, the next morning, about this sudden yen for liquor and tell her she would have to lay off quick, or else. But aside from that, things couldn't have been going better. Those pieces of Joe Racina's would put a stop to a lot of loose talk from people who didn't know enough to keep their big mouths shut. As to Ahani, he was a slick customer all right; but Castle was used to dealing with slick customers, in Aristan and everywhere else. And now that Ahani was all hot and bothered about those dopey dispatches, it would be like taking candy from a baby to manage him. Thorpe and De Valcourt both had a lot of class; so did the girl, Althea, and hell's big brass bells! so did her mother. And he couldn't for the life of him understand now, why he'd thought it would be just as well not to meet Janice again or why he hadn't even wanted to see her from a distance. "Magical"—he'd made fun of the word, often enough, saying it was in the same class with "glamorous" except that it wasn't quite so overworked. But at that, it had been the right word to describe her, twenty years before, and it still was. The bronze-colored hair of hers, which she had had the sense not to dye or cut—though of course someone must have told her she ought to be a blonde in* Gold of Pleasure, *even if she had held out against it until then—showed she still had her wits about her; her yellow dress was twice as effective because her hair wasn't yellow, too. She could wear any color, with that hair and that figure and that skin. He didn't believe she'd put on an extra ounce, either. And then her voice—well, that was golden all right, if Bernhardt's and Duse's had been, like people who'd heard them said they were. It was golden and it was magical, too. Why, she could still give any woman cards and spades. Any woman in the world . . . .*

Curtain call followed curtain call. Again and again,

Janice Lester responded to the crashing applause. The first few times she appeared between Claude Lucas, who played her middle-aged benefactor, and Evan Neville, who played his son; she smiled and bowed to each, as if acknowledging her indebtedness to their support, before she faced the audience; then she inclined her lovely head so deferentially that it seemed as if she were giving thanks for a tribute which she neither expected nor deserved. But at last she came out alone and stood, no longer bowed but proudly erect, no longer smiling but beautifully grave. The golden curtains parted in the middle once more to reveal her as she continued to stand in statuesque immobility. Confused shouts of "Bravo!" mingled with the applause, now louder than ever. Then the curtains swept across from each side before her and were not drawn back again.

Hilary gave Althea's hand a final pressure and hurried up the short flight of steps from the box to the Retiring Room. The attendant was just opening the door to the upper stairway, in order to admit a maître d'hôtel and two waiters, bearing linen, silverware and the champagne and lobster which Cornelia had demanded. Before Hilary finished giving swift directions for arranging the table, the door opened again and Ahani appeared on the threshold. He glanced around him, taking in the festive preparations without enthusiasm.

"I understand this is to be quite a long entr'acte," he said. "So I thought it might give me the opportunity I did not have at your house to speak quietly with Mr. Castle for a few minutes. No, no, that was not your fault. You very kindly offered me the use of your study, but Mr. Castle obviously preferred to remain at the tea table. And then, just as the curtain was going up, I received a note from Mrs. Castle, asking me to bring the ladies of my party here to meet Janice Lester who is, I must say, a very great actress."

"I hope you'll do so," Hilary answered cordially. "Of course I know that Madame Ahani doesn't usually accompany you to social functions, but this is to be such a small, private gathering—"

"No other guests? The note was obviously written in haste; it didn't say."

"Only the Racinas. And here they are now. Here's everyone."

"Everyone except Janice Lester and her side-kicks," Cornelia amended. But her statement was more or less lost in the general chatter about the play. Ahani slipped out and returned with his wife and her mother, who remained in the background, unobserved, until Judith went over and spoke to them; then they shook their heads and cast down their eyes. After a moment or two, she realized that their abashment was only partly due to their prescribed custom of withdrawal; it was also partly due to their inability to understand English. Her French was not fluent, but she knew enough to attempt it; the two ladies from Aristan brightened visibly under her halting but kindly efforts to converse with them and they finally consented to come nearer the others, while still keeping close to her side. Cornelia had briefly acknowledged their presence, when this was called to her attention, and told them to sit down, if they wanted to. But she had not tried to talk with them or with anyone else at length; all her attention had been focused on the door opening to the stairway which led backstage.

Again Joe's swift glance toward Judith was one in which love and pride contended for mastery. It was nothing short of miraculous, the way she always managed to do exactly the right thing! *I sure must have been living right the day I met her*! he told himself, just as he had on thousands of earlier occasions; and, for a few minutes, he only half heard what Ahani and Castle, who were deep in conversation just behind him, were saying to each other. Then he caught the import of words which sounded almost brusque.

"And I'm telling you, Mr. Ambassador, that unless I see it in black and white, I won't answer your questions. So let's change the subject."

"To Miss Lester's superb performance?" Ahani inquired. The glance he turned on Castle, from half-lidded eyes, was an unwavering stare.

"Why not? When you get right down to it, the play's nothing much. If it weren't for Janice Lester—"

As if the words had effected a summons, the door leading to the lower stairway was thrown open and Janice Lester entered the Royal Retiring Room. She had changed from the simple dress of yellow crepe which she had worn in the first act to a gorgeous gold lamé, and topazes alternated with the diamonds which encircled her neck and wrists. The two men in formal evening clothes who followed her were as completely overshadowed as the ladies who accompanied Ahani.

"I'm *so* sorry to have kept everyone waiting!" she exclaimed apologetically. "But I thought if I changed first, then we wouldn't have such a sense of haste when I did get here. This is Mrs. Castle, isn't it? I can't tell you how much I appreciate your invitation! And Win! How *are* you? Why, you've hardly changed at all! But I'm afraid introductions are in order, to the rest—except to Joe, of course. Joe darling, I *am* so glad to see you!"

Quite unaffectedly, she flung her arms around him, hugging and kissing him heartily. There was nothing studied or theatrical about the embrace. She turned back to Mrs. Castle, her face radiant.

"Do let me sit beside Joe, so we can talk about old times, won't you?" she asked. "You haven't any idea how good he was to me, in the days when he was a spear bearer and I was a happy villager."

"Well, of course if you want Joe on one side of you, that's all right by me. But Baldy'll have to be on your other side. You want to talk about old times with him, too, don't you?"

"Oh, no! I wouldn't dare, now that he's an ambassador. There, I'm forgetting as usual! This is my husband Hugo Alban, and this is my cousin Evan Neville. Now we all know each other, don't we? And do tell us just how you want us placed, Mrs. Castle, so we won't lose too much more time. And I was just joking. Of course, any place is all right for me, as long as I have Joe on one side."

The seating presented some difficulties, partly because

the marble-topped center table, now covered with a white cloth, was not large enough to accommodate a company of fourteen; and partly because Mrs. Castle, though she had pre-empted the role of hostess, was not yet well versed in matters of protocol, and was too preoccupied with the question of crowding to listen attentively to the whispered hints which Hilary was endeavoring to give her. Ahani came to the rescue by suggesting that, since the ladies of his party would not be drinking champagne in any case, perhaps they might be seated at a small supplementary table, which was now in a corner, but which could easily be brought forward; then, if Mrs. Racina and Miss Whitford would join them that would make an agreeable feminine group, and they would be delighted. It was, indeed, obvious that the ladies from Aristan were much pleased with this plan, which was quickly put into effect; both Zeina and her mother were now chatting unrestrainedly with Judith and, though they suffered a momentary relapse into timidity when Althea was presented to them, this was quickly overcome. Zeina had with her a beautiful little box filled with tiny sweetmeats, and this she passed to her table companions with the shy suggestion that perhaps the guests at the other table would like some, too.

"I am sure they would," Judith said cordially. She held the box for a moment, admiring its exquisite workmanship, and then handed it to Joe, after selecting a sugar-coated almond. He raised his eyebrows slightly, as if to indicate that sugared almonds would not make the most suitable accessory to lobster salad and, though the expression was quickly controlled, Ahani caught it. He spoke swiftly to his wife in their own language and at once she produced another box, smaller and even more richly jeweled, from among her draperies and, rising, presented it to her husband.

"The coating on these walnut fragments is salted," he said, opening the box, extracting a dainty morsel and offering it to Castle. "You must often have eaten walnuts prepared in this way, when you were in Aristan.

Such preparation is a specialty of the region I come from."

"Also a rarity elsewhere," Castle said, accepting the fragment and putting it into his mouth. "So I can't truthfully say I had them often. I always wished I could though, once I'd had a chance to sample them."

"Please honor us by accepting these then—and the box which contains them," Ahani replied. "There is no use in passing them around. No one else here would appreciate them—or even notice whether or not you had something they hadn't."

It was quite true. Everyone's eyes were fastened on Janice Lester, everyone was listening to her golden voice. Occasionally, in an absent-minded way, somebody took a mouthful of lobster or a sip of champagne; but food and drink had become quite incidental. Janice was talking about the days when she and Joe had first known each other and she was making a fascinating story of "suping."

"I'd been trying to get a master's degree, you see," Joe added by way of explanation. "All year I'd been teaching at a little jerkwater college in West Virginia to save enough for summer courses at the University of Chicago. Well, when this chance came along to earn seventy-five cents a night by suping with the Otis Skinner Company in *Kismet* for a solid month . . . ."

"You should have seen him!" Janice exclaimed joyously. "He was a Persian soldier, with baggy green silk pants and a bow."

"Stop belittlin'! I was also a civilian in the market place scene. In fact, I had two parts, while you and Otis Skinner had only one each."

"But I also had a line, you wretch. I said, 'Yes, mistress' to Kut-al-kulub in the harem scene." She turned to the others, radiant. "I had just been promoted from the ranks of the supes myself. It was my very first professional engagement. Joe took me to a cafeteria on Wabash Avenue to celebrate and told me to go ahead and take chicken, even if it did cost thirty-five cents a portion. And he also said—I'll never forget this! Never

–he said, 'Now that you've got the line, be sure they don't give you the hook!' "

Cornelia giggled shrilly. "This is a regular Old Home Week for you, Miss Lester, isn't it?" she asked. "Tell me, was that the time you met Baldy, too?"

"Oh, that was later, and much less exciting," Janice said casually. "I was acting a bit part on Broadway in a play called *Dusk in December*. Perhaps some of the rest of you saw it? . . . Well, it doesn't matter. Win did and he liked it. He was in New York on a theater-going spree, so he took in *Dusk* along with all the other shows. He liked me, too, in my part well enough to come backstage afterward. Pretty soon this became quite a habit and I found I liked *him*. So . . . well, perhaps you'll tell that story, Win."

"No. I'm not much of a storyteller."

"Did you know Miss Lester at that time, too, Mr. Alban?" Lady Laura inquired, addressing Hugo for the first time.

"Yes. I'd just become the star's manager. Janice and I were married later that same year. We'd both started small and we'd both gone ahead fast. So we had lots in common from the beginning."

"Did you start as a supernumerary, too?" Lady Laura asked, still politely simulating an interest she did not feel.

"No. My first line was entirely different–sleight of hand. It came natural to me and I made good at it right away. All the same, it's quite a jump–from magic to managing, I mean. Nowadays, it's Janice who deals in magic, as I don't need to tell you, and without any help from me."

As he spoke, Alban grinned, revealing strong yellow teeth. His smile formed a wide crescent in his face, which was almost as dark as Ahani's. It did not illumine, in the way Joe's smile lighted his countenance; but it had somewhat the same power of transformation. Until now Alban had been almost expressionless and had seemed amiably insignificant–just a small, retiring man, with scanty black locks brushed back from a high, mild forehead and a large nose which overshadowed a receding chin. But the teeth gave him a surprising appearance of strength and menacing purpose; it was almost as if some inoffensive-looking animal had suddenly bared vicious fangs.

"That's all nonsense," Janice said laughingly. "About his not helping me, that is. The next year *I* was the star and he was *my* manager. I couldn't have *lived* without his help, much less gone on and up! He's the most wonderful husband in the world—and the most wonderful manager, too. It wasn't such a jump from magic to managing as he's pretending, either. Why, he was at the very top of his profession in legerdemain! If I hadn't intervened, he might have become another Houdini. He still does parlor tricks once in a while—just for amusement, of course. He could shift everything around on this table so fast you'd never see when he did it, and put things in some people's pockets and take them out of other people's handbags, without anyone being the wiser."

"Really?" Lady Laura still spoke politely, but she no longer feigned an interest she did not feel; she could imagine nothing less appropriate to the occasion than an impromptu display of legerdemain. "What about you?" she asked Evan, turning to the *jeune premier*.

"Oh, I came along a little later, without any special display of talent! In fact, I was just an 'infant, mewling and puking in the nurse's arms'—or, if you'd like the expression prettified, an orphan angel. My parents were killed in an automobile accident and Miss Lester took pity on me and adopted me—Miss Lester and Mr. Alban I should say, of course. But I've had some kind of a part in every one of Miss Lester's plays—even *Dusk in December,* during the latter part of its long run. They began by using a doll for the foundling in the basket left on the doorstep. Then they decided to make the scene more realistic by using a real baby, who would probably cry. I was the baby and I obliged. That was the way I got my start."

"And now he's the leading man! It's marvelous, isn't

it?" Janice said, looking at him fondly. "That's still another story—Evan's rise to fame and fortune. I'm afraid we haven't time to tell it now. There goes the first call bell. But we've still time for one toast before we leave."

"You're right, lover. I'll prepare the drink and you propose the health. And perhaps Evan will help you out with a quotation."

With a sudden swooping movement, Hugo picked up an empty champagne glass and, lifting it high above his head, twirled it round and round, meanwhile flourishing a large white silk handkerchief he had taken from his pocket in his other hand and grinning toothily at every member of the group in turn. While his fellow guests watched him with bewilderment, the empty glass appeared to fill before their astonished eyes. Then they realized that the appearance was not an illusion: the glass was brimming and next it was bubbling over; yet no one had seen Hugo touch one of the bottles standing on the table, uncorked, but with contents still untasted. He wiped off the edge of the glass with a corner of the silk handkerchief and handed it to Janice, who turned to Evan.

"I can't think up a toast, just like that!" he said, almost sulkily.

"Why, of course you can."

Her tone was not only encouraging, it was challenging. Evan hesitated a moment longer. Then, still sulkily, he muttered, "I can't do better than say, 'Sweet health and fair desire consort Your Grace!'" and bowed in Castle's direction.

"Just a minute. I can't join in the toast if you give it to me personally. I propose that, instead, we drink to a happy future for that great and glorious country, Aristan, and to my share in assuring this, in whatever way I can, no matter how."

"Bravo! That's a toast in which you should all join!" Enthusiastically, Ahani picked up a champagne bottle and filled all the remaining glasses himself. As Castle drained the one Janice had given him, he turned to her and whispered something, inaudible to the company at large, momentarily looking straight into her eyes. Then, apparently satisfied with the response he found there, he turned away and spoke in his normal voice.

"It may surprise most of you, but I can spout Shakespeare, too, when there's a good reason for it," he said, reaching for another glass. "How's this?"

> 'Would our hearts love till now? forswear it, sight!
> For ne'er saw I true beauty till this night.' "

The quotation was all the more startling in its effect because it seemed so incongruous, coming from Castle's lips. There was a moment of electrified silence. Then Hugo touched his wife lightly on the arm.

"That's the second bell, darling," he said, "unless you hurry, you'll be late for your call."

CHAPTER VI

JOE HAD SUGGESTED to Judith, in a whispered aside, that they should not return to the Royal Retiring Room during the second entr'acte, since this was to be a short one, and she had instantly agreed, understanding that there was some reason besides the brevity of the interval why he wished to remain where he was. When he sat silent beside her in the stalls after another long succession of curtain calls, she did not try to make small talk about the progress of the play or draw him out by lengthy questioning. She guessed that he was making his customary astute appraisal of the persons with whom he had been thrown and storing up his impressions for future use. She accepted the coffee they had ordered before learning about the champagne supper, quietly adjusted the tray for their mutual convenience and, silent in her turn, became immersed in her own thoughts . . . .

Janice, Joe decided, had changed very greatly. Of course he had not expected to find the carefree *gamine* he had known in Chicago; while becoming an established star, she had, inevitably, ceased to be an aspiring soubrette. She was radiant now instead of roguish and she had gained immeasurably during the transformation. Moreover, the years had been very kind to her; she was infinitely more beautiful in her rich maturity than she had been in her untried youth. But the radiance and the beauty had other qualities for their undercurrent. Ambition? Of course. But she had always had that. Pride? That was not new, either. On the other hand, she had been singularly warmhearted as a girl; it was this warmheartedness ringing through her untrained voice which had made it so compelling then; now there was something vaguely disquieting about it. Inconsequentially, Joe thought of the *wundersame, gewaltige Melodei* sung by the legendary German enchantress. Naturally, that was absurd; Janice was no Lorelei, luring the unwary to their death by a song. Just the same, there was a devastating element in her charm; he would rather have her for a friend than an enemy. Or did he really want her for a friend any more? And why should he think she could ever be vengeful or hostile? He did not know. But the conviction persisted.

He looked up, with a slight start, as the attendant came to remove the coffee tray; his thoughts had taken him so far from his actual physical surroundings and so deep into the realm of conjecture that it took him a moment to realize where he was and what he was doing. But, when the attendant had unobtrusively departed, he lapsed easily into reflection again.

Hugo he characterized with a single muttered designation of "Whattaman!" Judith heard him, smiled, and reached for his hand. "Alban?" she asked and Joe nodded. Then, silently and judiciously, he considered the manager's blank expression, suggestive of a marionette, when his face was in repose, and his repulsive, revelatory smile, when it was not. The man was queerly built, too, his head set upon a short neck above spreading shoulders, his trunk thick, his hips narrow, his legs spindling. Offhand, he seemed as ill equipped intellectually and spiritually as he was physically. Yet he had excelled in his first chosen trade and later he had become an outstandingly successful manager; actually, he must be shrewder than he looked. And after all, Janice had married him; speaking with a ring of deep sincerity in her voice, she had said that she could not have lived, much less acted, without him. Obviously, she had not found him physically repulsive and she must have found him not only congenial but kind and helpful. There was a mystery here, too . . . .

Joe was a little cramped from sitting so long—his long legs made it hard for him to adjust himself to the limitations of a stall seat. He shifted his position, stretched himself and rose, turning to survey the house. Spectators were now streaming out for a smoke; just the same, it was easy to estimate that the theater must have been packed to the last seat; patient crowds must have "queued up" for hours, to get places in the "gods." Once, not so long ago, either, that was what he would have had to do himself. Fate had been very kind to him in many ways, but especially in his work and in his wife. He could not conceive that Alban could possibly have found such fullfillment in either and, for the first time, Joe's appraisal of the manager was tinged with pity.

As to Evan, he might be almost anything, despite the diffidence which had thrust him into the background of the Retiring Room and kept him there, except when he emerged from his shell long enough to quote Shakespeare appropriately. Janice had been much the same off the stage as on it—the very incarnation of a charmer, conscious of her power and a past mistress in the art of wielding it. On the other hand, Neville, the sleek sophisticate of the play, was anything but the presumptuous young gallant deliberately setting out to become his father's rival. While acting, his bearing, like his movements, had been unhesitant and assured; while slumped in his chair, withdrawn from his fellow guests, he kept his eyes downcast, except for occasional darting glances when he apparently believed himself unobserved; moreover, he seemed handicapped by a complete lack of direction. Once, when Castle addressed a sudden remark to him, he upset a champagne glass with a startled, aimless gesture; and when Castle righted it, saving part of its contents, Evan's acknowledgment of this rescue sounded almost as maladroit as a schoolboy's. He had finely chiseled features and a really beautiful brow from which abundant auburn hair swept back in graceful, if overlong, waves. But he was extremely pale, and though his skin was clear, the pallor had an unhealthful tinge. Something about him suggested the dreamy ascetic, unbalanced instead of uplifted by mysticism, rather than the alert, cocksure philanderer. It occurred to Joe that someday the boy might play Hamlet remarkably well. Unquestionably, he had great talent as an actor; otherwise, he would not have been able to throw himself into a part alien to his nature in such a way as to give a complete illusion of reality.

Joe was still visualizing him in this most demanding of all roles when he realized that someone behind him was courteously asking him to take his seat. The curtain went up again, revealing Evan as the false son and Janice as the false wife, locked in a close embrace . . . .

At the second rise of the curtain, the occupants of the box had taken their places as before, with Hilary behind Althea, De Valcourt behind Cornelia and Castle behind Lady Laura. When the second act ended, Cornelia, instead of joining in the general applause, twisted around and whispered to De Valcourt.

"Mr. Thorpe was telling us about some aspirin with a special coating," she said. "He told us you had an uncle, or someone, who was a doctor and used it for patients who couldn't take ordinary aspirin and that this gave you an idea for coating cyanide the same way. Have you got any with you?"

"What, cyanide?" De Valcourt inquired jestingly.

"Of course not," Cornelia replied rather crossly. "I've got a devilish headache and I happen to be one of those poor simps who can't take ordinary aspirin. I told Mr. Thorpe so, on the drive over from his house. I thought it was just possible–"

"Of course. I'm happy to say I'm well provided. I'm also one of those poor simps, as you put it–a fellow unfortunate, if you will permit a rephrase. My uncle was very fond of me, as I was of him. It was through his sympathy for me, and his desire to relieve me, that he made the experiments with aspirin which later inspired me to make my own with cyanide."

De Valcourt opened his wallet and took from it a small vial containing half a dozen tablets. "Of course you can't expect immediate relief," he said, handing it to Cornelia. "You understand the action's delayed by the coating. That's the purpose of it."

"Yes, I got that. And thanks a million. Now I'm just dying to hear more about those Dutch girls. Won't you–"

"Excuse me. It will be better if you drink a little water with the aspirin. I will get you some from the lavatory. Surely there must be a glass there."

"Perhaps you could get two glasses. And perhaps Mrs. Castle could spare one of the tablets you so kindly gave her. I can take ordinary aspirin, but I find I have none with me and even if the action of the medicine is delayed, it will be better than getting no relief at all. I have a headache, too."

Lady Laura smiled pleasantly at De Valcourt. "So I think I shall remain where I am during this entr'acte," she said. "I hope Mrs. Castle will keep me company here. If not, I shall be perfectly contented to stay alone, looking about the house from this vantage point and identifying my various acquaintances. I know that you and Althea and our host are all longing to smoke and I am equally sure that Mr. Ahani wants the Retiring Room put at his disposal for a chat with Mr. Castle. I wasn't supposed to overhear, but I couldn't help it, and from my involuntary eavesdropping I've learned that he's been repeatedly seeking a private conference. This would seem to me an excellent time for it."

"Dear Lady Laura, you are always so thoughtful!

While I am getting the two glasses, you must persuade Althea to join me for a stroll in the foyer; Hilary will will not need any persuasion, if she consents. I am sure you and Mrs. Castle will find that the discomforts of migraine form a bond of interest and that this will result in an absorbing discussion. Thus the Retiring Room will be available to our two distinguished ambassadors and *tout s'arrangera*!"

"Look here!" Castle protested. But it was already too late. De Valcourt slipped from the box, Althea and Hilary rose, and Ahani opened the door to the Retiring Room. As the lavatory proved to contain no glasses after all, De Valcourt hastened to assure the two sufferers from headache that he would find an attendant and send her back with some—also, with bottled water, which would probably be better than tap water in any case. Since the attendants sometimes proved very elusive, however, it would probably be a good idea if Hilary searched in one direction, while he, Jacques, and Althea went in another. Before Castle could raise any further objections, he was alone with Ahani, who promptly began what he was obviously prepared to make a colloquy of some length. Castle made an honest attempt to listen; but the sound of Cornelia's voice, brassy as Janice's was golden, came harshly from the box, rendering the endeavor virtually futile.

"Yes, of course I'd been married before. Good grief, I'm over thirty and I guess I look it now, though I didn't until a short while back. I didn't strike you as the type that would stay single to that age, did I? My first husband was a farmer, all right in his way, too. He fell for me the first time he saw me, which was the first time in his life he ever saw a play, and he got so excited that, somehow, he talked me into marrying him. I was down on my luck just then and his line wasn't bad, at that. But I never was cut out for life in the country, and the first chance I got, I lit out. He took it awfully hard and—"

"Look here," Castle said abruptly to Ahani, "if we can overhear what's being said in the box, my wife and Lady Laura can overhear what we're saying in the Retiring Room. And it could be entered from either corridor at any minute. For all we know, someone may be listening outside right now."

"Excuse me. We are not speaking in–ah–loud voices. On the contrary. And I feel sure there is no one in either corridor. But I will look." He rose and went first to one door and then to the other, opening and shutting both. "You see," he said, turning with a reassuring smile. "And now–"

Castle interrupted brusquely. "Let's understand one another, Mr. Ambassador. As I've told you before, unless I see something in black and white, to show that you have a right to discuss such questions, I won't answer them. I won't even discuss them."

"But Your Excellency," Ahani protested. "Proof of the fact that I'm authorized to represent certain interests is available. It is in my safe at the Embassy. You wouldn't expect me to carry such documents about in my coat pocket."

"All I can say is that I play table stakes," Castle retorted. "Put the whole works out in front of me with the rest of the chips and I'll sit in until times get better. But before it's where I can see it, there'll be no answers, no questions, no discussions."

Again the sound of Cornelia's voice reached them stridently. She was telling Lady Laura about her second husband now, the drummer who had come to the farm selling patent medicine–a city slicker. Castle made a gesture of impatience, and spoke even more brusquely than he had before.

"We're not getting anywhere this way, Mr. Ambassador. In the first place, I haven't had any instructions from the State Department to confer with you. I don't hold too much with protocol, but, on the other hand, I don't kick over all established precedents without a good reason. My stay in London's unofficial and, as far as that goes, my stay in Kirfahan will also be technically unofficial, until I've presented my credentials to the Sultan and he's accepted them. So–"

"But the matters I wish to discuss with you have

nothing to do with your official status; they're matters of private business."

"All right, I'll take your word for it–though, in that case, I don't see why they're so urgent. But in the second place, I can't concentrate here on what you're saying, the way I want to. In the third place–" He hesitated for a moment and then burst out, "In the third place, I want to go backstage. Not with the whole crowd; by myself. I asked Janice Lester, on the quiet, if I couldn't, and she didn't have a chance to answer–in so many words. All the same, I don't think I'll get thrown out if I go to her dressing room. Anyway I'm going to try. But I'll tell you what I'll do, if you'd like to have me. When the others start for the Savoy, I'll go to the Embassy with you and stay there until we've thrashed this thing out. I know you're going on to some official reception, but our discussion ought not to take long, once we get down to cases. Then, after your chauffeur has dropped you off at this party of yours, he can take me on to the Savoy–at least, if that would be agreeable to you. We can ask Hilary to tell the head waiter he's expecting me. Probably I'll get to his table before the rest of them have finished their soup. If I don't, I don't see that it matters much anyhow. Well, what do you say?"

"Why, I say yes, of course," Ahani answered.

Table conversation was lagging a little, Lady Laura reflected, with inward irritation, though her delicate features were still wreathed by a perfunctory smile. It was a mistake, and she had said so repeatedly, to keep the most congenial group together overlong or for an interrupted succession of meals. This time, both mistakes had been made, and the company, heterogeneous to begin with, found fewer and fewer common interests to discuss as the evening progressed. Even arrangements were not smooth running any longer, which one had a right to expect, at the very least. There had been confusion when it came time to leave the theater. First, Mr. Castle had announced tersely, the instant the orchestra stopped playing the national anthem, that he was going to the

Aristanian Embassy in the official car; then he had plunged off to Ahani's box to join the Aristanian Ambassador and the two ladies who had accompanied him. This had meant a complete readjustment of plans for transportation, with the inevitable arguments about it, in the midst of the crowds pouring out of the Terry and milling around on the pavement. Mrs. Castle had stated, in no uncertain terms, that she wanted to go with De Valcourt, that he hadn't told her yet about those Dutch girls, and she thought Joe and Judith would like to hear about them, too. Very properly, Judith Racina had said that of course they would do whatever was most convenient for the others; perhaps they had better take a taxi? But taxis were being snapped up so fast that none was immediately available; and then Joe Racina, who was obviously not as tactful as his wife, said he would like to hear about the Dutch girls, too, and off they had gone in De Valcourt's car, leaving Lady Laura and Althea with Hilary. Hilary's Mexican chauffeur Celestino did not seem to know there was a terrific fog, or at least he drove as if quite unaware of it; and since Hilary seemed to be unaware of both the fog and Celestino's driving–indeed, of everyone and everything except Althea–Lady Laura finally felt impelled to lean forward and caution Celestino herself.

This had only made bad matters worse, for he turned around, smiling broadly, and spoke to her in rapid incomprehensible Spanish, meanwhile paying less attention than ever to the tangled traffic. So she had lapsed into taut silence, not speaking again to anyone until, miraculously, they reached the Savoy safe and sound. The others, naturally, were not there yet, for De Valcourt's chauffeur was entirely different–a Norman, deferential, considerate and prudent. It was at least a quarter of an hour before Jacques and Mrs. Castle and the Racinas appeared in the cocktail room where, until then, there had been gaps in space as well as in small talk. And there was still a gap, for Castle had not appeared, even now, and his absence inevitably created a certain awkwardness. Jacques ordered a round of drinks, which nobody wanted very much, and finally he said, well, perhaps they had better go on into the grillroom and start on their soup; that was what the Ambassador had asked them to do anyway–and that was before he had realized how bad the fog was getting, let alone how long his conference with Ahani would last. Of course he would understand. Luigi, the maître d'hôtel, showed them to their table and the soup came, but it grew cold while they dallied with it, and still Castle was not there. The fish arrived and presently it would be time for the game and then for the sweet.

Judith had shown herself frankly delighted with the setting of the supper: the paneled walls, painted a delicate green, the rich crimson hangings, the effective lighting of the grillroom–all these had called forth expressions of admiration. She had been no less enthusiastic about the supper itself: the clear turtle soup, so different from the thick mixture, almost a stew, that was called turtle soup in Louisiana, but equally delicious; the *bonne femme* sauce on the sole, a triumph; they had been served sole on shipboard, filleted and fried; that was good, too, but it couldn't compare with this; as for the grouse, she had never eaten that before, and she was really thrilled to find it was not just something you read about. Joe said less about the setting and the supper but he was keenly interested in the occupants of the other tables, some of whom he knew, either personally or by sight–Claudette Colbert and Elizabeth Taylor among the movie stars, Gigli, the world-famous tenor–and Sir Malcolm Sargent, the well-known conductor, Sir Alan Herbert, the equally well-known author, Mr. Randolph Churchill, the Prime Minister's son, whom De Valcourt obligingly indicated . . . . Joe was also intrigued by De Valcourt's brief outline of the Savoy's story: so it had originally been a palace, built by Peter, Count of Savoy, on land given him by his friend, Henry III of England? It had housed such celebrities as Simon de Montfort and John of Gaunt, both famous for their entertainments? Froissart had described it in his "Chronicles," Chaucer had written many of his poems there and, centuries later, Henry

Fielding several of his novels? By order of Cromwell, the Confession of Faith had been drawn up here and by order of Charles II, commissioners had met for the revision of the Liturgy, in an assembly later known as the Savoy Conference? All very interesting, Joe said, making rapid notes on the back of his menu; but after all, a touch of romance always gives spice to history .... Ah, that could be supplied also, De Valcourt assured him: Anne Hyde, daughter of the Earl of Clarendon, had been married there to the Duke of York in 1660 at a midnight ceremony performed in a tapestried, candlelit room; and his clandestine wedding had had many a reverberation; for the Duke of York had later become James II and two of his daughters—Anne and Mary—Queens Regnant of England! That was the ticket, Joe exclaimed, writing still more rapidly. Usually he stuck to current events, but this time he was going to dive down into the past and, who knew? He might even come up with his first novel! A wonderful idea, De Valcourt exclaimed. Hilary and Althea and Judith were equally enthusiastic and presently had their heads together discussing possible plots. But all this while Mrs. Castle did not join in the conversation and Lady Laura was finding it increasingly uphill work to do so. Instinctively, she kept looking from the table in the direction of the door.

Eventually, Cornelia gathered her white foxes around her, and announced that she supposed this was as good a time as any to go to the little girls' room. She rose, uncertainly, but managed a laugh as she caught hold of her chair to steady herself; then she started across the floor, swaying more noticeably with every step. The three men had risen at the same time; now Judith did, too.

"I think perhaps I'd better go after Mrs. Castle," she said quietly. "I'm afraid she's ill."

"Ill!" Lady Laura exclaimed scornfully.

"Yes. You see, I used to be a nurse, so it's more or less second nature to look for symptoms. I think it's far more likely Mrs. Castle is one of those unfortunates called a periodic drinker, and that tonight, for some reason, she couldn't overcome her weakness. So, if you'll excuse me, Lady Laura . . . ."

Judith was gone almost as swiftly as she had spoken. None of the men looked at Lady Laura as they reseated themselves. But they looked at each other.

"Judith's probably right, you know," Joe said at last. "It's uncanny how few mistakes she makes–about anything."

"Now I think of it, Castle spoke to his wife pretty sharply while we were on our way to the theater," Hilary remarked. "He said, 'Look here! I thought you never drank!' or something of the sort. I didn't pay much attention to the exact words. To tell you the truth, I was too much shocked. I thought it was unpardonable of him to speak to his wife like that, under any circumstances, and especially in the presence of a complete stranger. But he must have had an awful shock, too, a lot worse than mine. If Judith's right, if Mrs. Castle doesn't go in for this sort of thing often, possibly he never saw her drunk before."

"Which would explain a great deal that's been puzzling me," De Valcourt added. "I couldn't understand how a man of his importance could have married an alcoholic–because you have to concede that he *is* a man of importance, whether you care for his type or not. I couldn't understand, either, how he could have accepted a position of such responsibility, realizing how his wife would handicap him. Don't you agree with me, Lady Laura?"

"Nearly always, as you know, my dear Jacques. But I am afraid in this instance you gentlemen are all being too charitable–to both Mr. and Mrs. Castle."

The finality of her pronouncement put a further damper on conversation. Cornelia and Judith did not reappear and nothing happened to break the awkward silence. At first Luigi, and his assistant Pelosi, had both hovered solicitously around them, making suggestions and supervising the service. But now all the suggestions had been followed and the service was so excellent that it really needed no supervision. Besides, even without

Hilary's warning that Luigi should keep a sharp lookout for the Ambassador, this functionary would have done it anyway, because he greatly enjoyed showing persons of distinction to their seats. He did not hover any longer, but periodically he returned from his station near the main door, shaking his head; and, in spite of his correctly blank expression, Lady Laura had a conviction that he was conscious of an increasing tenseness in the situation.

Finally he came across the floor with great rapidity. This time, however, he did not come alone. Two other men were with him, one of whom Hilary and Jacques instantly recognized as the manager of the Savoy. None of them recognized the third man, who was lean and sinewy, with bleached-looking hair which might once have been ginger colored, and a scrubby mustache, still belligerently red. Unlike the other two, he was not dressed with formal precision; his pepper-and-salt suit hung rather loosely on his wiry frame and his tie was carelessly knotted. Joe, after one swift glance in his direction, stifled a startled exclamation and waited. He did not have to wait long.

"I should like to present Mr. Gradie Kirtland," the manager said suavely. "Mr. Kirtland is–ah–in a position to be very helpful when–ah–anything of a distressing nature arises. The sort of circumstances, for example, in which Scotland Yard is concerned."

"Scotland Yard!"

The words had been echoed simultaneously by almost everyone present. The manager bowed and turned to Mr. Kirtland.

"I regret to intrude on your supper party," Mr. Kirtland said courteously. "But I am afraid I shall have to speak to Mrs. Castle–privately."

"I'm very sorry. Mrs. Castle isn't here just now."

"She isn't here?

"No. She wasn't feeling very well. My wife–who used to be a professional nurse–went with her to the ladies' room."

Mr. Kirtland looked from Hilary, who had spoken first, to Joe, whose explanation had followed with trigger quickness. "I see," he said imperturbably. "Then I'm afraid I shall find it necessary to speak with someone else . . . . You are the host, I believe?" he asked, turning back to Hilary.

"I was, earlier in the evening. The Marquis de Valcourt wanted to take over the party after the theater and I consented."

"I see," said Mr. Kirtland again, including Jacques in his comprehensive glance and then turning back to Hilary a second time. "But you *are* Mr. Thorpe aren't you? The Counselor of the American Embassy? You have been more or less in charge of the Castles' program since their arrival?"

"Yes, sir."

"Then I should like to speak to you alone for a few moments."

In the pause that followed Hilary's departure, Joe sat down beside Althea, whose hands were trembling, and began to talk to her, in an apparently effortless way, about the Thorpe family–what grand people they all were, especially Hilary's father, a dyed-in-the-wool Vermonter, if there ever was one. Lady Laura, after glancing in the direction of her daughter, tried to say something inconsequential to De Valcourt. But he did not answer her, he did not even look at her, and presently she realized that she was trembling, too, and that they were all watching for Hilary with an intensity which forbade further speech.

It seemed to her an eternity before she saw him coming toward them alone. He spoke without preamble.

"I may as well break a tragic piece of news to you straight off," he said. "It concerns all of us: that was the Chief Detective Inspector of the Bow Street station who came for me, or rather who came for Mrs. Castle and who accepted me as the best available substitute. A few minutes ago, Ahani's car came up, driven by his chauffeur. The tonneau of the car had only one person in it–Castle. And he was dead."

Part II

CHAPTER VII

STANDING BESIDE THE handsome marquetry desk, in the spacious sitting room of the suite which the management of the Savoy had put at his disposal, the Chief Inspector did not present an especially impressive appearance; on the contrary, he seemed somewhat overshadowed by his imposing surroundings. The suite was one of those "facing the sea"—that is, the river Thames—generally reserved for film stars, chief executives, commanding generals and visiting royalty or near royalty; everything about it, in both size and style, was suggestive of appropriate surroundings for such luminaries. The large porcelain lamps in the sitting room were extremely decorative; but the light which filtered through their shades of painted parchment was designed to prove becoming rather than revealing. In its tempered radiance it would have been hard to determine whether Mr. Kirtland's eyes, shielded by glasses with large tortoise-shell rims, were blue or gray; but their gaze was direct, and the movement of his hands, as he occasionally selected a sheet from the stack of engraved note paper before him, was swift, definite and without waste of effort. Joe Racina, at least, had felt no surprise on learning that this was the Chief Detective Inspector of the Bow Street police station, who, in view of the circumstances, had taken over the investigation of "this unfortunate occurrence" in person. In his long experience as a journalist, Joe had come to learn that it is the man of undistinguished appearance, which does not stand out from the crowd at any gathering, who is frequently the most successful detective.

Inspector Kirtland rubbed the knuckle of his right forefinger across his mustache and looked quietly at the group before him. "First of all, I want to thank each and all of you for consenting to come here at my request," he began. "I am sorry to inconvenience you and, as a matter of fact, you are all free to leave. There's no question of detaining you, not the slightest, or of insisting that you make any statements.

"But after all, it is my plain duty to make inquiries, ladies and gentlemen, into such a regrettable happening as this. Mr. Castle, who passed the evening in your company, is dead, as you know. The body has already been removed, in charge of Sergeant Griffin, to the Horseferry Road Mortuary, where the coroner will hold an inquest after the police surgeon has completed an examination. There are circumstances which indicate that Mr. Castle did not come to his end from natural causes. Both the house surgeon and our police surgeon are of the opinion that he was poisoned."

"Poisoned!"

The exclamation was as simultaneous as the one which had greeted the announcement about Scotland Yard, but it was far less uniform in its effect. The word came in a frightened gasp from Althea, a smothered oath from Thorpe and a sharp ejaculation from De Valcourt. Joe and Lady Laura made no audible reply. The former lighted a cigarette and stood with it between his fingers, watching the Inspector and waiting for him to go on; the latter pressed her lips closely together and looked away.

"It will make things easier, of course, if I may talk to you separately," the Inspector continued imperturbably, after glancing toward each in turn. "I therefore suggest that the ladies withdraw to the large bedroom which connects with this sitting room at the right, where I am sure they will be very comfortable, and the gentlemen, who will, perhaps, not be in quite so much need of rest, take the smaller bedroom at the left. I will then ask you to come to me, one by one. Sergeant Griffin, who should be back from the mortuary at any moment, will write down in longhand replies to my questions, and I shall ask each person to whom I have talked to read what

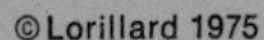
©Lorillard 1975

the sergeant has written and to sign it, if it is found to be correct–otherwise, of course, there will be an opportunity to make corrections before the signature is affixed. I shall take notes on what seem to me salient points, but I shall depend on the sergeant's record for details. There are perhaps some matters you will desire to impart only in confidence; I assure you that confidence will be properly respected. And before we begin, I feel it is due you to let you know, as fully as I am able to do so, what has taken place up to now."

He paused, as if in indecision, and again brushed his knuckle back and forth against his mustache.

Hilary Thorpe cleared his throat. "On behalf of myself and the Embassy, with which I have been in touch by telephone, I want to express my appreciation for your courtesy, Inspector," he said. "And I'm sure I also speak for the others here present in saying so. But that thought impels me to point out that we are not all here. I mean all who, at one time or another, were together during the course of the evening."

"If you're referring to His Excellency, the Ambassador from Aristan," replied Inspector Kirtland, "he's on his way here. This was at his own suggestion, not at ours," he added almost hastily. "When he heard what had taken place he offered to come here at once and give us whatever information he had."

"There were others, too," Hilary continued. "Miss Janice Lester, her husband and her leading man all joined us for refreshments in the first entr'acte; so did the wife and mother-in-law of the Aristanian Ambassador, though the latter remained in the Retiring Room only a few moments. But if this is a question of poison . . . ."

"Aye, perhaps so," agreed the Inspector. "But I can't very well send for them, you know. Perhaps after I have gathered and studied all the particulars, I may ask them in the morning to assist us, if they will. But just now I'm afraid it wouldn't do."

Joe Racina rose. "May I make a suggestion, Inspector?" he asked.

Kirtland glanced at him, then dropped his eyes to the

papers on the marquetry table before him. He began to shuffle through these.

"I'm Racina," Joe added, smiling. "I suppose you were looking through your notes to see which one of us I might be."

"Quite right, Mr. Racina," agreed the Inspector, courteously but without warmth. "I had meant to speak to you about your presence here. You're a journalist, I understand."

Joe nodded. "I suppose that would be the classification," he agreed.

"Well, it's just that we do things a bit differently over here than seems to be the custom in the States," said the Inspector. "I am told you reporters work right with the police and can publish any details even while an investigation is still under way and so on. That sort of thing wouldn't do at all, here. The reporters . . . ."

"Perhaps I can clear that up, if you'll permit an interruption," Joe broke in. "I've not been a reporter in that sense for quite a few years. I'm no longer concerned professionally with what we call spot news. I'm a writer of magazine articles and books, and I'm here solely in that capacity, having traveled with the Castles from New York on the same ship, to do a series about the new Ambassador and about the Middle East and its international tensions."

"Very good, Mr. Racina. I can see your point. And as long as it's understood nothing's to be published until . . . ."

"Check!"

"Then, if I'm not mistaken. you were about to make a suggestion?"

"Only this. Miss Lester and I are old friends. I've known her for years. If you'd like, I could telephone her, or even go direct to her hotel, explaining the situation and ask–as a favor to me, you understand, and without so much as mentioning you, unless you wish it–that she and her husband and young Neville join us. In that way, you could have everyone here who could have any connection with this–this unfortunate affair. Except the Aristanian ladies, and they didn't eat at the table with Castle—in fact, I don't think they even spoke to him."

"If you wish to do that on your own proper responsibility, Mr. Racina. I couldn't stop you, of course. But it's not within my province even to suggest it."

"That's good enough for me, sir. So, while you're conferring with whichever one of us you'd like to talk to first, I'll step out and see what can be done about it."

"That will be quite satisfactory to me. But before you go, I'd like to have you hear the preliminary remarks which I think the occasion calls for."

"As a matter of fact, I'd like very much to hear them," Joe replied, reseating himself.

"Well, as I was saying, before I discuss anything with any of you individually, I feel you have a right to know what has transpired so far, as fully as I can put the facts before you. I was summoned from Bow Street station, which is only a short distance from here, when the officer in charge of a police wireless car reported that he had been called to this hotel and had found a gentleman dead in a motor car carrying diplomatic plates."

This time the response to his statement was less of a startled exclamation and more of a respectful and regretful murmur. The surprise and shock occasioned by the news of Castle's death had passed, and the Inspector's hearers were now intent on learning more about the details of the tragedy.

"I decided to take charge of the investigation myself. When I reached here—and it was only a matter of minutes before I did so—we had no clue as to the gentleman's identity. The chauffeur could only assure us that the Aristanian Ambassador had directed him to drive a guest to the Savoy, and that this passenger had appeared in possession of all his faculties when he entered the car. We immediately got in touch with His Excellency by telephone and he told us who his guest had been; also, that Mr. Castle was expected to join a supper party at the Savoy, where Mr. Castle's wife—or perhaps I should say his widow—was awaiting him. As she was of course the person who should have first been notified, the manager of the Savoy thereupon went with me to the grillroom, intending, after proper preparation, to break the dreadful tidings of her husband's passing to Mrs. Castle as gently as might be. But it developed that Mrs. Castle had been taken ill, and that Mrs. Racina had assisted her to the Ladies' Room; also that she was still quite unable to appear. We therefore called Mr. Thorpe aside, as being the most logical member of the party to approach, in Mrs. Castle's absence. This explains why you first learned of Mr. Castle's death from him.

"You understand, we must take things as we find them, ladies and gentlemen. Had Mr. Castle died in the car of apparently natural causes–a heart attack, let us assume–there would have been no question of an investigation. The car belongs to a foreign diplomat, and we take it as a matter of course that foreign ambassadors are men of character above suspicion. But the house surgeon and the police surgeon both gave it as their opinion that Mr. Castle had been poisoned, and a small circular box of obviously foreign workmanship was found open on the floor amid a scattering of what looked like white pellets of some sort. Specimens of these are being analyzed by our laboratory.

"Now, when you come to poison, there are only three possibilities. The poison was taken accidentally; the poison was taken by Mr. Castle of his own volition and in the full knowledge of the fact that it was poison; or the poison was administered through design or ruse by someone bent upon murder. It is my duty to find which of those three alternatives is the correct one."

Once more the Inspector rubbed the knuckle of his right forefinger through his mustache before continuing. "It is my profession to make such a tangled skein come out straight, and we usually manage to do just that in an ordinary professional way, without flamming it up with magic tricks or unknown arrow poisons and so forth and so on. In this case, I hope quite earnestly we learn it was not a murder. But the surgeons both mentioned a very quick-acting poison. If, therefore, the fatal potion, whatever it may have been, was not accidentally taken, or Mr. Castle was not intent upon self-destruction, the murderer is one of those who was with him during the past few hours. In short, one of you."

CHAPTER VIII

"SIT DOWN, MR. THORPE."

Inspector Kirtland was now settled in a businesslike manner at the marquetry desk, with a plentiful supply of paper spread out before him and a fountain pen in his hand. Slightly behind him, at his left, Sergeant Griffin, whose plain clothes added to his generally unobtrusive appearance, was installed at a small table; he was even more plentifully supplied with paper than his chief, and also held a fountain pen, which, in his case, was already poised for action. The Inspector, after glancing briefly in his assistant's direction, as if to assure himself that the latter was prepared, motioned Hilary toward one of the deep armchairs, upholstered in flowered cretonne, which stood near by. The counselor let himself easily down into it.

"I'm at your service, Inspector."

"Then suppose you begin by telling me all you can about Mr. Castle."

"Joe Racina can probably give you more details than I can and I'm sure he'll be glad to. I'm a career man—Castle wasn't. So I don't know as much about him as if I'd been associated with him, at one post or another, over a period of years. He was one of the good men and true, who also happened to be wealthy, that came to the aid of the party—the winning party—in the last election. So he became an ambassador."

"You mean that's all there is to it?"

"No—although that's been the case often enough to

make it likely here, too. Conceivable, anyway. Understand, I'm not criticizing the way our Foreign Service is run, I'm just telling you about it, because it's so different from yours. As a matter of fact, Castle wasn't *just* a wealthy man—I mean, he could have been important to our government in lots of ways, even though he wasn't trained for diplomacy."

"Could you tell me some of them?"

"Well, to start with generalities and then get down to cases—at least, as many as I can supply—my country alone now uses more petroleum than it can produce. So the oil reserves in the Middle East, especially in Aristan, are supremely important not only to the United States, but to all the free world."

"Quite so. For fuel and all that."

"Not only fuel. If we didn't have gasoline, we'd work out something else; alcohol, maybe. But lubricants. Even a steam engine can't be run without heavy oil for the bearings and greases and what not. You can have all the fuel in the universe, but without the lubricants from petroleum the world's machinery would come to a standstill within a week."

"And Castle was a petroleum tycoon, as they say in the States?"

"Yes. But what's much more important, he was the man who managed to secure a treaty between Aristan and the United States, which gave us a concession for oil exploration and development, when several others had failed. He was quite young then, too. I don't know much about the circumstances. But there was some sort of compact among the nations to the effect that they should not bid against each other for those rights in Aristan. They figured that the old Sultan—the father of the present one—could be left to dangle and that, eventually, they'd get hold of the concession on their own terms."

"How long ago was this?"

"I should think it was twenty-four or twenty-five years—something like that. Maybe a little earlier."

"And just what part did Castle have in all this?"

"A rather theatrical one. While the syndicate people were letting some stuffy major get away with acting very pompous and high hat at parties in Kirfahan, Castle grew a beard, adopted native dress and assembled a hunting party in the same general area where Sultan Suleiman ibn Hamis–the one the stuffy major was supposed to sew up for the British syndicate and its Red Line Compact–was in the habit of hunting. Castle could already speak Arabic after a fashion, having made a thorough study of it before he left the United States, and he quite adroitly found means of getting to meet the Sultan on the pretext of presenting him with a very fancy shotgun that he'd ordered in Vienna and that had just come through. Castle made the presentation, allegedly on behalf of his countrymen, 'because the Sultan's fame as a mighty huntsman had penetrated to their land.' "

"And this proved to be a helpful gesture?"

"Exactly. The old Sultan was tickled to death and invited Castle to join him in a hunt the next day. This was a hawking party for houbara, which I believe is a kind of oversized plover. Castle hadn't provided himself with a hawk–apparently this was almost his only oversight, but he'd assumed that the hunt was for gazelles. So the next thing he had to do was to complete his equipment . . . . Am I making this too long? I wouldn't tell you so much, except that it does have a bearing on what happened afterward."

"Please go on. I'm very much interested."

"Well, I'll keep it short. I suppose Sultan Suleiman was glad Castle didn't have a hawk, because that gave him a chance to catch and train a wild one for Castle's personal use–a very great compliment indeed. They set about it at once. One of the soldiers came up with a dead jerboa–that's a sort of kangaroo rat, only larger–and pegged it out on the brown sand with a net of brown linen threads above it.

"Before long a hawk began to circle the spot, but at just that moment, the signal for one of their five-a-day prayer sessions was given, and everybody but Castle whipped out a prayer rug, faced toward Mecca and began the usual ritual. While they were in the midst of their devotions, the hawk made his stoop, and became entangled in the net. As, of course, Mohammedans won't let anything interrupt their prayers, no one but Castle paid any attention. He didn't want the hawk to get away, so he stepped quietly over and grabbed the fierce bird with his bare hand. The hawk slashed at him with beak and talons, but he stood there and let it rip at his fingers, thanking his own gods, no doubt, that Mohammedan prayers are brief, and don't include sermons. The moment the prayer was ended, some of the soldiers relieved Castle, and Suleiman's own master of the household bandaged his bleeding hand. As the Aristanians regard courage of that sort as the greatest of all virtues, it isn't surprising that Suleiman immediately embraced Castle before everybody and pronounced him a man of great bravery and resolution, whose reward for bravery should be something far greater than a mere hawk; what–the old man wanted to know–could he bestow on his newfound friend that would adequately represent a token of his great esteem? So then, Castle promptly began to murmur something about oil concessions, which would put plenty in the royal treasury right away, and millions and millions more if black gold were eventually found–endless money for roads and hospitals and education and sanitation, in short, all the things an impatient people were clamoring for, and which they could then have without in the least affecting the Sultan's own bulging moneybags. If you'll believe it, in almost less time than it takes to tell, the trick was turned: the stuffy major was out on his ear and Haroun al Castle had the inside track. The whole story's in the files at the State Department."

Inspector Kirtland nodded reflectively. "All very interesting," he said. "And I can see where that might have made Castle some proper enemies. But this happened a long time ago–about twenty-five years, you said?–so it doesn't seem much of a motive for present-day murder."

"Oh, it isn't. At least, I shouldn't think so. The point is that the old Sultan's throne was pretty shaky at the time—a ruler who is broke soon becomes a ruler who is broken. When you can't pay your army, I mean. So Castle's cash payment for the concession was manna in the desert, all by itself. Then, on top of that, one of the world's most important oil pools was discovered, and pretty soon the Sultan was firm as a rock in his palace. Meanwhile, the people got more schools, hospitals and all the other benefits they had been clamoring for, and Castle became somewhat the same sort of legend in Aristan that Kipling had made of Nicholson in India."

"But Castle didn't stay in Aristan."

"No. He returned to the States and went right on up to the top as head of Perisphere Petroleum and Ameristan and a few more corporations, while the millions kept rolling in. And that might have been all there was to the story, if it weren't for a lot of political unrest in Aristan, some of it probably engineered from outside; and Izzet ibn Hamis, the present Sultan—son of the one Castle dealt with in his youth—isn't the same sort of person Suleiman was, by a long shot. He's a playboy, who doesn't go in for hunting, flouts native traditions, wears Western clothes and puts an impossible drain on the treasury—you see him on the Riviera with a new dancing girl every time you turn around. Sooner or later, there'll be a revolt against him. When it comes, something will have to be done quick in order to put Aristan on a sound governmental and financial footing. And I imagine—remember I'm only guessing—all this is unofficial—"

"That's understood, Mr. Thorpe."

"I imagine the powers that be thought Baldwin Castle was the man who could do this. Anyhow, the President called him in—as I said, he'd contributed rather handsomely to the political war chests, so he might well have expected the offer of an embassy, I suppose. But no doubt he counted on one of the top ones—London, Paris, Rome, Madrid—those are nearly always political plums; it's only occasionally that they go to career diplomats like me. No sour grapes—that's just the way things are. Castle must have been rather taken aback by the suggestion of Aristan, and I believe he'd have turned it down, ordinarily. But it's my guess the President put it up to him as a patriotic duty, to pull another rabbit out of the Aristanian turban for the United States and for the free world, as he did in the twenties . . . . I think perhaps he might have done it, too."

"At any rate, he was on his way to have a go at it. But"–Kirtland brushed a knuckle in a worried way through his mustache–"that brings up a question I hardly know how to ask. It's a matter of great delicacy. I mean about Mrs. Castle."

"I'm afraid there's nothing I can offer you there in the way of information. They were only married about two months ago; it was after he had been appointed, and during the period of delay he had asked for so that he could put his business affairs in order and turn them over to subordinates. I never saw her before tonight, when she made a–a most unfortunate, I suppose *you* would term it, impression."

The Inspector took off his glasses, polished them with his handkerchief, replaced them and drew from his pocket a flat, round box of lacquered ebony inlaid with jewels, not unlike a compact in size and shape. He held it in his palm, moving his hand appraisingly up and down, as though he were trying to estimate its weight.

"You realize, Mr. Thorpe, I'm quite sure you do, that we wouldn't be making such an inquiry if it could be avoided." He snapped open the lid of the box to reveal a number of white, salted nut fragments.

"This little case was found open on the floor of Ambassador Ahani's car beside Mr. Castle's body," he went on, "and these"–he stirred the contents of the box with a stubby finger–"were scattered all about. Some of them are in the laboratory at the Yard, waiting for our chemists to analyze them. They are . . . ."

"Why . . . why . . . those are salted nuts," interrupted Hilary, staring.

"You've seen this before?"

"Indeed I have. It was at the theater, during that first entr'acte. Madame Ahani had produced some little box of sweetmeats for Judith Racina, and Ahani then asked for the other box–the one you are holding now. He said Castle would prefer the salted nuts in that–it seems they're a specialty of some region in Aristan and considered a great delicacy. And Ahani pressed the box on Castle as a gift."

"I must ask you to consider the matter and weigh your words well, Mr. Thorpe. You could not be mistaken about what you have just said?"

"I saw Ahani hand Mr. Castle, earlier this evening, either that box you now have in your hand, or one exactly like it. I believe Mr. Castle put the trinket into his pocket."

"That was during the first interval? In other words, several hours before Mr. Castle's death?"

"Yes, Inspector. And I could not be mistaken about that–provided this is the same box and not merely an identical twin. The design is so striking and the jewels are obviously so valuable that I couldn't be mistaken–unless there were two such boxes exactly like the other."

"Well, then, assuming you are not mistaken, what purpose could the Ambassador have had in wanting Mr. Castle out of the way?"

"Why, to . . . ." Hilary had begun with animation. Now he paused, and turned a look of blank astonishment on Kirtland. "I'm afraid you've really stumped me with that one, Inspector," he conceded. "I hadn't looked at it that way before. As representative of Izzet ibn Hamis, Ambassador Ahani would have every reason for wanting to get Mr. Castle safely to Kirfahan, that he might render the present Sultan the same service he rendered his father–stabilize his throne and put his government in order. Ahani would, indeed, have every motive *not* to do what . . . ."

"Let us leave it at that for the time being, Mr. Thorpe. And I may say you have been very helpful, far more so than you seemed to think you could be, at the beginning of our talk. But I must ask you to say nothing about this conversation to His Excellency, when he arrives, or to anyone else, for the matter of that."

"Of course I shan't." Hilary rose, then turned abrutply

back toward the Inspector. "I appreciate the fact that you haven't even intimated that I might be so much as indirectly responsible for the evening's tragedy," he said. "But, under all the circumstances—I mean since the case involved poisoning—perhaps you'd like to question my cook Lalisse. After all, she prepared everything Mr. Castle ate while he was my guest at the cocktail party before the theater."

"Is this a cook you have only recently acquired?"

"No, I've had her a number of years—ever since I was vice-consul in Martinique, which was my first post. She's a native of that island."

"Have you ever had any reason to question her integrity?"

Hilary hesitated, but only for a moment. "She's been highly satisfactory, as far as I'm concerned—clean, honest, obliging and a wizard with a cookstove. But she's—well, she's very good looking; you might almost call her a beauty."

"That's nothing to hold against a woman, is it?"

"No, of course not. But I believe several men have been quite appreciative of her charm. And one of them came to an untimely end, in a mysterious way. I've never believed she had anything to do with it. Certainly, she was terribly cut up when it happened and she was completely exonerated by the police. But my friend Jack de Valcourt has always sworn she knew more about it than ever came to light."

"I see. Well, I may want to send for her later on; but it isn't necessary at present and it may not be necessary at all. Of course, it may be indicated, before we get through, that we should send for the caterers who furnished the collation you ordered at the theater, and the waiters who served it in the Royal Retiring Room between the acts. But we shan't bother with any of that until and unless we learn something that indicates such a course would be the proper one. So suppose you and I suspend our conference at this point and that I talk next to—" The telephone at the Inspector's elbow rang and he picked it up. "Yes—yes—thank you very much," he said, speaking into the transmitter. "Will you please ask him to come up and send someone suitable to escort him? Sergeant Griffin will meet him at the door of the ascending room." He replaced the instrument on its cradle and looked up at Hilary with a rather whimsical smile. "I don't know how well you're acquainted with this part of the Savoy," he said. "But in case you're puzzled, the ascending room is what you'd call an elevator and what we'd ordinarily call a lift. But an ordinary term wouldn't do for this one–it's paneled in red lacquer and ornamented with gilt scrolls. Quite suitable, one might say, for the accommodation of ambassadors and such. And Ahani is 'ascending' in this 'room' at the moment–that was the doorman calling, in accordance with my instructions, to let me know when he arrived. So the question as to whom I should see next is quite automatically settled."

CHAPTER IX

EVERYTHING ABOUT AHANI'S appearance and bearing as Sergeant Griffin ushered him respectfully into the presence of the Inspector, indicated self-confidence and self-importance. He was now wearing a long flowing cape of black broadcloth, lined with crimson satin; and as he unfastened it and handed it to the astonished sergeant, who later informed his colleagues that it was the first time he had been treated like a footman, the Ambassador's somewhat startling display of orders and decorations again came into full view. He stared levelly, almost insolently, at Kirtland through half-lidded eyes; and his facial expression, though masklike, somehow suggested condescension not untinged by arrogance. His manner of addressing the Inspector did nothing to lessen this impression.

"Mr. Kirtland? Ah, yes, I believe we have already spoken with each other on the telephone. You will recall that I offered–*offered* quite voluntarily to come here–I was of course under no compulsion to do so and–"

"I have tried to make it very clear to everyone with whom I have spoken, your Excellency, that so far no one who was in Mr. Castle's company this evening is under the slightest compulsion."

"No doubt. And no doubt all my fellow guests, not to mention my host, have said they would gladly be as helpful as possible. But none of them is in quite the same position as I am. Hence their voluntary co-operation does not have the same significance."

"If you're referring to diplomatic immunity, I may perhaps remind you that Mr. Thorpe and Colonel de Valcourt could also have claimed that, had they chosen to do so."

"Ah–well perhaps at a pinch they might have." It was obvious that Ahani had not considered the matter from this angle; but it was equally obvious that he was not prepared to admit either the oversight or the similarity of circumstances. There was no change of expression either in his insolent voice or in the half-lidded stare from the black eyes whose opaque surface had something like the appearance of polished volcanic glass. "But after all, neither is a chief of mission," he continued. "And to avoid the possibility of any future misunderstanding, let me say at the outset that my offer of co-operation does not include either my wife or my mother-in-law."

Kirtland adjusted his glasses, looked steadily at Ahani for a moment and then glanced away. In his opinion, the interview was getting off to a very poor start. He did not like this man, ambassador or no ambassador–peer in his own country, no doubt, red ribbon across his shirt front, CD plates on a Rolls. Granted and all that. But what the flaming hell! Another ambassador–an *American* diplomat at that–had been found dead in the privileged car; and under such circumstances what did his ruddy Excellency expect the C.I.D. to do? Send him a written note of apology on a silver salver? Well, in that case he was in for a rude awakening. But in the meantime, it behooved the Inspector to show more respect that he felt and, above all, to walk warily.

"I do not foresee any reason why we should inconvenience the Ambassadress or her mother," he said civilly. "As I understand it, they were in Mr. Castle's company for only a few moments, had no conversation with him and did not even sit at the same table with him while refreshments were being served. It would be very farfetched to imagine that they might have had anything to do with this unfortunate affair."

"Exactly. And it is almost equally farfetched to imagine that I could have."

"Which is an additional reason why the department appreciates your co-operation. It is most obliging of you to give it. I think I need ask only a few questions to clear up some minor points, for the record. One is this: would you know of any clique, group, party or individual that might have gone to deplorable lengths to keep the new American Ambassador from your country?"

"Certainly not—in the sense of having knowledge, that is. If you care for bazaar talk . . . ."

"Anything that might be helpful, Excellency."

"In Aristan, as in every other democracy, one hears that agents representing other forms of government—avowed representatives and secret provocateurs alike—are eager to promote internal unrest and are always prepared to move into a vacuum."

"And how would Mr. Castle's presence in Kirfahan affect such matters?"

"It was believed that both by formal treaty and by unofficial American aid he would strengthen the financial stability of my government."

"Did it need assistance to such an extent that—"

"No more than our country did and does," retorted Ahani, for the first time raising his voice sharply. "Britain, France, Greece, Turkey, Spain, Japan, Israel—all of them not only receive aid from the United States but desire to continue doing so. So does Aristan—no more, no less."

"And Castle had the key to such aid."

"Since you've already talked to Thorpe, you probably don't need me to tell you that, as a young man, Castle developed the oil resources which enabled Suleiman to restore his government to stability at a time when it was greatly impoverished. Thanks to Castle, the Sultan also bettered the lot of all our people, in many ways. Mr. Castle understood our customs and our needs. With his help, help backed not only by his oil company but by his great government, there was no need to fear any other outside influence."

"I take it then that your government—your sultan and you as his representative in Britain, as well as your ambassador in Washington—all of you were most eager to have Mr. Castle reach his destination."

"We used every shred of influence in our possession to have Mr. Castle appointed. That is no secret."

"Yet you did insist that Mr. Castle should confer with you in secrecy." Kirtland raised his hand, palm outward, as Ahani's heavy brows drew down in a frown . . . . "In privacy, then, if that's more like the proper word. Where what you discussed would not be overheard. You insisted on this so urgently, I am told, that Mr. Castle finally agreed to meet you at your embassy after the theater and before a supper party given in his honor. Would it be too much to ask what matters it was necessary to discuss in secr—that is to say, in privacy—before Mr. Castle went on to Kirfahan, where you and your government wanted to see him installed as soon as possible?"

Ahani stared unblinkingly at his questioner for a moment and then looked away in his turn and gazed out of the window. In the Embankment Garden beneath it, the surface of a dark pool, lightly sprinkled with lilies, shone like black onyx under its encircling lights. But instead of this, Ahani seemed to see a pool that was wider and deeper, where the water flowed over turquoise tiles and radiant goldfish glided indolently from end to end.

Instead of Kirtland's voice, he seemed to hear that of his bearded kinsman Toufik Mikhardi, who was seated in the shade of a spreading pomegranate tree and who looked up in welcome at Ahani's approach.

* * *

"You are with your people, Jevad," Toufik said gravely.

"And I come to my friends in peace."

"It was good of you to come at all, knowing that my sympathies and yours lie far apart."

"We cannot always think of each other as politicians," Ahani replied, settling himself in a low chair of woven wickerwork. "Sometimes we must remember that my sister is your wife and the mother of your son."

"Set your tray down here, Esmah, and depart," Mikhardi said to a maid who had just come in, as he pointed to an ebony taboret, elaborately inlaid with ivory and mother-of-pearl, where a samovar was singing. "If there is anything further we need I shall summon you. Meantime, we will serve ourselves."

The maid put down a silver tray set with tiny eggshell cups and small dishes of sweetmeats. "Blessed be the Giver by Whose will food is brought forth from the earth," Mikhardi murmured ritually, as he passed a freshly filled cup of tea to his guest and indicated the tray at his elbow.

"With peace," replied Ahani, savoring the fragrant infusion and reaching for one of the sweetmeats.

"We're creatures of tradition," observed his host, meditatively. "My grandfather, inviting one of your ancestors into his house, or his tent, would have offered him a bit of bread and a dish of salt. I tender you tea and a pastry made with honey and walnuts. There is something here"—he pointed to his breast—"that responds to the old ways. What a pity that Izzet has so forgotten and forsaken them!"

Ahani shook his head.

"The old ways die out everywhere," he argued. "Esmah, your maid, wears a dress her grandmother would rather have died than wear publicly."

"But the old moralities, the old definitions of right and wrong, do not change. These cannot be flouted with impunity now, any more than they could aforetimes."

"Meaning?"

"Izzet. Our unworthy sultan. Does he ride or hunt as did his great sire? No. At least, he hunts nothing but some other man's woman or filthy trinkets purchased in Havana or Paris. A dancing girl or a harlot along the Riviera can get more gold from him for an hour's dalliance than he will grant to a school for a few desks and a bit of chalk."

Ahani set down his cup and made as if to rise.

"No, do not leave—yet," cried Mikhardi earnestly. "Hear me out. Izzet's day is done. His sun is setting. He will abdicate or . . . or . . . ."

"Or he will be assassinated after a mockery of a trial. Is that what you hesitated to say? Look, then, Toufik. It was you who spoke so highly, just a moment ago, of the ancient virtues, of the rite of bread and salt. I am one of those who remains loyal to his salt. If Izzet goes down, I go down with him. I stand or fall at his side."

"But it is that which we do not want."

"We?"

"The Federationists."

"That Aristan-for-the-Aristanian pack of jackals who demanded expropriation of the American oil properties?"

"We need a rallying cry and that is a convenient one. We have no idea of really abrogating the treaties under which our resources are being turned into gold. There will be some abracadabra, of course. But in the end, capable interests now in charge of the oil production will remain in charge. We have no one who could do the work one tithe as well. Nor have we enough of those trained in statecraft and public administration. That is why we need men like yourself, career men . . . ."

". . . Who are willing to betray the cause they serve?"

"Nonsense! Who asks treason of you? If it pleases you to withdraw after Izzet has abdicated, you will be free to do so. Meanwhile, only one service is sought of you–not for my party, but for our people, and I ask it by the ties of blood that have bound our houses since our forefathers herded camels and goats as nomad chieftains."

"If I consent to listen, I do so on condition that this implies no promise of any sort."

"Agreed. You return to London when?"

"Within the fortnight."

"To meet the man Castle whose appointment as ambassador has just been announced."

"The Embassy will extend him an official welcome, of course."

"Then ascertain from him whether he will work for the restoration of peace and plenty in Aristan with any responsible administration that is in power, or whether he will deal only with Izzet and his leeches. We plan to replace the Sultan with a council of five, who will name a temporary president to govern until a constitutional election can be held. The Royalists have agreed to join us. They too fear the Muscovites, as you do, as Castle's government does. For if the weak profligate Izzet is not replaced by a strong and honest coalition the Communists can step in."

"You think Castle, or any other ambassador, would even discuss such a thing?"

"There is no need to speak to him of uprisings. Find out merely if he is prepared to help Aristan or only to help Izzet as he once helped Suleiman. He can get from us for his government as liberal an agreement on oil as Izzet would concede, and we will deal with him more honestly after an agreement is made. If it is his purpose only to maintain the rule of Izzet–he must be kept from setting foot in the Embassy at Kirfahan."

"You mean you . . . ."

"Oh, no need to be melodramatic. You can save him his life and your country her future by cabling Izzet some reason for declaring Castle *non grata* if you like. Or you need do nothing. Once you ascertain what his real purpose is, you will have done all I ask of you. Think on it, and let me have your answer before you return to London."

Both men rose.

"I leave the house with your permission," Ahani murmured.

"And peace go with you, brother of my wife."

* * *

The turquoise of the tiles was fading to misty blue, the glitter of the goldfish was almost gone. Toufik's voice came from a great distance. Ahani's gaze was fastened again on the onyxlike pool in the Embankment Garden, and the voice he heard was that of Kirtland, who was repeating his question.

"Would it be too much to ask what matters it was necessary to discuss–"

"Yes, it would," Ahani said in level tones. "They were matters of the utmost delicacy, which I must decline to divulge."

"That is your privilege. As you reminded me at the beginning, you are here by your own volition. But as long as you *are* here, and voluntarily, perhaps you will be good enough to 'divulge' how this box"–he picked up the jeweled bauble which had hitherto been covered by his papers–"happened to by lying open on the floor of your limousine, beside Castle's body, and these white pellets scattered over the rugs and cushions?"

Ahani glanced at the box without a change of expression and answered without hesitation. "The trinket is one which has been in my family for generations," he said. "I gave it to Mr. Castle tonight, in the Royal Retiring Room of the Terry Theater. In my country there is nothing unusual about the proffer of gifts to newcomers who we hope are to become our friends."

"But the pellets, Excellency, the round white pellets. Are those also customary gifts?" Kirtland let half a dozen of the minute objects roll out upon the desk top from among his papers. "These are a few of those we found in your limousine. The others are now being tested in the laboratory."

Ahani's thin sallow lips parted slightly, and he ran the tip of his tongue over them before answering. Again, he did not seem to be seeing what was actually before him. This time he seemed to be standing in the fog at the entrance of his embassy, motioning to his chauffeur that his guest was leaving, that the car should be brought closer to the doorway flanked by trumpet-shaped urns, which long ago had been used to hold the torches lighting the way for the bearers of sedan chairs. Again, he did not seem to be hearing the actual speaker; this time he was listening to Castle's abrupt rejection of his inquiries, the heavy bass growl of the American's voice.

* * *

"I'm not the type to be bluffed, Ahani. I'm always ready to push a few more blue ones into the pot just to see what the other fellow really holds–to keep him *honest,* as we have a way of saying. I've got a job to do after I get to your country. It's a big job and it was entrusted to me by a big man. If you think for one moment I'll give you a chance to report back to your sultan that I was ready to talk shop with that Federationist crowd–well, all I can say is, you're not a sharp enough judge of character to hold down a branch managership in my outfit. But then, I pick men for their integrity. . . . By the way, if you'd rather I called a taxi, under the circumstances, instead of taking this showcase of yours, I've no doubt I can find one parked along the middle of a roadway hereabouts. . . ."

* * *

"The others are being tested in the laboratory," Kirtland repeated.

"Those *pellets*!" Ahani said to the Inspector. "Those are walnuts from one of the provinces of Aristan, broken into small bits and then covered with a glaze of salt, in the same way that you put sugar-coating on almonds. I assure you, Inspector, that there is no need to have those analyzed."

"Perhaps it does not seem so to you. But in view of the circumstances under which they were found, I should be failing in my duty if I did *not* have them analyzed. And, as I have just told you, that is what is now being done."

"Very well. Nevertheless, I assume that you do not expect me to remain here indefinitely, awaiting the report on this analysis?"

"The wait should not be very long. However, you are, of course, entirely free to go–immediately, if you wish."

"Thank you."

The Ambassador's words were spoken with extreme sarcasm. Kirtland rose and bowed.

"Please do not mention it. After all, *I* am assuming that I can always reach you quite easily and quickly at the Embassy."

CHAPTER X

KIRTLAND HIMSELF ESCORTED Ahani back to the lift, and waited until the operator had opend the door to disclose its imposing red lacquer interior, and then shut the door again, hiding the "ascending room" which was now *de*scending. The Inspector had not failed to observe either his sergeant's expression when the Aristanian had tossed over his cape, or Griffin's apparently deep absorption in his papers when Ahani departed; and Kirtland did not much blame the man for the one or the other, especially as Griffin now sprang to immediate attention. Without making any reference to the departed Ambassador, Kirtland said gravely that he would like to talk with Lady Laura next, if it would be convenient for her to come at that time to the sitting room.

"I'll ask her right away, sir," Griffin replied with equal gravity.

It would be entirely convenient, Griffin reported promptly; and he had hardly done so, when Lady Laura herself entered the room, smiling pleasantly. She accepted with grace the chair which the Inspector drew out for her. Then she clasped her hands lightly in her lap and looked toward him with attentive expectancy. Everything about her attitude was easy and disarming.

"I'm very sorry, Lady Laura, that it seems necessary to include you in this general interrogation," Kirtland said, almost hesitantly.

"Please don't apologize, Mr. Kirtland. Of course I realize that it is nothing but a formality."

"Quite so. Now of course I am familiar with your background and family connections, so I shall not need to tire you with useless questions about those. But I do not know whether you met Mr. Castle for the first time at Mr. Thorpe's house last evening or whether you were already acquainted with him."

"I was already acquainted with him."

"Slightly or well?"

"I think I might say that I was fairly well acquainted with him at one time, though I had not seen him in a long while."

"And the acquaintance began in—"

"In the early summer of 1925."

"And this was where?"

"Here, in London. Mr. Castle was on his way to Aristan, in connection with his father's interests in the Perisphere Petroleum Corporation—a large company. I believe the original plan had been that he should represent Perisphere at a world petroleum congress in Moscow. Then the schedule was changed and he was instructed to proceed directly to the Middle East. This change of schedule involved some delays and he remained in London longer than he had orginally expected. Because of his father's prominence, he had letters of introduction to the American Ambassador and other important persons, and doors opend for him rather quickly."

"So you happened to meet him because you and he were moving in more or less the same social circles?"

"Yes. That was the year I came out. I was presented at the second Drawing Room. It was a very gay season and I went to at least three or four parties every day. Mr. Castle went to some of the same parties—not many, but some. I really don't remember at which of these he was presented to me. I met so many charming young men, for the first time, in those days."

"I can quite understand that, and the exact date of your meeting isn't important as long as nothing significant happened on that occasion. You're quite sure of that?"

"Yes, quite sure."

"But he did impress you as a charming young man?"

"Perhaps charming isn't exactly the right word. I think arresting or even dynamic might be a better one. As I said, I don't remember when I first met him, though I think it was at a ball, and he couldn't have asked me to dance with him often, or been an outstandingly good dancer, for then I do believe I would have remembered it. But I remember my first real conversation with him, very well indeed. I must have met him several times by then, because he asked me for the supper dance and I accepted; then while we were eating chicken patties, he told me that his 'old man' had put him to work successively as 'a roughneck on a drilling rig, a dynamite monkey with a seismographic exploration crew and a still tender in a refinery.' Of course, I hadn't the slightest idea what any of those terms meant, and when I said so he replied that he'd be very glad to explain, if I'd invite him to tea the next day. I told him I couldn't do that, as I was going to Ascot; and he exclaimed, 'Why that's so, I've got a ticket for the Royal Enclosure myself. I'd forgotten about it, but I'll see you there.' I couldn't understand how anyone with a ticket for the Royal Enclosure could forget about it, especially someone who'd never been there before, but he did seem to be telling the truth. And the next morning I had a long letter from him, explaining all the terms I hadn't understood, and illustrating them with diagrams! Then we did see each other that same afternoon. I was talking to one of the attachés of the Egyptian Legation—or perhaps it was the Persian Legation, I'm not quite sure—when Mr. Castle came strolling up and spoke to this young diplomat in Arabic! I thought it was really rather rude, for of course I couldn't understand a word, and I was simply left out of the conversation. But after Mr. Castle had strolled off again, the Egyptian—or the Persian, whichever it was—said, 'That brash young American is going far,' and I said, 'Yes, to Aristan.' The diplomat laughed and said, 'I didn't mean far in that sense; I meant he'd make his mark in the world. His Arabic isn't very good yet—at least it isn't very fluent. But that's not surprising; he's got a good foundation, and with a little more practice, it won't be bad at all. It seems he didn't study it along with his engineering; since he graduated from the University of Oklahoma, his father's assigned him to an experienced tutor for indoctrination in all the Eastern languages, culture and other lore he could absorb. It's evident he's absorbed a good deal . . . .' I suppose the reason all this made such an impression on me was because I was terribly astonished that a young man who'd described himself to me as a dynamite monkey could impress a diplomat as a promising linguist."

"I can understand your astonishment, Lady Laura–and your awakened interest. Did you eventually find an afternoon when you were free to fall in with Mr. Castle's suggestion that he should be invited to tea?"

"Yes. Eventually my mother invited him to an afternoon party at Haverford House."

"Is there something you could tell me about that occasion?"

"Not much. It was a rather large party, as I recall it. You know the grounds there are immense. That is, I believe they're more or less covered with undergrowth now. They were never kept up by the new owners, as they were in my father's time; and after the house was converted into a temporary office building and struck by a bomb, during the war, of course, the empty shell and its surroundings were deserted for a long while. The ruins had to be barred off, for the sake of safety, and I suppose no one was interested in the grounds without the house. I've heard something about a movement to restore them, but I'm afraid it's just talk–so many other things must be done first. But when I was a girl there was a beautiful terraced garden, with statues and arbors and pools and waterfalls, on one side of the house, and on another a great greensward, smooth as velvet, enclosed by rare trees which my father had brought home with him from all parts of the world–he was a great traveler. We always had music at the large alfresco parties, and refreshments served in several different places–on the terrace, on the lawn and occasionally in one of the pavilions as well. I think we did that day, though I'm not sure."

"And that's all you can tell me about this particular party at Haverford House?"

"Yes, that's all."

* * *

I haven't told a lie, not even a white lie. He asked me if there were something I could tell him about that occasion, and I *have* told him something. Then he asked me if that was all I could tell him, and I said yes, it was. Because naturally I couldn't tell him that was the first time I was certain that Baldwin Castle was in love with me.

Of course, I'd suspected it before; I'd been vaguely aware of it—a girl does suspect those things; she does have a vague awareness of them. My suspicions began as far back as the time he'd talked to me about roughnecks and dynamite monkeys and still tenders—he was hoping to intrigue me with all those unfamiliar terms and he did. My suspicions became even stronger when he burst into Arabic—that was the kind of showing off a man does sometimes, when he's courting, just the way a peacock spreads his tail before a peahen. But I wasn't sure until that day at Haverford House when he said, "Look, can't we get away from all the others for a while? Isn't that a summerhouse about half a mile away, at the other end of the grounds?" And when I said, "Yes, there is a *pavilion* there, but you and I can't walk way off there by ourselves," he came back with, "All right, if we can't do it now, when can we do it? Because I don't want every Tom, Dick and Harry listening while I tell you that you're the loveliest creature I ever saw in my life—and some other things."

I knew what the other things were likely to be, for he wasn't the first man who'd made love to me, or tried to. I'd been a success from the very beginning of the Season—I really *was* pretty and my frocks were all made by Reville, which helped, too, and of course Haverford House and everything it stood for gave me a tremendous advantage anyway. I'd already had two serious proposals of marriage, besides one that was half in jest and half in earnest and another that was just a feeler, to see if I'd be interested. So I recognized the symptoms and I tried to stave Baldwin Castle off. I didn't want him to propose to me seriously or even half seriously; I didn't want him to put out any feelers. He did intrigue me very much, but he bewildered me, too. He was so different from anyone I'd met before, even from any American I'd known before. I'd met one or two Rhodes scholars and some of the younger attachés at the American Embassy and that was all. Baldwin Castle didn't look like any of the others or talk like them or act like them. I was actually a little frightened of him. The Inspector couldn't have expected me to say I was frightened of a man just because he was different from anyone I'd known before. It would have sounded so silly. It wasn't silly; I was quite right to believe there was something frightening about Baldwin Castle; but I hadn't found out then what it was, and I'd have just made myself ridiculous if I'd given any of the reasons why I felt shy with him as a girl.

Of course it didn't do me any good to try and stave him off. He finally succeeded in cornering me, out of earshot from everyone else, and then he plunged right in, without any preliminaries at all, and said, "Look here, I'm crazy about you. Why don't you marry me and come along to Aristan?" I told him he certainly *was* crazy to so much as suggest such a thing, but he went right on saying the trip would make a wonderful wedding journey, and what would it matter if we had to travel in a caravan and sleep in caravansaries, and live in a tent after we finally got to Aristan? That would all be part of the newness and the fun. It made me shudder just to hear him talk about caravans and caravansaries in that casual way; and when he started talking about the Arch of Ctesiphon and the ruins of Persepolis, and said we could take a look at those along the way, I was surer than ever that Baldwin Castle must be crazy. But I couldn't very well tell the Inspector that, either. He might be the kind that admires ruins himself.

In the midst of all this weird talk, Baldwin Castle had somehow got his arm around my waist. I was very indignant, and told him, in no uncertain terms, that he wouldn't have done such a thing, without my permission, if he'd been a gentleman. He just laughed, and said anyway, he was a man, and it would do me no end of good to find out what a real one was like. I was afraid he was going to say something coarse after that, and I was ashamed because I didn't dislike having his arm around me as much as I'd thought I would and as much as I knew I should; I could feel the color coming into my cheeks and the tears into my eyes. I must admit that the minute he noticed this, he took his arm away from my waist and pressed my hand and said very earnestly, "Look here, honey, I didn't mean to put the heat on too fast or too hard. It's just that I want you like hell, and I know that if you'd only give me a chance, I could help you find out that you want me, too." When he spoke like that I simply couldn't be too hard on him, it just wasn't possible, so I said, "If you'll promise not to speak of this again until after the Garden Party, I'll listen to you–I won't promise to do anything more than that, but I will listen." He clasped my hand a little more firmly and said, "All right, it's a deal. What garden party?" I didn't think he could be serious, but it turned out he really didn't know I was talking about the Garden Party at Buckingham Palace. And when I explained, he said, "Oh that? Yes, I think I did have a card; I hope I didn't throw it away." I was quite shocked, and I said I hoped so, too, because the Lord Chamberlain had a strict rule that such cards couldn't be replaced, if they were lost. Baldwin Castle laughed again and said, "Well, if I've lost mine, I could go in on someone else's." Really, it was hard for me to believe that anyone would be so uninformed about proper social usages, but he was. And I didn't worry too much because, after all, I'd won my point–I'd persuaded him not to propose to me again, or talk about deserts and tents and dreadful things like that until after the Garden Party. And there was no knowing what might happen in the meanwhile. Someone else much more important might propose to me.

But how could I explain all this to the Inspector? He wouldn't understand how a girl used to feel, her first glorious Season, even if he understands how they feel now, when everything is so different–no Drawing Rooms, no big houses with lawns all around in the center of London, no great families who are also wealthy families, or hardly any, and therefore hardly any private entertaining in the grand manner. He might get a wrong impression and think I'd been just a heartless flirt; and after that, he might believe anything of me.

* * *

"And following this party at Haverford House, did you continue to see Mr. Castle fairly frequently?"

"No. I didn't see him again until the day of the Garden Party."

"In other words, not for several weeks?"

"It must have been about that long."

"It take it this was not because of anything unpleasant that had happened the day you invited him to tea?"

"No, not at all. He'd never been to the British Isles before and he wanted to see as much as he could of them–for some reason, he was more interested in doing that than in going to more and more balls. He went to Scotland and Ireland and Wales–cities like Birmingham and Manchester and islands like the Hebrides and the mines in Northumberland and in the Rhondda Valley. But he did come back in time for the Garden Party. He was leaving England within the next day or so anyhow, and therefore it didn't curtail his sightseeing much to take that in."

"And you did see him at the Garden Party?"

"Oh, yes. After Royalty withdrew, we strolled around the grounds and talked together for some time."

"In a pleasant, inconsequential way?"

"Yes, I think that would be a very good way of putting it."

* * *

It *was* pleasant, because Baldwin Castle didn't do anything to frighten me or even to disturb me that day. He said, "I've kept my word, haven't I? No love-making, no proposing until after the Garden Party?" And I had to admit that he *had* kept his word. So then he said, "Well, I won't grab hold of you again, because this is all pretty public, even if it is supposed to be a very exclusive party—there must be several thousand people here besides us and it looks to me about as private as a ball park. Besides, you didn't seem to like my former technique very much. But I will lower my voice"—and he did—"enough so I'll be reasonably sure that no one else in this mob will hear me telling you that I love you a lot and that I want to marry you more than I want anything else in this world." I can't deny that somehing about the way he said this touched me very much, and I was touched, too, that he'd refrained from giving me another unwelcome caress. I was more than pleased. I was really a good deal moved.

But just the same, the conversation was inconsequential. I told Baldwin Castle I was glad he'd kept his promise and that of course any lady realized it was a mark of great regard when a gentleman made her an honorable proposal of marriage. (He looked at me in a queer way just then, as if he didn't quite understand what I was saying, but for a wonder he didn't interrupt me.) Then I told him it was quite out of the question that I should go to Aristan with him as his bride or, in fact, that I should go there at all; since I was rather delicate, I knew I couldn't stand the hardships of that sort of a life. (At this point, he started to mutter something about the extraordinary amount of dancing some delicate girls could do, without injuring their health; but he checked himself and I knew he hadn't actually meant to be sarcastic, that he just didn't understand the difference between the demands of an active social life and the privations he had suggested.) However, I added that I would be glad to hear from him, if he cared to write, and that when he came back—I understood he expected to be in Aristan about two years—if he wanted to bring up the same subject again, I might be prepared to listen. He asked me if I couldn't go a step further than that and say that, meanwhile, I'd be thinking the matter over, and that perhaps when he brought up "the same subject" again, I might be prepared not only to listen, but to say yes. And he was so very earnest about it all that I allowed myself to be overpersuaded and said, well, perhaps. But that was all. Then he asked if he couldn't come to see me at home, later that evening, to say good-by, and I told him that, unfortunately, I wouldn't be at home later that evening, as I was going on to another party so we had better say good-by then and there. And that is what we did.

* * *

"After Mr. Castle went to Aristan, did you and he correspond?"

"Yes. That is to say, it wasn't a correspondence in the sense that we wrote each other regularly—nothing of that sort. He wrote to me fairly frequently, without waiting for answers to his letters. I wrote to him only two or three times."

"Would you say that the contents of these frequent letters from Mr. Castle were in any way significant?"

"The first few just told me about his trip to Aristan, which was, apparently, very uncomfortable, though he made light of that. He went by sea—Messageries Maritimes from Marseilles to Beirut—then by car to Damascus and after that by motor caravan across the desert to Bagdad and north by car over mountain passes, which were often blocked by snow, the rest of the way. Then he wrote me that he'd succeeded in accomplishing the purpose for which he'd been sent out there much more rapidly than he'd expected and that very soon he was coming back to England."

* * *

Of course the Inspector doesn't want details about the way Baldwin Castle accomplished his purpose. And the personal part doesn't matter—at least I shouldn't suppose it would. But I hope Mr. Kirtland doesn't ask me whether I kept that letter. It was such a silly thing to do, especially as I'd read it so many times that I knew it by heart. But it wasn't any sillier than the things most women do. They all keep some letters they'd have done much better to throw away, just as most men write letters they'd much better have left unwritten.

* * *

"Did this early return have any significance—I mean to you personally?"

"No."

* * *

That was true, too, because it didn't—in the end. The Inspector doesn't want to know how everything worked out, step by step—it would take too long to tell him. He only wants to know what happened in the end. Of course when Baldwin Castle wrote me that he didn't expect me to go hurrying off to Aristan after all, that we could have a suitable engagement, and a beautiful wedding, and live luxuriously in a civilized manner, this did make a great difference. I did write back in a way that made him think matters were more or less settled between us; I did tell him I'd be very glad to see him on his return to London. But how could I know that before he could get here, no matter how quickly he wound up his business in Aristan, and how fast he hurried back, I'd have had time to meet Guy Whitford?

It wasn't strange that I hadn't met Guy before, even though our fathers belonged to the same clubs and our mothers exchanged cards and went to each other's larger parties. He was nearly fifteen years older than I was, and he'd been out of England a great deal, collecting butterflies. This was his great hobby and he had one of the finest collections in the world; he liked to keep adding to it. But he finally decided that before he did so any more extensively, it should be properly catalogued by an expert, and that after this had been done, he'd like to provide an appropriate setting for it, by making extensive alterations in a suite of rooms at Helston Abbey, the magnificent property in Gloucestershire, that he'd inherited from his Uncle Dirk. Then, while he was arranging for the cataloguing, he took over the town house that he'd inherited at the same time as Helston Abbey, and started going out in society again. We met almost immediately and we fell in love.

It seemed so exactly right to say yes the very first time Guy asked me to marry him that I didn't hesitate for a moment. We had the same kind of background, we knew the same kind of people, we enjoyed the same kind of a life and—as Baldwin Castle himself would have said—we spoke the same language. We understood each other perfectly and the understanding was harmonious and happy. We never had to explain anything to each other, much less apologize to each other; we never surprised or startled each other. And Guy's Uncle Dirk had left him plenty of money; Helston Abbey wasn't going to be a burden to him, or the town house, or Shepherd's Haven, the lovely little shooting lodge in Scotland. I didn't have the figures, of course, but it seemed safe to assume that Guy was just as rich as Baldwin Castle; and if I married Guy, I could live in London instead of Oklahoma, and it didn't seem to me there could possibly be any choice between them. Besides, I really did love Guy. He didn't excite me, the way Baldwin Castle had excited me, but then I didn't want a life of excitement. I wanted a life of leisure and comfort, with a well-bred, considerate husband who would always treat me very tenderly, and who would realize that women adore romance and wouldn't be afraid of seeming quixotic by catering to this taste. I'll never forget standing by one of the pools at Haverford House with Guy and two other suitors who'd come in for tea, and saying in a casual sort of way, "Those water lilies are just exactly what I need to complete the costume I'm wearing at Lady Kenncally's ball tonight. If I had them, I'd put them in my hair." One of the men with me said, "Why water lilies close up at night; they wouldn't look like anything after sundown!" And another said, "They'd drip all over everything and spoil your wave." But Guy didn't say anything. He just stepped right into the pool, white flannels and all, and picked the water lilies. Then he climbed out, soaking wet of course, but looking as if he didn't notice that, and handed me the lilies with a beautiful bow. If I hadn't already decided to marry him. I'd have done so then.

If I could have said all this in a letter, between the time I met Guy and the time Baldwin Castle started for London, I'd have explained everything. As it was, Baldwin Castle burst in on me without any warning, one afternoon when I was sitting in the drawing room, waiting for Guy, whom I was expecting any minute. Baldwin Castle "grabbed" me, to use his own hateful expression, and hugged me so hard I couldn't breathe; and when I tried to get free, he just laughed and said, "Look here, honey, you got away with that before, but now you can't get away from *me*. We're engaged, remember?" Then he began to kiss me, and when I tried to speak, he said it was no time for talk, and stopped my mouth again. I was so nervous I didn't know what to do, for I thought that Guy might walk in and find me in Baldwin Castle's arms, and what would happen then I couldn't imagine, for I'd never even mentioned Baldwin to Guy. (There didn't seem to be any real reason why I should, for of course I thought Baldwin would write or telephone when to expect him, and then I would tell him, quietly and kindly, that though I would always value him as a friend, I found I had been mistaken in believing even briefly that my feeling toward him could ever take any other form.) Fortunately, however, I did manage at last to disentangle myself, and to tell him that he must never do anything of the sort again, that he mustn't even come to see me again. I tried to keep very cool and collected, but it wasn't easy, because he kept interrupting me, and he didn't understand what I was trying to say to him. He kept repeating, "My God, you can't be engaged to someone else, you're engaged to me; I have your letter promising to marry me right here in my breast pocket, I reread it about fifty times a day."

At last I did make him understand though, and while he stood staring at me, not saying anything more once he understood, the butler drew back the curtains leading from the drawing room to the hall and said, "Sir Guy Whitford calling, my Lady." (Guy never rushed in, unceremoniously, even after we were engaged; he always had himself properly announced.) Guy came across the floor with his usual dignity and kissed my hand and waited quietly for me to present my other caller, whom of course he hadn't expected to find there and whom he couldn't place at all. And I was still so nervous and upset that I said something I know I shouldn't have. I said, "Guy, this is Mr. Baldwin Castle of Oklahoma, a businessman whom I happened to meet last year when he was briefly in London on his way to Aristan. Now he's on his way back to the States again and he came in to tell me about putting over the best deal this side of Tulsa. It's all been very interesting, but I think he's finished now." And Baldwin said very shortly, "You're right, I'm through now," and turned and went out. He went so quickly that I don't know whether he heard Guy say, "Darling, has that awful man been annoying you?" But somehow, I think he did hear. He couldn't have heard my reply though, because I didn't make any right away. I just put my head down on Guy's shoulder and had a good cry; and he comforted me lovingly and said, "There, there, dearest, don't think about it any more right now. If Baldwin Castle ever comes near you again, just let me know and I'll deal with him."

* * *

"How long, approximately, did Mr. Castle remain in London at that time?"

"I think only a few days. I saw him only once, and that was in the presence of my fiancé. I was already engaged to Sir Guy Whitford then."

"Quite so. And you didn't see Mr. Castle again after his return to the United States?"

"No."

"Until last night?"

"Until last night."

"Then you did not resume your correspondence with him after your marriage?"

"As I said before, we never did correspond, in the usual sense of the word. And I didn't write him at all, or hear from him again, during my husband's lifetime. But I heard, indirectly, that he'd married–a former schoolmate; and then, several years later, I heard, again indirectly, that his wife had died–you know how the press delights in printing news items about rich Americans. Almost at the same time that I heard about the death of Mrs. Castle, I had the great misfortune to lose my dear husband. I wrote Mr. Castle a brief note of condolence, telling him that I was, unhappily, in a position to understand the extent of his bereavement, because of my own, and asking him to accept the sympathy of an old friend."

"And he answered?"

"Yes."

"Gratefully and cordially?"

"His answer was rather formal. But it was quite correct."

"And after *that* did you resume your correspondence–or, if you prefer a different phraseology, was there any further exchange of letters between you?"

"Yes. I wrote him once again, a number of years later, and he answered."

"I take it that there was again some special reason why you wrote."

"Yes, I think one might put it that way."

"And would you say that, this time, his reply was cordial–or merely correct?"

"Really, Inspector, this was a long time ago. I can't remember every detail of every letter I receive–I get a great many."

"I realize that and I'm not asking for every detail. I am only asking for a general impression."

"My general impression is that Mr. Castle wrote rather briefly, recalling something that happened in the course of our previous acquaintance and that I didn't feel it required an answer. At all events, I didn't reply and I haven't heard from him since."

"And you think this covers everything you can tell me about your acquaintance with Mr. Castle?"

"Yes, I think so."

"Very well. You understand I may wish to recall you, in the light of information I may gather from others?"

"Yes."

"Just a minute, Lady Laura. There are one or two other questions I should like to ask you, which are not directly connected with Mr. Castle, though they may have some indirect bearing on the case . . . . You did not mention it, but I believe that your late husband was a collector of butterflies."

"That is so"

"It was, if I'm not mistaken, a very notable collection—one that he spent years and traveled extensively in assembling, and eventually located in a specially arranged suite at Helston Abbey, his country estate in Gloucestershire."

"You are not mistaken."

"Do you still have this collection, Lady Laura?"

"No. I was unfortunately obliged to dispose of it—my income, like that of most English people, has been very materially reduced, and I could not afford the luxury of keeping such a collection."

"You had a great deal of sentiment about it?"

"Yes, a great deal. It was the last of my valuable possessions from which I parted."

"You accompanied your husband on some of the trips in the course of which he collected butterflies?"

"Yes. On all of those he made, after our marriage."

"And took an active interest in the specimens after returning to England?"

"Yes. I helped my husband select names for them. He told me I showed a very real talent for this."

"I am sure you did. No doubt you were also acquainted with Sir Guy's methods of capturing and mounting the butterflies?"

"Only in a general way."

"You did not know then that cyanide was a factor at one stage?"

"I suppose I must have–in a general way, as I said before. But I must remind you that my husband has been dead for a number of years now, and that his collection passed out of my possession some time ago, too. I have had no occasion to consider the treatment of butterflies for a long while."

"Quite so. But I must remind *you* that Mr. Castle has just died as a result of poisoning–possibly cyanide poisoning. As you said in the beginning, these questions are largely a matter of form. But I feel it is my duty to ask you whether you can think of anything that occurred in the course of your meeting with Mr. Castle last evening which might point to cyanide poisoning?"

"No, Mr. Kirtland, I cannot."

"You did not see him eat or drink anything?"

"Certainly I did. I saw him eat some kind of scones, which were called biscuits, and drink tea at Mr. Thorpe's house, and I saw him drink champagne and eat lobster salad in the Royal Retiring Room during the first interval."

"These biscuits were prepared in the kitchen?"

"Yes; by a quadroon cook from Martinique."

"Ah–that is very interesting. And the tea–was that also prepared in the kitchen, by this quadroon cook, and passed, already in the cups?"

"No, it was prepared at the table."

"By–"

"By me. Surely, Mr. Kirtland–"

"I am very sorry, Lady Laura, that I have had to press you with such questions. However, I shall require nothing further of you at present. But I should like to question your daughter for a few minutes now."

"Althea? Why, she's hardly more than a child! And she's simply exhausted–we all are, as far as that goes. I'm sure she couldn't help you at all. She'd be frightened at the mere suggestion that you wanted to question her, she'd get confused–"

"I shall take all that into consideration, Lady Laura, and make everything as easy as I can for her."

"At least you will let me remain with her while the questioning is taking place."

"I'm afraid I can't. You know, it was agreed in the beginning that all members of the party should be questioned separately. Now, if you would just read through what Sergeant Griffin has written and, if you find it correct, affix your signature . . . ."

Inspector Kirtland waited patiently while Lady Laura, with obvious irritation, complied with his request; then he rose and, going swiftly to the door leading into the bedroom at the right, knocked and stood blocking the entrance while he waited for an answer. After a moment it was opened by Judith, who put her finger to her lips.

"I'm Mrs. Racina, Mr. Kirtland," she whispered. "The manager very thoughtfully sent one of the housekeepers to the ladies' room to tell me I might take Mrs. Castle into a near-by room that was vacant until she felt well enough to come upstairs, and then to bring her here. We moved about half an hour ago, and now she's fallen asleep—she couldn't before. I'm sure a good rest will do wonders for her, and that when she wakes up she'll be able to co-operate with you, and that she'll want to. Of course, I will, too. While Lady Laura has been with you, Althea's been explaining the sad situation to me in an undertone. She's been very helpful."

"Well done. I'm sure she'll continue to be helpful. Will you come into the sitting room for a few minutes now, Miss Whitford? I shan't keep you long."

He moved away from the door, clearing the passage, and Lady Laura swept by him into the bedroom. Althea came hesitantly out of it, glancing back several times at her mother. The Inspector motioned toward a chair.

"I have only two or three questions to put to you, Miss Whitford," he said kindly. "And you may take all the time you like, if you feel you must think over your answers. However, I do not believe you will find it necessary to do so—I believe the answers, like the questions, may be fairly simple. First, I am right in assuming, am I not, that you had never met Mr. Castle before last evening?"

"Yes."

"And did your first impressions of him correspond to the mental picture you had already formed of him?"

"I didn't have any mental picture of him. No one had ever described him to me."

"I see. You cannot remember ever having heard any previous reference to him?"

"Not until just before I met him. Hilary Thorpe telephoned to say that he had the new American Ambassador to Aristan on his hands for the evening, so that we wouldn't be able to go dancing together, as we'd planned. But he didn't describe Mr. Castle to me. And then my mother said she was very glad *she* had happened to hear that the Royal Box would be available, after Hilary and Mr. Castle had failed to get tickets, because—well, because she doesn't like Americans very well, on general principles, and she was rather proud to think she had succeeded where two important Americans had failed. She spoke of the Ambassador and his wife as 'these Castles'—perhaps in a rather supercilious way, but that was because of this queer prejudice she has. She didn't describe Mr. Castle to me, either. She couldn't have."

"She couldn't have?"

"Why, no! Because last night was the first time *she* ever saw him."

"You're quite sure of that, Miss Whitford?"

"Of course I'm sure! I've got a rather good memory—I can remember things that happened when I was only four years old. If Mr. Castle had ever come to our house since then, I'd know it. I'd know it if he'd come before that, too. My mother and I have always been very close and if she'd been acquainted with Mr. Castle, she'd have told me about it. She told me everything about her girlhood and her debut and her meeting with my father and her early married life."

"You're quite certain of that?"

"Of course I'm certain. She's rather fond of recalling the past—those days were so much happier for her than the present. I don't mind the way things are now, because I'm used to them. I've never known anything else. But

Mother'll never get used to them. She can't accustom herself to going without what she took as a matter of course when she was younger. It's very hard on her. If she weren't so sweet, she'd be rather bitter about it."

"I see," said Mr. Kirtland thoughtfully. He permitted his gaze to wander from the girl before him to a floral painting which formed the panel surmounting the door leading into the bedroom where the ladies were resting. In the faces of his quiet detachment, Althea felt increasingly that her fears of him had been quite without foundation.

"Besides," she continued, warming to her subject, "when Mr. Castle came to Hilary's house yesterday afternoon, it was apparent from everything Mother said to him and the others that the Ambassador was a complete stranger to her. I was in the dining room while she was pouring tea and I remember the conversation distinctly. He and Ahani both seemed to think, from the way she made her preparations, that she must be quite familiar with the customs of the Middle East. But she said, on the contrary, she'd never heard more than a few passing references to them, from returning educators and diplomats, that everything she knew about teamaking she'd learned in England. Mr. Castle was quite persistent. He asked her if she'd never had any long letters, describing Middle Eastern customs, written by someone who'd lived in that region for a long while, and she was even more emphatic in her reply. She said, 'No, never,' and then added, 'I must confess that the subject's never concerned me closely or, to be truthful, intrigued me very greatly.' I don't think I ever heard her speak so positively. I suppose that's why I remember what she said, practically word for word. It was so unlike her."

"Well, thank you very much, Miss Whitford. I don't need to detain you any longer. That wasn't very trying now, was it?"

"Why not at all! I can't imagine why I thought it would be. The answers were just as simple as your questions, the way you said."

She rose, drawing a deep breath of relief that ended

in a little laugh. Then she left the room swiftly, almost gaily. The Inspector turned back to his notes and, after studying them for a few minutes, glanced in a questioning manner toward Sergeant Griffin. The sergeant was also apparently studying his notes and his expression was impassive. But presently, as if conscious that his chief was watching him, he looked up with a responsive gleam in his eye.

"I believe you were thinking the same thing that I was, Griffin," Mr. Kirtland announced, "that there is—shall we say a slight discrepancy?—between the stories of those two ladies. And that it would be interesting to find out which one was telling the truth. Meanwhile, perhaps Mrs. Racina would be good enough to let us know whether, in her opinion, Mrs. Castle is now sufficiently recovered so that it would not be an imposition to question her."

CHAPTER XI

As Judith came into the room, Kirtland was immediately struck both by the complete tranquility of her manner and by its slight formality. He did not need to consult his notes or search his memory to be reminded that she either was or had been a professional nurse. Despite the quiet elegance of her dress, which in no way suggested a uniform, she had so far reverted to type in her person that he knew she was regarding him almost in the light of a physician who had called upon a trusted assistant to help him diagnose a difficult case, rather than as a police inspector who wanted information from a complete stranger, which might lead to the arrrest of a murderer. She did not seem to expect that he would ask her to be seated and he refrained from doing so, not through discourtesy or negligence, but because he realized that she was actually more at her ease, standing erect before him, than she would have been when apparently relaxed in a chair. Moreover, it seemed in no way unnatural that, having been summoned, she should take the initiative in speaking.

"Althea says you'd like to know whether I think Mrs. Castle's well enough to be questioned now. She's had a good nap and I've broken the bad news to her as gently as I could. She took it very hard, at first, but eventually she got her second wind, as we say. I think it would be all right to send for her almost any time, though if you could give her a few minutes more, I believe that would be all to the good."

"Of course I can give her a few minutes more—or as much time as you think advisable. Meanwhile, perhaps you'd let me ask you a few questions. If I understand your husband correctly, you are, or were, a hospital nurse."

"I was what we call a registered nurse, which is the nearest American equivalent of a 'sister' in your hospitals. I haven't done any nursing, professionally or regularly, since my marriage, which took place in '43, but I've taken care of the members of my family whenever they've been ill, and the attending physicians have always seemed satisfied."

"And what was your training? Your previous experience?"

"I took my first training at a cottage hospital in Vermont and then went to a large hospital in Boston for postgraduate work. After that, I did private nursing in the rural community where my parents live until I volunteered for service in the Army Medical Corps. I prepared for that in a military hospital in Fayetteville, North Carolina, and served in the African theater for some months before I was invalided home as the result of an accident. I married immediately after that."

"It would appear from this that your training was excellent and your experience quite varied."

"Yes, I think I may say they were."

"And you feel quite sure, from what you observed of Mrs. Castle, that she isn't habitually intemperate?"

"Of course that was more or less guesswork at first. Now I do feel quite sure of it—both from what I've observed and from what she's told me."

"You have every reason to believe she was telling you the truth—I mean, that she was sufficiently recovered to tell a straight story, not that she was willfully lying?"

"Yes, sir, I have. She's terribly upset—I don't mean just by her husband's sudden death; of course her horror over that is natural—inevitable. I mean by the realization that her behavior was—well, nothing short of a disgrace to him. I think she really wanted to make him a good wife. She's terribly ashamed."

"She didn't strike you at all as the sort of woman who was, let us say, on the make?"

"Yes, she did, in one sense. I think it meant a great deal to her to become an ambassadress—that it was terrifically important to her."

"More important than to be immensely rich?"

"But she would have been both!"

"In other words, you have reason to believe that her husband made a large settlement on her at the time of her marriage?"

"I don't know about that. I never saw Mrs. Castle, or her husband either, until Joe and I took the same ship with them, so that Joe could get a good start on his Castle articles. I never talked with her confidentially until tonight. But I should think it most unlikely. Marriage settlements are much more unusual in the United States than they are in Europe. Most Americans like to pay for their wives' expenses out of their own incomes."

"On the other hand, if I'm not mistaken, rich Americans are apt to provide very liberally—in fact, very prodigally—for their *widows* through life insurance policies."

"Yes, sir, that is true."

For a moment, the Inspector and Judith looked at each other in silence. She met his gaze squarely, without averting hers. It was he who finally glanced away, and reshuffled his papers before resuming his questioning.

"I'm very much interested in everything you've told me, Mrs. Racina," he said at last. "And I should now like to ask you some questions of quite a different nature. In the course of your varied experience as a professional nurse, you must have had many, or at least several, opportunities to observe the effects of poisoning."

"Yes, sir, I did."

"Therefore you are fairly well acquainted, perhaps, with the effect of–cyanide, let us say."

"Yes, sir."

"How would you describe this?"

"It is the fastest acting poison known to medicine."

"Quite so. But I believe there is also a way of delaying action so that there may be no results for several hours?"

"That is correct. At least, such coatings as are put as a matter of common practice about aspirin would certainly delay the poison's effect."

"So you would concur in the opinion, already expressed by the surgeon we have consulted, to the effect that Mr. Castle's death might easily have been caused by poison, administered either at Mr. Thorpe's house or at the theater?"

"I'm sorry, but I shall have to."

"Can you enumerate for me, from your own observation, all the various items of food and drink that Mr. Castle consumed while you were in his company?'

"No, because I wasn't in the same room with him all the time, at Mr. Thorpe's, and I wasn't watching him very closely at the theater–there wasn't any reason, that I knew of, why I should. I saw him drink a highball at Mr. Thorpe's–he helped himself from the same butler's-tray that everyone else was using. I think he'd had something to eat and drink in the dining room before that, but I can't speak of it from my own knowledge. At the theater I did see him eating lobster salad and caviar sandwiches and drinking champagne."

"And he helped himself to these?"

"If he didn't, he was served by the maître d'hôtel or one of the maître d'hôtel's assistants. They were there to wait on everyone who wanted them to. But I think most of the guests did help themselves. The salad was on a large platter at one end of the table, and the caviar sandwiches on another large platter at the other end, with napkins and plates and forks neatly arranged beside each. We didn't need any help."

"And the champagne?"

"Well, the waiters served that."

"Right along?"

"I think so. Except–"

"Yes, Mrs. Racina?"

"Except that just before the end of the first entr'acte Mr. Alban did a trick with an empty champagne glass."

"A trick?"

"Yes. It seems that at one time he was a professional magician; he specialized in sleight of hand and was very good at it. Now he only does it at home for the amusement of his family, for his own amusement or the amusement of fellow guests at private parties. That was why he did the trick this time–to add to the gaiety of the occasion. It was very clever: he picked up the empty champagne glass and twirled it round and round; meanwhile, he flourished a large silk handkerchief, and suddenly the glass began to fill. It really did fill up; it actually bubbled over. All of us saw it do that, though none of us had seen Mr. Alban take one of the champagne bottles that was standing on the table and fill the glass. Mr. Alban wiped off the dripping edge with his silk handkerchief and handed the glass to Miss Lester, who immediately passed it on to Mr. Castle, in plain sight of us all."

"And Mr. Castle drank from this glass?"

"I think so. Mr. Ahani filled or refilled all the glasses that were standing around, so that everyone could join in the toast to Aristan which Mr. Castle had proposed. He changed the one Mr. Neville had proposed, at Miss Lester's instigation, because it was to him–I mean to Mr. Castle–personally, and he said of course he couldn't drink that. We all drank the toast to Aristan with him. My impression is that Mr. Castle drank out of the same glass Mr. Alban had just filled. But I can't swear to it."

"Quite so. And I'm not asking you to swear to anything; I am only asking you to tell me what you think you can state with reasonable accuracy and I am more and more interested in what you are telling me. Now just two or three more questions, Mrs. Racina. I do not need to tell you that cyanide is not casually sold over the counter, at every chemist's, to anyone who happens to ask for it. It is sold only for specific purposes, to reliable persons, and even such sales are properly safeguarded. Among your fellow guests last night was there anyone who you believe might have had occasion to buy cyanide for a proper and logical reason?"

"How can I say? I never met any of my fellow guests except the Castles before last night. I don't know very much about them."

"I realize that. But you do know that Mr. Alban, now a theatrical manager, was once a professional conjurer. On the face of things, there is no logical reason why he should have cyanide in his possession. You do know that Miss Lester and Mr. Neville are both actors; that Lady Laura and her daughter are both ladies of leisure; that Mr. Thorpe and Mr. Ahani are both diplomats; that Colonel de Valcourt, though now attached to an embassy, is primarily a military man–and that the same lack of logical reason applies to all of them . . . . Yes, Mrs. Racina?"

Kirtland had been quick to note the swift change in Judith's expression which, until then, had been almost professionally blank. He was sure this change was involuntary and would not have occurred if she had not been taken, suddenly and unexpectedly, by surprise. He pressed his advantage.

"I can't force you to tell me anything, you know, Mrs. Racina."

"I know. And I don't want to say anything that would cast unjust suspicions on an innocent person."

"On the other hand, I'm sure you don't want to refrain from saying anything that would *remove* suspicion from an innocent person by helping me to find the guilty one."

"Well, then . . . . I learned, quite by chance that, with the help of an uncle who was a physician, Colonel de Valcourt had perfected a method for coating minute cyanide crystals. They were used in Holland, by Dutch girls, during the Occupation. These girls would slip such coated crystals into the food or drink of the Nazi officers who took them out, and a few hours afterward the victims would die. De Valcourt's experiments were made with the best possible motives. The girls had been using cyanide for some time; but in its customary form it worked so quickly that they could very easily be identified and paid for the Nazis' lives with their own. With the delayed action, it was almost impossible to trace them. Hilary Thorpe and Jacques de Valcourt are great friends, so Hilary knew all about this from Jacques himself. And when Mr. Castle questioned Hilary about Jacques's career, on the way to the theater, Hilary told him this, among other things."

"And you were in the car at the time?"

"No. But Joe and I were in Colonel de Valcourt's car when we went from the theater to the Savoy, and so was Mrs. Castle. She'd been so intrigued by what she'd heard about the Dutch girls from Hilary, in the course of the previous ride, that she wanted to hear more about them, from De Valcourt himself. And he seemed perfectly willing to tell her."

"I am more and more interested in what you are saying, Mrs. Racina, and just to reassure you, let me state I feel quite certain you are not throwing suspicion on an innocent person. After all, the Occupation of the Netherlands by the Nazis was terminated several years ago; there is no sound reason why Colonel de Valcourt should be carrying tablets of coated cyanide around in his pocket at this late day; nor would he talk about his successful experiments so freely if there were the slightest danger that they might be used as a basis for suspecting him of murder."

"I know. But—"

"Yes, Mrs. Racina?"

"But it seems that Colonel de Valcourt's avocation is horticulture. It was their mutual interest in this that formed the basis of the friendship between him and Hilary–not that Hilary's much of a gardener himself, but practically all the family money that doesn't come from talc mines comes from the elder Thorpe's nurseries–they're famous throughout the United States. It seems that the grounds of Colonel de Valcourt's château in France were laid out by the landscape gardener of Francis I, and they've made the estate a show place for generations. Moreover, he's very proud of the way he's improved and developed the gardens on the property he's rented at Chiswick. He was very much intrigued when I told him about the Lancaster and York rose that we have on my father's farm. Anyway, he said he was going to try to get sent on a mission to the United States, so that he could come and see it. Of course that was just a joke, but there was genuine enthusiasm back of it. And he asked Joe and me to come to tea tomorrow–or is it today?–with Lady Laura and Althea, to see his flowers at Chiswick. He's especially proud of his roses. He says the English climate, which otherwise he doesn't like very much, is wonderful for them. And–"

"Yes, Mrs. Racina?"

"Nothing. Except that, as a horticulturist, Colonel de Valcourt would, of course, be able to purchase cyanide without any difficulty. I don't need to tell you that."

There was a long pause. Then the Inspector straightened out his papers and rose.

"Thank you very much, Mrs. Racina," he said. "I think we will not disturb Mrs. Castle just yet, after all. I think that before we do that, as soon as I have put in one telephone call, I had better have a short talk with Colonel de Valcourt."

CHAPTER XII

THE MULTICOLORED PATCH of ribbons on Jacques de Valcourt's blue tunic glowed in the lamplight like a magnified fragment of some intricate mosaic, whose pattern was no longer discernible in so minute a fraction of the whole. He bowed with chill formality as the Inspector waved casually toward one of the large chairs.

"Sit down, do, Colonel," Kirtland urged. "No use being stuffy about this, is there? After all, neither one of us is here from choice, eh?"

De Valcourt inclined his head slightly and let himself down into the designated armchair. From one of the pockets of his tunic he drew a thin case of platinum, ornamented with his crest and a facsimile of his signature; at a touch, this case flew open, to reveal its gold-tipped and monogrammed contents. Still without speaking, De Valcourt proffered this to Kirtland, who shook his head and picked up from among the scattered sheets of note paper on his desk a packet of Woodbines.

"A chap gets used to these," he said, rather apologetically. "After a bit, none of the others seems to have any tang or whatever it might be."

He struck a match, which sputtered for a moment like the bomb fuse in an old-fashioned cartoon before the cigarette achieved an even glow. Jacques snapped flame from a slim platinum lighter, and inhaled the aromatic smoke as though surrendering to a caress.

"I'm a man of few words myself," the Inspector said, rather dryly, after waiting some moments for a reply to his civil overtures. "Apparently, you are, too, Colonel. And, as I've already said, anyone who does not care to be questioned is quite free to go. On the other hand, since you all realize that this is a very serious situation—"

* * *

Do I not, my old one? But in my place, at present, one needs to walk most cautiously, though without seeming to do so. All may yet march as it should, if I remember I cannot afford to utter one careless word, while leading you along a trail which gives promise of reaching the goal you desire. No red herrings though—merely a cat of another color! But now I must tread as lightly as one myself.

* * *

"Let me assure Monsieur Kirtland of my willingness to answer any questions of which I know the reply."

"Well done, sir. Then if you're really prepared to assist me, suppose we begin by asking whether you ever met Mr. or Mrs. Castle before."

"Until this afternoon, at Mr. Thorpe's cocktail party, I never laid eyes on either of them. In the case of Mrs. Castle, I express the hope that today marks not only the first, but also the last time that I do so."

"But you knew of Mr. Castle? I mean you knew who he was, what he did and so on? As a young officer, you served for a time in Lebanon, I believe."

"Certainly the name was familiar. So was that of Lawrence of Arabia. But nothing in my work ever brought me into contact with either one."

"I can understand that—I was thinking merely of possibilities. And I suppose it is not even a probability that your work in Lebanon had political as well as military and diplomatic significance."

"Quite right. You are of course aware that the French had a high commissioner in Lebanon at that time; but our interests stopped at what was then still called the Near East. They never went as far as Aristan, and they were in no way connected with oil—which, if I am not mistaken, is the political connection for which you are groping at the present moment. Now if I were a German instead of a Frenchman, your question and my answer might both have more significance. The Germans at the period under discussion were greatly interested in Aristanian oil. But I think you would hardly suggest that a French officer with my record could plausibly be associated with the hereditary enemy of his country, the despoiler of his home, the slaughterer of his nearest and dearest, for the treacherous purpose of private gain!"

De Valcourt spoke with an increasing degree of heat. Kirtland answered him with an even more marked increase of calm.

"Permit me to say that I have not suggested anything of the sort. I am well acquainted with your record, Colonel de Valcourt; and if I had not been, it would have been a simple matter to secure your dossier before this interview began. Now let me ask you something quite different: you have other interests besides those that are strictly military and diplomatic, do you not, Colonel de Valcourt? That is to say, I understand you are quite an authority on horticulture. Is your interest in that more serious than your interest in tennis and polo, for instance? By that, I mean—and I hope it is not impertinent to ask—is it a hobby on which you spend money, or is it a pursuit out of which you make money?"

"I spend money on it in England, but I make money on it in France. We not only have flowers, fruit and vegetables in abundance for our own use on the estate which my mother and I jointly own; we sell them extensively. From our kitchen gardens we ship melons to the London market—you might easily have bought some yourself, during the season, at Selfridge's or any other large store. There is a large and growing demand for our camellias in the southern part of the United States; and, from our greenhouses, orchids have gone to every part of the world. It was while I was in Martinique where, incidentally, I first met Hilary Thorpe, that I began to collect orchids in a small way—a fascinating pursuit if one hunts one's specimens in the jungle. The collection grew until it formed the basis for a flourishing business, in the chance way that one thing often leads to another."

"So that, all in all, your kitchen gardens and your greenhouses together have proven a very successful financial venture?"

"We have our good years and our bad years, like everyone else. On the whole, however, I think I may say that it has been."

"So that you can, as you yourself put it, spend money in England, since you make it in France. I have heard a great deal about this establishment of yours in Chiswick, Colonel de Valcourt—apparently it is a very fine place, very fine indeed, and you live there in almost princely style and entertain in a very lavish manner."

"These things are all comparative. I do not do too badly by myself and my friends. I should be very pleased to have you visit me in Chiswick, one of these days, and see for yourself if the setting and the entertainment justify the reports you have had."

"Thank you. Now, besides this place in Chiswick which you rent, you own an estate in France—a château with extensive grounds, as I understand it, which is situated just where?"

"In the lower part of the Loire Valley—which we call the Loire-Inférieure. It is not far from Nantes, which is sometimes known as Nantes la Grise—Nantes the Gray—or, more pleasantly and I think more appropriately, the Camellia City. The first designation always makes me think of nuns, the second of flowers—the human variety as well as the other kind."

"And this château in the Loire Valley, near Nantes, is called—"

"Vaujours."

"And this is the only property that you own in France?"

"No, I have a *pied-à-terre* in Paris and a small villa on the Côte d'Azur."

"Could you be a little more explicit in regard to the location of the latter?"

"It is not far from Menton."

"And, as I recall it, Menton is not far from Monte Carlo."

"Your geography is admirable, Inspector."

"And do you also make money on the *pied-à-terre* in Paris and the villa near Monte—I beg pardon, near Menton?"

De Valcourt selected another gold-tipped cigarette from his platinum case, lighted it and inhaled its perfumed smoke before answering. "I assume that, considering your calling, you must have asked that question seriously, Monsieur Kirtland," he said, with a slight drawl. "Otherwise, I should certainly conclude that it had been asked merely *pour rire,* as we would say. It is inconceivable that a *pied-à-terre* in Paris and a small villa on the Côte d'Azur should represent sources of income, unless they were rented to rich Americans, which mine are not. However, the *pied-à-terre* might be said to save me money, since it obviates the necessity of hotel bills and I am obliged to spend a certain amount of time in Paris, in connection with my business interests. I might stretch a point, and say that the villa also saves me money, since it provides me with a means of escape from the terrible climate and arduous duties of London and permits me to relax in the sunshine. No doubt many doctor's bills are averted in this way."

"And am I to understand that, when you are in Paris, you devote all, or practically all, your time to your business interests, and that, while you are on the Riviera, you seclude yourself for a rest cure?"

"Again I find it hard to believe that you expect to be taken seriously, Inspector. Naturally, I lead the life of a normal man in both places—that is, a reasonable amount of my time is given to diversion."

"And these diversions include occasional visits to the casino at Monte Carlo?"

"*Cela va sans dire*—that goes without saying."

"You also entertain and are entertained a good deal?"

"Certainly I welcome my friends to my house, whenever I may be in residence, and certainly I go out among them. But neither the *pied-à-terre* nor the villa is on a scale to permit entertainment in the grand manner. I myself do not have either a yacht or a private beach."

"You do, however, give small parties, with persons of prominence among your guests?"

"Yes, occasionally. Not as often as in London."

"Do you happen to be acquainted with the present Sultan of Aristan, Izzet ibn Hamis?"

"I have met him, yes."

"I understand that he spends considerable time on the Riviera."

"My understanding is the same."

"But is your understanding based only on report? You have not seen him there, frequently, yourself?"

"As I said before, all these things are comparative. I do not know just what you mean by 'frequently.' "

"I will try to be more explicit. You yourself have spent approximately how much time on the Riviera this last year, Colonel de Valcourt?"

"About six weeks, all told, at intervals."

"And was the Sultan also on the Riviera each time you visited it?"

"Not as far as I know."

"Once perhaps?"

"Yes."

"Or perhaps twice?"

"Perhaps."

"And you were out in company with him—once or twice perhaps?"

"Yes."

"At private houses?"

"Yes, and elsewhere."

"Elsewhere including the casino?"

"Yes, elsewhere including the casino."

"And you entertained him at your villa—once or perhaps twice?"

"As I recall it, he came once to a small dinner and once to a large cocktail party at my villa."

"As guest of honor?"

"As ranking guest, naturally. Now that you speak of it, I believe the dinner was planned especially for him. I could tell by consulting my diary. I am sure, however, that the cocktail party was not, that I was giving it anyway, just before my departure, and that the Sultan graciously signified his intention of honoring it with his presence."

"So that, all in all, you were in his company, either in your own house or elsewhere, at least four times. On one of these occasions he was the guest of honor at a dinner you planned especially for him and on another he signified his desire to attend an entertainment you were giving."

"As I said, I should like to consult my diary on one of those points. But I believe you have stated the case correctly."

"Yet, when I first questioned you about the Sultan, you only admitted that you had 'met' him. Permit me to say that I should consider your acquaintance with him a good deal closer than that."

"It is not my habit to boast about the prominent persons who have been good enough to admit me to their immediate circle. I hear enough of such pretentious remarks from others–usually either from *noveaux riches* or down-at-the-heel aristocrats. I think I may say without arrogance that I belong to neither group. But since you are interested in the company I keep, I may mention that I have known several princes well enough to call them by their first name–and even one or two princesses."

De Valcourt's lips curved in a slight smile. The cigarette which he had been smoking intermittently had gone out, and again he reached for the platinum case and again proffered it to Kirtland.

"No, thank you very much," Kirtland said quietly. "Perhaps a little later . . . . Meanwhile, could you tell me, Colonel de Valcourt, whether, in the course of these various meetings with the young Sultan, the name of Baldwin Castle ever came up?"

"It well may have."

"Yet you told me—"

"Excuse me. You asked if I had ever heard it in connection with my work, *as a young officer in Lebanon.* And I told you, quite truthfully, that I had not."

"Well, now, I should be much obliged if you would tell me, *quite truthfully,* in what connection you heard of it on the Riviera."

"In connection with the possibility of a presidential appointment."

"Could you remember just what form the reference took?"

"Only that it was very casual. But I will search my memory and also consult my diary, if you would like to have me do so, to see if anything about it struck me particularly."

"I should be much obliged. Not that there is any hurry. I shall probably wish to question you a second time and, if I should, you can tell me then. You are quite sure that the reference was casual?"

Again De Valcourt's lips curved in a slight smile. "Quite sure. The little dinner at which I heard the passing reference was not a political meeting, Inspector. It was a social gathering with ladies present."

"I will take your word for it that this particular social function had no political significance. And I gather that it had no financial significance, either?"

"I'm afraid I don't quite follow you there."

"I believe that fairly large sums of money are sometimes won—and lost—in certain circles under certain circumstances on the Riviera. I assume that, sooner or later, a day of reckoning comes."

"And you think I was reduced to borrowing from the Sultan—or that he was reduced to borrowing from me?"

"I had not thought of either of you as being 'reduced,' Colonel de Valcourt. But money does enter the picture quite prominently, in one way or another, as I have just said, under certain conditions."

"You must know that the Sultan is one of the richest

men in the world. And you are quite at liberty to investigate my financial status, if that is not as well known to you as my diplomatic and military record."

Once more De Valcourt spoke with considerable heat, and once more Kirtland answered with increased calmness. "Well, perhaps I shall . . . . Now we seem to have dismissed the dinner party. And the cocktail party which the Sultan expressed a desire to attend—this had no political or financial significance, either?"

"None whatsoever. It was in the nature of a farewell fete."

"So you had no time for private conversation with anyone?"

"Practically none."

"If you should recall anything later, which you cannot seem to think of at the moment, I should be obliged if you would tell me . . . . I take it that His Excellency the Aristanian Ambassador was not vacationing on the Riviera at the same time as the Sultan—and as yourself?"

"Not to my knowledge."

"But you often see him in London?"

"Naturally. Since we are both members of the Diplomatic Corps, we inevitably move in much the same circles."

"And you are on good terms with each other?"

"It is the business of diplomats to be on good terms with each other unless and until their respective countries are actually at war. We are not intimate friends, if that is what you mean. After all, an ambassador's rank is so far above that of a military attaché's as practically to preclude intimacy."

"So you have never discussed Aristanian politics with him?"

"Never."

"And you have no reason to believe that he was displeased with Mr. Castle's appointment?"

"None. I should have said it would be quite the opposite—that he would be delighted with it."

"And, in the light of what you can recall about your

casual conversations with the Sultan, you have no reason to believe that he was displeased, either?"

"The same answer applies . . . . I hope I have answered your questions fully, Monsieur Kirtland, but I confess that you have roused my curiosity. May I inquire why you asked them?"

The Inspector rolled his fountain pen between the palms of his hands. "Because a man's political affiliations and their possible connection with his finances sometimes affect not only his attitude, but his actions," Kirtland said quietly. "Because cyanide is a component of many insecticides used in horticulture, especially in greenhouses. Because Colonel de Valcourt is an amateur in horticulture and the owner of profitable greenhouses. Because he is also famous for having introduced into the French Resistance new ways of using cyanide against the Nazis' occupying forces. Because Mr. Castle died of what appears to be cyanide poisoning. Quite enough reasons, shouldn't you say?"

"Most assuredly, I would *not* say! For every one of your reasons, I could cite you a dozen why it would be nonsense to think I had anything to do with Mr. Castle's death."

"Beg pardon!" Kirtland glanced up sharply, and placed his pen beside the notes on the desk. There was no hint of any apology in his tone. "I've never so much as suggested you might have done this, you know, any more than I suggested a treacherous political affiliation." The syllables were clipped and sharp.

* * *

On guard! That could have become a serious slip if by good chance he had not caught me up so quickly. For he has not intimated in words he suspects me—except that in the very beginning he said one of us in this suite must have killed the man Castle. How to shake his conviction on this point? How suggest it might have been someone who was *not* in the room with us? Ah, one needs to prompt him to talk. If he talks enough, that will give time for thought.

* * *

"In words, you have not said I am suspect, no, Monsieur Kirtland. But you have said it was one of us, and now you question me. Yet, why in the name of what you will should I desire to kill a man I did not even know?"

"Aye, there's the matter of motive, I grant you," agreed Kirtland and let his eyes wander, as if idly, to where the lighted Shot Tower gleamed against the south bank sky line. "One of the three *M*'s. You know, Colonel, police work's mostly just a routine job. The wireless and the two-and-six mystery books have their super sleuths, who trip up the guilty wretch by knowing precisely which island in the Fijis a given feather dart comes from or what sort of oak galls were used in making the ink the will was written in. These chaps are forever pointing out to us dull C.I.D. fellows some perfectly obvious thing we've really taken note of long since. But actually, when you stop to analyze even such a regrettable affair as this, the business boils down to the three *M*'s: method, moment and motive. As to method, once you find a body dead from having the neck bent back until it breaks, you immediately eliminate the possibility that any ordinary woman could have done it. They haven't the physical strength. Then you take moment—you must find someone who wasn't off in Greenland at the time the victim had his head bashed in at Northwick Mews. In short, you eliminate everyone who couldn't have been on hand. Motive—well, that explains itself, I fancy."

"And in my case you have method and moment, but no motive?"

"If you'll pardon me for saying so, I'd put it a bit differently. I'd say we haven't established a motive in your case, *as yet*. Just the same, I'm not at all sure that there couldn't have been one. Meaning no manner of offense."

"Ah, *toujours la politesse,*" murmured Jacques. "But in your preoccupation with my 'possible' political affiliations and my financial standing, not to mention my favorite avocation and the excellent opportunity this affords for quietly and quickly disposing of anyone who interferes with my interests instead of furthering them, have you forgotten one very famous motto of the *gendarmerie* of my own land, a police force of no small repute, you will concede, no?"

"Carry on, sir."

"Cherchez la femme—look for the woman."

Kirtland shrugged and glanced toward the door of the east bedroom of the suite. "Lady Laura and her daughter Miss Althea, Mrs. Racina, Mrs. Castle and Miss Lester are all in there, as you know. I have spoken with the first three already and—"

"And of course found them all completely above suspicion."

"As I said, I have spoken with them already," the Inspector replied levelly. "I have not yet spoken with Mrs. Castle."

"May I make a suggestion in that quarter?"

"Certainly, if you feel it would be helpful. But to avoid needless repetition, I may perhaps tell you that Mrs. Racina has already informed me that Mrs. Castle was greatly intrigued—I think that is the exact word she used, intrigued—by what she had heard about certain experiments of yours from Mr. Thorpe, on the way from his house to the theater; that she asked you further questions about them, on the way from the theater to the Savoy; and also that you seemed perfectly willing to tell her about them."

"Ah . . . . I see that Mrs. Racina, no less than her husband, could qualify as an observant reporter. But did Mrs. Racina also tell you that while we were at the theater Mrs. Castle asked me for an aspirin tablet, to relieve a headache."

"No, she did not mention that."

"Ah!" De Valcourt said again. "Well, any reporter worthy of the name needs to know what to omit as well as what to relate. I am glad to say that I was able to oblige Mrs. Castle, since I was well provided with aspirin–and with the coated variety, which is what I always take myself."

"Yes? And you are suggesting?"

"Nothing, really, any more than you were. I am only mentioning potentialities about which you will naturally wish to consult one of your chemists. But it does not seem to me to be beyond the range of possibility that, with the requisite type of tablet in her possession, a clever woman might have found a way of impregnating it with poison. As you doubtless know, there is a lavatory connected with the Royal Retiring Room. Mrs. Castle could easily have absented herself there a few minutes for quite natural reasons."

"Did you see her absent herself, as you put it, after giving her the aspirin tablet?"

"No, because during the second interval Miss Whitford and I took a stroll in the foyer. But there would have been plenty of time for Mrs. Castle to do so."

"I see. And since you are so positive on that score, you should be able to tell me yourself, Colonel de Valcourt, whether you think the impregnation you mentioned would be possible under the given circumstances. After all, you have had considerable experience with it."

"I should not say it could be done easily. But neither should I say that it was impossible to do, in the hands of a clever woman with a destructive purpose."

"And that is how Mrs. Castle struck you–as a clever woman with a destructive purpose?"

"I believe you have been told that she was 'indisposed.' Well, in the case of an indisposition such as hers, it is of course difficult to judge character correctly, and what is more, many characters seem to change completely. But again I should not say it was utterly impossible to assume that Mrs. Castle is far more clever than she seems and not in the least impossible to assume that she might have had a destructive purpose–considering how much she stood to gain, in certain ways, if she could accomplish such a purpose."

"And you would not put it past her either to have poison already in her possession, hoping that she might learn how and when it could be used to best advantage?"

"Certainly I should not put it past her."

"So it was Mrs. Castle you had in mind when you suggested we should look for the woman in the case?"

"She was one of those I had in mind. Miss Lester was another."

"Yes?"

"Yes. I did not know this before tonight, but it was quite obvious then that Miss Lester and Mr. Castle were not meeting for the first time, when they did so at supper."

"And so?"

"Something in the atmosphere gave me the impression that they had not only met before, but that at one time they had known each other quite well."

"I am afraid that in cases of this sort we cannot be guided by anything so vague as atmospheric conditions."

"She called him by a *petit nom*–what you would designate as a nickname or, in certain cases, as a pet name. This is one of the cases where I think the latter term would be applicable. And as Miss Whitford and I were returning from our stroll, I distinctly heard Castle tell Ahani that he had an appointment with Miss Lester in her dressing room. Moreover, he obviously set great store by this appointment–so great that he cut short a discussion of international import in order to keep it."

"Then it would appear that they were on friendly terms rather than otherwise, wouldn't it?"

"Yes, it would appear so. But it's a cliché to say that appearances are often very deceptive. And to refer again to atmospheric conditions, on which I put more dependence than you do, I did not gather that Mr. Alban and Mr. Neville entertained very cordial feelings toward Mr. Castle. However, I must say that since one is a cheap charlatan and the other a morbid brooder, we should not take too much stock in their feelings, which are hardly those of a well-balanced man, in either case."

"We can discuss them later on if it seems best, Colonel de Valcourt. For the moment, suppose we confine ourselves to the aspects of the case which you yourself suggested: namely, the part which the–ah–ladies might have played. Did Miss Lester also show evidences of being intrigued by your experiments with cyanide?"

"No, but she and the other principals in the cast of *Gold of Pleasure* visited me at my place in Chiswick about ten days ago–my house, my garden and my greenhouses. You have taken some pains to stress the fact that cyanide is a component of many insecticides used in horticulture, especially in greenhouses. If Miss Lester had wished to help herself to this deadly poison, it would have been quite easy for her to do so unobserved."

"Easy, yes. But would it not also have been pointless? What could she possibly have thought, ten days ago, that she might wish to do with it?"

"That of course is for you to determine. You have mentioned three *M*'s–motive, method and moment. I have supplied you with the possible motive and a certain method. Certainly a man of your talents and experience should be able to supply the third M for yourself."

Kirtland appeared to be undisturbed by the mockery in De Valcourt's tones and indeed quite unaware of it. "I should indeed," he said pleasantly. "So if that is all the information you are prepared to give me about Miss Lester, let me ask you if there is still another woman about whom you believe I haven't thought?"

"There is indeed."

"And she is . . . ."

* * *

In Paris, the police would have seized that she-devil long ago–do the English then search for white women and no others? Naturally, I must admit you were not the one who saw her come out from behind the garden wall of Thorpe's villa that evening in Martinique, when I was waiting impatiently for the swift tropic dusk to end, so that I could discreetly make my presence known at a certain barred window of a villa which had nothing to do with my friend Thorpe. But behind his garden wall was a niche where once a gate had given on an orchard of mango and papaya—an excellent place to wait. The wall itself was covered with a cascade of purple and red, for the bougainvilleas came tumbling down on it from above; and against the sky were etched the broad leaves of banana plants and the huge bud, like a heart hanging from a chain. Above these, highest of all, were the palms, like great standpipes, with fountains of fronds spraying out from the tips. And beyond and over them all, old Pelée with its plume of smoke drifting away with the trade winds . . . .

I knew that darkness would soon drop a curtain between me and these sights. Then there would be only fireflies and stars, bright jewels on the bosom of the night, yet less bright to me than the eyes looking down into mine from that window less well barred than the old people thought; and I can still see before me the figure that stole out from behind the wall at its far end—the gay striped skirt, looped up over a white petticoat, the bodice with its kerchief outlining the breasts, the knotted *tignon* covering the black hair. I can still hear the tinkle of the ornaments worn by the girl so clothed, when she slipped past my niche to the buttresses at the foot of a great silk-cotton tree. And I still think to myself, not only for me are nights the times for lover's meetings . . . . .

* * *

"I'm waiting for your answer, Colonel de Valcourt. Can you tell me any other lady we should look for in trying to get to the bottom of this tragedy?"

"Yes, Thorpe's cook Lalisse. Has it occurred to you that she prepared and served food that Mr. Castle ate only last evening?"

"Certainly it has. And I may say, Colonel, that Mr.

Thorpe offered to send for her. But since, if we did that, we might also logically have to consider the caterer and waiters responsible for the collation at the theater, I suggested that we might wait before taking such action. However, upon reflection, I decided that the two cases were not necessarily comparable, and that I would not wait too long after talking with Mrs. Racina. I telephoned to headquarters and sent a sergeant to fetch Lalisse at Mr. Thorpe's house. And she has disappeared. There is not a trace of her to be found."

CHAPTER XIII

DE VALCOURT SPRANG to his feet. All his lassitude, all his indifference, had vanished as if by magic. He gave a triumphant exclamation.

"Why then, your mystery is as good as solved! I cannot understand why you have kept me here, prattling about politics and finances and horticulture, and leading me on to make possibly damaging remarks about completely blameless women, when all the time–"

The Inspector raised his hand in the characteristic gesture.

"Not quite so fast, if you please, Colonel de Valcourt. The fact that Lalisse has disappeared from Mr. Thorpe's house does not necessarily establish her guilt as a poisoner, though certainly it serves to place her among the suspects."

"*Among* the suspects! At the top of the list, I should say!"

"Not even that. The list has no top and no bottom as yet, Colonel de Valcourt, and I would not know just where to place this cook of Mr. Thorpe's on it. However, after he found he would probably be here most of the night, he sent his chauffeur Celestino home, telling the man to stay on call, but saying he was welcome to snatch what sleep he could, as long as he remained where he could hear the telephone and the doorbell. When my sergeant went to the house, Celestino admitted him and showed him the way to the cook's room. The door was locked and repeated knocking elicited no answer; so the sergeant had no choice but to force his way in. There was no one in the room, but it was in perfect order, and there was clothing in the closet and in the chest of drawers—as much as such a woman would have been likely to possess; in fact, rather more. Everything pointed to a precipitate departure, but—"

"Of course it was a precipitate departure! A departure which is clearly a revelation of guilt!"

"*If* you please, Colonel de Valcourt . . . . Celestino admitted telling Lalisse about the murder and the investigation which is now taking place, and he probably painted the proceedings in the most lurid colors. He also admits that Mr. Thorpe told him we might wish to send for Lalisse later on—a piece of information, needless to say, which Mr. Thorpe cautioned him *not* to relay. The only reason it was given was to expedite the cook's arrival, in Mr. Thorpe's car, should we decide to question her. All in all, Celestino obviously succeeded in giving Lalisse a terrible fright. She is undoubtedly an ignorant superstitious woman and, as you know, she has had one bout with the police already—the French police—which may have left a very sad impression on her, even though she was exonerated in the end. I do not know with what crime she was previously charged, but—"

"I do. And I shall be very happy to tell you."

"Later perhaps—after you have consulted your memory and your diary on those other points under consideration. I may even wish to question Lalisse in your presence, though we do not habitually follow such a procedure."

"After you find her!"

"Exactly. After we find her. For I have not the slightest doubt that we shall find her, considering the thoroughness of the search which is now being made." The Inspector spoke rather dryly. "Meanwhile, Colonel de Valcourt,

I will excuse you—for the present. It is getting rather late and, as I wish to spare Mrs. Castle as much fatigue as possible, I think I should perhaps talk with her now, so that she may have that ordeal behind her and get some rest."

De Valcourt hesitated, obviously unwilling to leave the room without further discussion of Lalisse. It was, however, equally obvious not only that the Inspector had no intention of obliging him in this respect, but that he had been dismissed. He bowed with even chillier formality than when he had been ushered into the Inspector's presence and, turning abruptly on his heel, left the room with exaggerated military stiffness. Kirtland waited until the door had closed behind the Frenchman before nodding to his sergeant.

"Consult Mrs. Racina again, will you, Griffin? Then, if she feels this would be a good time, ask Mrs. Castle to come in."

"Right away, sir."

Compared to Lady Laura's impeccable appearance, Cornelia's inevitably suffered. She had done her best to repair the ravages wrought by her 'indisposition' and Judith had tried to help her; but neither had been able to make her disordered hair smooth again, or to apply cosmetics with sufficient skill to hide the traces of tears or erase other telltale signs of malaise and emotion from her face. Her magenta-colored velvet had also suffered, first from her sickness and then from her restless slumbers; there had been no chance of changing it; and its original unsuitability had now become tragically incongruous. She was herself so painfully aware of all this that she spoke of it, on her own initiative, before the Inspector had framed his unwilling questions.

"I guess I ought to apologize to you for looking the way I do, Inspector. I know I need a good wash and a hairdo and all that the worst way. And—a nice plain black dress. But we didn't know when you'd call me again, or any place where I could get the right clothes, either, at this time of night. So—"

"Please don't give that a thought. I realize the circumstances. I'm sorry I had to send for you at all and I don't think I'll need to keep you long. Mrs. Castle, I hope you'll believe me when I say I'd like to make this just as easy as possible for you. I'd avoid it altogether if I could, and if you'd rather not talk to me tonight, we could do it later."

"I do believe you. And I'd rather have it over with. It's got to be sometime, hasn't it?"

"I'm afraid it has."

"All right then. Go ahead. What do you want to know?"

"Perhaps you'll tell me how you happened to meet Mr. Castle and where."

"He saw me modeling evening dresses in a fashion show and he liked my looks. I'd been an actress–that is, I'd been in the chorus, and the road company I'd joined up with in Chicago had actually made Broadway. But I knew the show would never last there, and I wasn't getting any younger or any slimmer; so I went around looking for a modeling job and by good luck I got one right away. Miss Hickey, the head woman of the Salon Superbe at Haas and Hector, was looking for someone who could show the most important type of gowns. At least, that's the way Hickey described them. Of course, what she really meant was dresses for dames that couldn't get into the misses' sizes any more or who had reached the age where they'd begun to look silly in fluffy ruffles, but who had enough dough to buy anything that took their fancy. Baldy–I mean Mr. Castle–brought his wife to an opening–she was the sort who didn't like to choose her clothes without her husband's advice–and she ordered three of the dresses I was modeling–or rather, he did. One of them cost eight hundred and the other two a thousand apiece; but when she came to try them on, they didn't look the same on her as they had on me, and I was called into the fitting room to show them again and see if there was anything that could be done about changing the model to make it more becoming. Of course there wasn't, but the Castles were both nice about it—he came to the fittings, too. And the next year they came back again. Finally, he came alone, and told Miss Hickey that his wife had died, but that the invitations to the openings kept on coming, so he thought he'd attend one just the same, as he was going to be in New York anyway at the time. Then, as I went past him, showing a beaded number—Sultana, the name of it was—he asked me to stop a minute, so he could look at the material, and while he was doing that he asked, in a lower voice, if I could meet him at Twenty One for dinner at eight that night."

"And you accepted?"

"Yes, I did. I couldn't help but be pleased that he'd remembered me and that he'd wanted to see me again. And he didn't—I mean—it was all on the level. He took me out three or four times, always to nice restaurants and once to a swell show afterward. He gave me orchids to wear and saw me home in a limousine. But that was all. I mean, he didn't ask to come in afterward or anything. But I had a one and a half room apartment by that time—a bed-sitting room, bath and kitchenette—and so after all those feeds and flowers I thought it would be only decent to ask him, wouldn't he like a home-cooked meal for a change, and how about a spaghetti supper at my place around seven? So he came, and we had a very nice evening, but no monkey business then, either, if you know what I mean. And the next day he came around and asked me to marry him. My, was I ever surprised! And was I ever pleased!"

"And this was how long ago?"

"Just last June. We were married in August and went to Hawaii on our honeymoon."

"You spoke of Mr. Castle's wife. Had you been married before, too?"

"Yes."

"So you were a widow at the time you met Mr. Castle?"

"Well, not a real widow—what we call a grass widow. I don't know what you call it here."

"We call it that to describe a woman who's briefly separated from her husband. Is that what you mean?"

"No, I mean we'd separated for good."

"You had divorced your first husband?"

"No, I'd divorced the second one. The first one divorced me."

"That's rather unusual, isn't it, in the States? That is, I've understood that, generally–"

"You've understood right. Generally, a man lets his wife divorce him. But this time . . . . Well, I didn't have a thing against my husband. He's one of the best men that ever lived. And he had plenty against me. Look, I've told Judith–I mean Mrs. Racina–all about it already . . . ."

* * *

"Honest, Judith–it's all right for me to call you Judith, isn't it?–I didn't mean to touch a drop of liquor again, never as long as I lived. You believe me, don't you?"

"Yes, of course I believe you. Don't worry about it now, just try to get some rest."

"I'll rest a lot better if I can talk to you first. Won't you let me?"

"Yes, if you're sure it'll make you feel better."

"Well, my own folks were all teetotalers, and so were most of the other folks I know. All Minnie Brown's folks."

"Minnie Brown's?"

"Yes. Minnie Brown was Baldwin Castle's first wife. Her younger sister Mabel and I went to grammar school together–that is, Mabel was two or three classes ahead of me and Minnie was already in high school then, but everyone knew those Brown girls. They were the kind who won all the spelling bees, and were chosen to speak pieces when there were visiting teachers and never got any marks lower than an *A*. All that didn't make them very popular–you know how girls are, jealous of such good students and pretending it's just because they're nasty nice. You must have seen the same thing yourself. It does make those bright girls stand out."

"Yes, I have, many times."

"The Browns moved away from Hudson to Oklahoma City when Mabel was twelve, so I didn't see anything of them after that. But we all went right on hearing about them and by and by reading about them in the papers. Both girls kept being valedictorians and Phi Beta Kappa and things like that, and then they were serving on school boards and library committees and running church fairs. But neither of them got married, and we hicks used to joke about that and say the Browns got degrees, but we got men. And then, right out of a clear sky, came great big headlines saying that Baldwin Castle–*Baldwin Castle, the biggest catch in the state*–was marrying Minnie Brown."

"Mrs. Castle, I'm interested in what you're telling me, of course, but I really think you ought to rest."

"You mean that, if I'm going to talk, you think I ought to stick to talking about what I started out to tell you, which was my drinking. Well, in a way you're right, but in another, it all fits into the same picture. You'll see. Like I said, my folks were teetotalers; it wasn't until I ran away from home, and fell in with a little road company, that I ever saw liquor swilled around. I got high once or twice, and pretty soon I got fired, because I put some dirtier language into my lines than what belonged there, when I was under the weather. The next job I got, I was careful to keep. I needed it bad–I mean badly–and the liquor hadn't got me then–it was just that I enjoyed the taste of the stuff and the way I felt after two or three drinks. Then Sam Martin saw me in a show, like I think I told the others tonight at the theater–I'm not too sure yet what I did do and say–and talked me into marrying him. There never was a drop of liquor on our table, either. It wasn't until that damn city slicker came along—excuse me, I didn't mean to say that, it just slipped out."

"If it's really helping you to talk, Mrs. Castle, I think it would help you still more if you do it the way that seems most natural. If it seems natural to say damn or even something stronger now and then, don't give it a second thought. I don't mind in the least."

"Thanks . . . . Well, this damn city slicker came along and he had a fifth with him. I guess he had my husband sized up, at one swift glance—me, too. Anyway, it wasn't until Sam went out to the barn to finish up the chores that Herb—that was the city slicker's name, Herb Styles—said he's been feeling the heat and needed a little stimulant and wouldn't I like to join him. I was getting supper and the baby was sitting right there in his high chair, beating on it with his rattle, and I knew I oughtn't to listen. But Herb asked did I want him to turn into a lone drinker, and where was the icebox, he could make his own setups, and the first thing I knew we were sitting at the table drinking ice-cold highballs.

"I had just time to get the glasses over to the sink and start to give them a good rinse when Sam came in from the barn; but I didn't have time to go to the pantry to get cloves or anything like that, and of course he could smell the liquor on our breaths. I must say he was swell about it, too. He just told Herb he didn't like to seem narrow-minded, but he'd taken the pledge when he was ten years old and he meant to keep it and have the members of his household keep it, too; so he hoped Mr. Styles would understand he couldn't permit any beverage with alcoholic content to be used in his home. And Herb said sure, sorry, and we all sat down to supper as if nothing had happened. It had been close to suppertime when he came, in the midst of a mighty bad thunderstorm, and it was Sam that had asked him to stay.

"Supper was a nice enough meal. Herb praised my cooking and asked Sam about the stock and chucked the baby under the chin—that sort of stuff. The weather had cleared, and pretty soon he said well, he'd be pushing along, thanks for everything, no offense meant and he hoped none had been taken. I put the baby to bed and then Sam read a chapter from the Bible out loud, like he always did, and afterward we knelt down together while he prayed out loud, like he always did, too. He said a lot about not being led into temptation and not yielding to it if we were, while he was praying, but he didn't say anything more after that; and then he put the cat out and wound up the clock, and we went to bed, in the room off the kitchen, where we always slept, with the baby next to us in his crib.

"Sam was asleep in no time, but I wasn't. I wanted another drink the worst way. I kept thinking how good that one had tasted, before supper, how cool it had looked in that glass with the ice in it. I couldn't seem to think of anything else. I went on thinking about it all the time we were in church the next day, which was Sunday, and all Sunday afternoon, when there wasn't a thing to do, after dinner, but sit on the back porch. Sam took a nap Sunday afternoons, but I wasn't sleepy, and anyway, I had to watch the baby. He was just starting to creep and he got into everything and hurt himself, too, if he wasn't watched. I watched him all right, every minute, but all the time I watched, I was thinking about that drink.

"Then, Monday morning, when I went to hang out the wash, I found the bottle. Herb had tossed it down by the clothesline when he left. He'd taken a swig as soon as he got down the steps and he thought he'd emptied it—at least, that's what he said afterward, and I'll give him the benefit of the doubt. Of course he couldn't see very well, in the dark. Be that as it may, the bottle was empty all right when I got through with it. And when Sam came in from the fields, the baby was crying and the stove was cold and I had passed out on the bed.

"Sam changed the baby and tried to feed him some milk out of a cup. Then he got the dinner and made some good strong coffee, so that it would be ready for me when I woke up. And he was nice that time, too—at least, he was a little more biblical than before, if you know what I mean; he quoted that verse about wine being a mocker and some others I've forgotten now. By and by he reminded me I was still nursing the baby and I didn't need him to tell me that made what I'd done all the worse. He brought the baby and put him down on the bed next to me and sat there watching us while I nursed him. I cried good and hard and said I was terribly sorry and that I'd never never do such a dreadful thing again.

"But I did. I won't try to tell you how everything happened, but Herb kept coming back with a different line—I mean a different line of goods. He was a drummer, did I say that before or didn't I? And he had plenty of the other line, too. And every time he came, he sneaked me in some more liquor. So it wasn't long before Sam wasn't patient and soft spoken or even biblical any more. He ordered Herb off the place and said he'd take a gun to him if he ever came back, and that the law would be with him for destroying another man's home and leading his neighbor's wife astray like that.

"Herb had led me astray, as far as liquor was concerned, and he'd had it easy, too. When it came to the other, he had it harder. But finally it happened of course—when I was under the influence. Sam found us together in the spare room—Herb thought he had locked the door, but the catch didn't work. The baby was out on the porch all alone, crawling around. It was a miracle he hadn't fallen down the steps and been hurt.

"Sam told Herb he wasn't going to kill him then after all, because he'd have to marry me as soon as my divorce went through—if he didn't, that was when the shooting would start. And Sam told me he wasn't going to risk having his only child grow up to be a drunken sot, like his mother. The baby was weaned by then, and Sam bundled him up and took him to *his* mother—I mean my mother-in-law, damn her! And he locked me up in the spare room alone, after he fixed the catch. He did the cooking and everything the next few days and brought meals to me on a tray, not bad ones, either, considering he didn't know the first thing about cooking. But he didn't speak to me at all until he told me my father had answered the letter he'd written and was coming to fetch me.

"Those next few months were pretty awful. I lied when I told the others I wasn't cut out for life in the country, that I made a swift getaway the first chance I had. I loved that farm, I loved my husband, I loved my baby. It nearly killed me to lose them all. And my father was a hard man, harder even than Sam. He cursed and called me bad names. It was terrible, staying in his house. He never talked to me except to compare me to Jezebel, or some such whore. If my mother'd been alive, she might have helped me some, she might even have made my father and Sam see different—differently. She was one of those soft-spoken women who can really turn away wrath, like the Bible says. But she was dead already. There wasn't anyone in that bare little house except me and my father. I wrote to Sam and begged him to give me another chance. I said I knew how bad I'd been, but did he really think just one act of adultery, committed under the influence, turned a woman into a sure-enough whore? He never answered the letter. And by and by the divorce went through and I was married to Herb the same day by a justice of the peace. Sam stayed right outside the courthouse with a gun . . . ."

* * *

"It would be kind of hard for me to tell it all over again—and anyway, it's easier to tell that sort of a story to another woman than to a man. So if you wouldn't mind, Inspector—"

"It will be quite satisfactory, Mrs. Castle, for me to get the gist of the story later from Mrs. Racina. I don't believe I need the details, at least for the present. But you said something about a second husband, whom you divorced?'

"Yes, and I told Judith all about that, too."

* * *

"It was pure-D hell, living with Herb Styles. But I might have become a liquorhead anyway. I know that now, Judith. There's something in me that means I'm no damn good at drinking, that I'm a gone Greek the minute I take drink one.

"Sam could have kept me straight—maybe. He was the world and all in my book. For him, I might have pulled myself together before it got me down. I mean it was really as much my fault as Herb's that I went the route I did. Of course I couldn't help marrying him—not when Sam was standing right outside the courthouse with a gun. But when I saw that third-floor walk-up in a six-apartment building, with two bays exactly like a jillion other South Side houses, my drinks died on me sure enough. This dump had been furnished by Herb's first wife, and I expect all the taste she had was in her mouth. Any jury that ever set eyes on that sitting room rug, with roses that looked like a cabbage all broken out with heat rash, would have said it was okay for him to kill her.

"In fact, if they'd ever seen that dining table, so

big you could barely squeeze between it and the china cabinet on one side, or between it and the sideboard on the other, or the boneless doll propped against the bolster in the bedroom, with its legs tied in a knot—any jury that saw those things would have given him no less than a hero medal for killing her.

"If he'd only let me do the place over, like I begged him! But he wouldn't hear of it. He said money was too useful for keeping us in hooch to waste it on furniture when the furniture you already had was as good as the day it left Grand Rapids.

"To this minute, I couldn't for the life of me tell you which was worse, the times he was in off the road and sharing the apartment with me, or when he was out in his territory and I had to shack up in that dump all by my lonesome. When you get right down to it, there wasn't a hell of a lot to choose from, either way. While he was in town, we'd go out to supper at the place of some friend of his, or some friend of his would come to our flat to eat. Either way, it was the same difference. The friends he had lived in the identical kind of six-flat walk-up, and whether it was in their place or in ours, there'd be drinks before, and during, and after supper. That was a good thing, in a way, because if I had been sober while I listened to those same stories about the old maid in the upper berth over and over and over again, God knows what I might have done. It was bad enough even when I was tight.

"Those were the times I'd think about Sam and the farm, and the quiet evenings, with the baby asleep in his crib. I'd be sitting by the table lamp, and like as not mending one of Sam's blue work shirts, and he would read out loud to me from the country paper about who was visiting which kinfolks, or maybe about somebody we knew taking a trip to Omaha. I remember how tickled to death Sam sounded when he read about the stork bringing us a baby boy. That was the way the paper wrote it up. Sam pasted the clipping in our baby book and said the rest of the page would be left blank for the clipping giving the election returns when our boy became president.

"Mornings everything was quiet, too, except for maybe just a bird starting to sing. Sam would be up a long while by the time I woke, he having the cows to milk and such as that. Then, while I was fixing our breakfast of sausage or side meat and pancakes and eggs and so on, he'd finish with the chores.

"What kept reminding me of that, I guess, was on account of being married to Herb was so different. Every morning I'd wake up with a horrible slimy taste in my mouth from the drinks of the night before, and just the bare idea of food made me sicker and sicker. So did the sight of Herb, sleeping with his mouth open, and his hair pushed around to where the baldness showed plainer than big print, and those gray-brown bristles sticking out of his creased jowl. Unless I got a quick nip to pick me up, it would have been just too bad. Fortunately, I was never so looping tight the night before that I forgot to leave some whisky in a bottle by my side of the bed. It would take about three good jolts to clear the gooky taste off my tongue; even then, the first thing I noticed each morning wasn't the birds beginning to sing, but the bricks in the wall on the other side of our air shaft; bricks that looked like they had been streaked with soot and grime before they were even built into a new wall.

"I used to enjoy fixing meals when I was on the farm, and cleaning up in the big kitchen afterward. We had nice fresh garden stuff all summer long, and a root cellar full of potatoes and beets and things like that in the winters. But in town, especially in that walk-up of Herb's, I hated it worse than the devil hates holy water. We always had the same old pot roast and mashed potatoes and canned peas and store-bought apple pie; that was all Herb cared about having, and it was the least trouble to fix. And there was always that business of squeezing past the china cabinet on one side and the sideboard on the other, to put things on the table.

"Anyway, after a while I got to sending out to the delicatessen for everything, when we were having company. That would still leave the greasy dishes and smeared glasses to wash up the next day, but at least I wouldn't have the pots and so on to scour.

"Now and then I'd try to cut down on my liquor, but somehow I just couldn't. I'd tell myself that I was heading for a crack-up, and all it would take was will power–and not even much of that–to cut down a little. I'd try to drink less often, but that wouldn't work at all. I'd get so nervous just thinking about not taking a drink until two hours had gone by that I'd want it more than ever. Then I'd try making each drink about half the regular size, and drinking as often as before, but that wouldn't begin to take the slimy taste out of my mouth or the knots out of my body where I was all tightened up and tense.

"Things kept getting worse and worse. The more I drank, the less I ate, and the sicker I was in the mornings. It got so I'd wake up in the night, once or twice, and have to take a drink before I could get back to sleep. I used to think, along at first, that when Herb was out on the road, I could have a chance to straighten up. But it didn't work out that way. Sitting in the dump all by myself, I'd feel like I was getting ready to have the screaming meemies, as the drinks died on me, and I'd be scared, knowing there was no one around to help me if I ever let myself go.

"So I'd try to keep busy. I'd go window-shopping along 63rd Street, or even down on State Street, but it didn't take my mind off wanting a drink. I'd begin to jitter, and then I'd hurry home, saying I'd take just one quickie to steady my nerves, and that is the way it would go, no matter what I tried. Like embroidery. I figured give me something that I'd have to keep my mind on and my hands busy with —and staying at home. But my fingers would get too twitchy, and my eyes, too, and I'd say to myself well, just a short one so you can keep on working . . . and the next thing I'd know it would be morning, and I'd be fumbling for the bottle on the floor by my bedside.

"I don't know whether this is anything to be proud of, but for whatever it's worth, the one thing I could never have brought myself to do was what the wives of some of the other traveling men did when their husbands were out on the road. Oh, it wasn't any thought of Herb or what he had coming to him that kept me from being a little prairie flower, growing wilder every hour. I knew he wasn't spending any lonely nights; not if he could find a waitress in some hick town hashery to mouse around with.

"But this business of letting some bohunk from the South Chicago steel mills, or some sailor from the naval station, or maybe even a college boy pick you up just wasn't for me. As I said, it wasn't the thought of Herb that held me back, but it might have been the thought of Sam. Somewhere, deep down, I must have had the notion that if Sam and I ever did make up, I could go back to him if I'd been no worse than a mixed-up gal who'd pulled one chump mistake because she couldn't let liquor alone. But I could never go back to Sam and my baby, no matter what happened, if I'd just been a push-over for any guy walking along Clark Street on the make.

"Anyway, it wasn't any of those ideas or anything else I tried on my own that finally pulled me up short. It was just plain getting too sick to go on. This was about three weeks after Herb had been fired for padding his expense account to make up for the commissions he didn't seem to be earning any more. While he was out of a job, he kept hanging around the house, griping because I wouldn't cook for him. That was because the sight and the smell of food made me too sick. But so did his bitching about being a misunderstood, hard-working guy, trying to make a living for his family, and not being about to come home to a decent meal after all the grease burners where he had been eating while he was out on the road.

"Finally he took to going out and looking for a job, and coming home with a bigger grouch than ever. But I will say this for him. He cut out all drinking for himself—I envied him and tried to do it. too, but it was no go for me—and he lost that bleary look under his eyes and at the corners of his nostrils. He was a sharp number when he put his mind to it—shoes you could see to shave in and a trouser crease you could use for the razor. Handsome was the word for Herbie, all right.

"After about a week of looking, he came busting into the apartment one afternoon yelling like a Comanche, and grinning, and headed straight for the sideboard to take a hooker of bourbon out of a cut glass decanter he was awfully proud of. He had a new suitcase, and packages with new shirts, and ties and things, and while he's packing, he tells me he's landed a wonderful job with a new radio manufacturing house. He'll only have to make the big towns to contact jobbers, and no more hick storekeepers and hamburger stands for grub. This was the kind of break all his life he had been looking for . . . just watch him burn up those old sales charts with new records! It wouldn't be long before we would move to a new apartment, either. Something with class, up on the North Side, Sheridan Road or any place I wanted. So step on it, honeybunch, and help him get going on account of he had to catch the train for Peoria right now.

"I helped him all I could. It was such a relief

to know he wasn't going to be grumping around the apartment about how he was misunderstood and abused by everybody, getting fired for a little nothing that everybody else expected a traveling man to do, and after all those years of piling up sales for them. He gave me some money before he left—saying they'd come up with a nice advance on his drawing account. He was never chinchy, I'm bound to say that for him. There was enough in the roll he handed me to keep me going for a long while, especially as I wasn't going to spend a cent of it for liquor. No siree, I was through with that stuff for keeps. No more halfway deals like trying to cut down. I was taking the pledge, but for life. That is, after tonight. I felt like I owed myself one good farewell party, especially after those last three weeks . . . .

"I woke up in the hospital. The cleaning woman —who came in two days after Herb left—found me. I'd passed out cold as a mackerel fillet. I had got too sick to hold even liquor on my stomach, and too weak from not eating and from sickness to get help, if I was conscious at all, which I don't know.

"By the time I really woke up in the hospital, I hadn't had a drink in it must have been five days. The doctors and nurses had kept me on some sort of sleepy dope while they got my system cleaned out or whatever it is they do. It was like being born again not to wake up with that foul slimy sensation in your mouth, and have an appetite, and feel myself getting clean and strong.

"I had plenty of time to think, and for once a clear head to think with. So I could make up my mind about what would come next. I mean about what I was going to do. Herb was on his feet with a good job, so there was no need for me to go back to that kind of life on his account. Nobody could say I was quitting him when he was down and out, after sticking around like a leech while he was in the chips.

"After they discharged me, I took what money was left and what clothes I had and moved to a furnished room. I didn't have any kind of training; the only thing I knew how to do was cook, aside from being a walk-on in a chorus line. So I got a job as waitress in a drive-in at night and hit the theatrical agencies in the daytime. After all, I still had everything a gal in the chorus line needs. So that's how I got on with a road company of *Rose Marie,* when one of their girls quit while they were in Chicago. It wasn't a bad troupe, either, and we wound up back in little old New York with nobody having to walk home from Weehawken; and, before the show closed, I had got a job modeling in the Salon Superbe at Haas and Hector.

"Herb didn't make any beef about letting me divorce him. I've a hunch he was kind of glad to get rid of me. So far as he knew, I'd never be anything but a liquorhead. But I stayed sober. I mean I didn't so much as sniff the cork of a bottle of anything that had alky in it. I was scared, but really scared, when I came out of the fog in that hospital. My mind was a total blank on what had happened to get me there. It suddenly came to me that when I was like that I might maybe do anything. I wouldn't know what I was doing while it was going on, and I wouldn't remember what I'd done after I came out of it. That was just too big a risk for the sake of something I couldn't stand the taste of any more.

"I wrote to Sam, too, to tell him what had happened. But Sam wouldn't answer my letters, and I can't say I really blame him, and after a while I got my second chance—not with Sam, like I'd kept on hoping against hope, but with Baldwin Castle of all people.

"The first time I met him he came to the Salon Superbe with his wife—her that had been Minnie Brown. But it wasn't until after she died that he gave me this chance. In fact, she'd died quite a while back. She'd been a good wife and, far as I know, he'd been a good husband. Just the same, it'd been one of those marriages that hadn't quite come off, if you know what I mean. She'd gone along serving on school boards and library committees and she'd given lots of money—Baldwin's money—to good causes, so her name was in the paper all the time. But when it came to throwing dinners for the big shots in the oil business, or getting up week-end parties out in the country, I guess she wasn't so hot. Even the Salon Superbe couldn't do anything for her and, when it comes to that, I don't think Balenciaga or Schiaparelli could either. She always looked sort of dowdy, no matter what she wore; and that was always the same kind of hat, like Queen Mary or Alice Longworth, only being neither the one nor the other, she couldn't get away with it and still look important, the way they can. Besides, her skirts were never the same lengths as other women's and her fur pieces were always crooked—well, I guess you get the general idea.

"What was a lot worse than her clothes, she'd never had any children. She wanted them all right—Baldy told me she did. In fact, they both did. But whenever she got in the family way, she'd carry the baby three or four months and then she'd lose it. Finally she went seven months and their hopes were high; but it was a blue baby that lived just a few hours and something went very wrong with her, too, and she never had any more expectations.

"Baldy told me about this himself, like I said. He did it in a nice way. He never said a single word against Minnie and I admired him for that. In fact, he told me that what he first liked about her was that she listened with so much interest and intelligence to everything he tried to say about oil in Aristan, the first time he came back from there, and that she continued to be a good listener as long as she lived. He made such a point of this it wasn't hard to guess that some women to whom he'd tried to talk hadn't been good listeners, and that her interest and intelligence meant a lot to him. Just the same, I could tell his wife had been a big disappointment. And I could see him looking me over. I don't mean mentally undressing me, the way some men do, but saying to himself, 'That dame's mighty good looking and she's healthy looking, too. I shouldn't wonder . . . .' You probably wouldn't believe it, seeing me just tonight, Judith, but everyone did call me a beauty, when I was a girl; and even if I'd put on a little too much weight and begun to touch up my hair, people did still turn around and look at me, men especially. I had nice soft skin and good natural color still; I really didn't need any make-up; and I carried myself well. I'd learned to do that on the stage and modeling had helped, too. And I *was* healthy. I was never sick–I never even got tired, once I got the liquor cleaned out of my system. I didn't have an off moment until the Atlantic Ocean got me down–I'll tell the world that's some different in October from the Pacific in August! And I–well, I may as well tell you this, I've told you everything else: I was crazy to have another kid before it was too late, and I'd begun to count the years. Of course with luck I might have had a little more time than I thought; I knew one woman who had a kid when she was nearly fifty. But I couldn't count on anything like that. I'd never got over having to give up my baby, and I'd always been sorry Herb and I hadn't had one, though in one way it was a mercy, because if we had, I'd have been tied to him for life maybe. Be that as it may, there wasn't any such kid, and here were Baldwin Castle and I both thinking of the same thing, him from his point of view and me from mine.

"But don't get me wrong. I wanted another kid, I was thrilled at the idea of being rich for the first time and well, respectable again, too. But I wasn't just selfish about it or grasping. I liked Baldwin, I liked him a lot. I didn't love him the way I had Sam, but that was because I was older, maybe, or maybe because you don't love but one man that way, ever . . . ."

* * *

"I can understand that it would be very trying—very hard—for you to tell me everything you have already told Mrs. Racina. It will be quite satisfactory if she will give me the gist of your remarks in this instance, also, Mrs. Castle. So suppose we go back to the point where you told me you had been married twice before. Did either of your previous husbands give you alimony?"

"No."

"Not any sort of an allowance?"

"No."

"Isn't that also unusual in the States?"

"If I'd had a child to support and couldn't have done it myself, I guess most courts would had given me some kind of an allowance."

"But you didn't have a child."

"Yes, I did. I had a beautiful baby boy. But my husband kept him. That—that was my first husband's child. He had a right to the baby. I didn't have a child by my second husband, and I wouldn't have asked a man I'd gone off and left for alimony or any sort of an allowance, as long as I had my health. I don't know as I would have anyway."

"I understand. Then I gather that when you met Mr. Castle, you were not a wealthy woman?"

"No."

"Not even comfortably off, as the saying is?"

"Well, I wasn't too bad off. I had enough for that nice little room and a half apartment I told you about, and I got a rake-off from the Salon Superbe on my clothes, so I could be well dressed. And I was putting something by. I knew I couldn't go on being a model forever—not more than five or six years probably, at the most. But I'd have found something after that. I could always cook and, believe me, cooks earn good money these days in America."

"Yes, I've heard that the wages are almost fantastic, as one might say. But though the modeling and–ah–cooking would have assured you of a competence, so to speak, they wouldn't have done more than that, now would they?"

"No, I don't suppose so."

"But in marrying Mr. Castle, you became, potentially, a very rich woman."

"I don't believe I know just what you mean by 'potentially,' Inspector."

"Well, even if there were no marriage settlements–"

"I'm not sure just what those are, either. But there couldn't have been any, or I would have known."

"Mrs. Racina has already told me that they are not as customary in the United States as they are in other countries. But you must have had some sort of financial arrangement with your husband for spending money and other necessary expenses."

"Sure. I had charge accounts, as many as I wanted. And there wasn't any limit put on the bills I could run up. Of course Baldy ran up bills, too, for things he thought I needed and wanted and that he liked to give me for presents. And every few days he would hand me a big wad of bank notes and say, 'I suppose you'll be needing some petty cash.' But there wasn't any system to it. I suppose there would have been later on, after we got settled down. But I didn't like to ask him. As a matter of fact, I didn't think I needed to ask him. I'd never heard anything or seen anything to make me feel afraid he was close."

"He never mentioned–life insurance, for instance?"

"Why yes, he did! He told me he'd taken out two policies, with different companies."

"So you did know that, in the event of his death, you would be an extremely wealthy woman?"

"I–yes, I did."

"I'm sorry to ask you these next questions, Mrs. Castle, but I feel I must. I understand, both from Mrs. Racina and Colonel de Valcourt, that you've expressed great interest in the latter's experiments with—well, with coating cyanide. Don't misunderstand me. Mrs. Racina has spoken of you only in the kindest way; the information I speak of was quite incidental, and no stress was laid on it at all. I think I may go so far as to say that she feels not only sympathy for you, but affection and—confidence."

"But that Frenchman—what did he tell you?"

"He told me something Mrs. Racina had not mentioned; that during the second interval you asked him for a coated tablet—an aspirin tablet, of course—and that he believed afterward you went—or rather, that you might have absented yourself—that was the expression he used—a few minutes, ostensibly for—ah—natural reasons."

Up to this moment, Cornelia had answered the Inspector with the utmost gravity and earnestness. Now, to his surprise, she laughed. The laugh was scornful, rather than hearty, but there was nothing about it that suggested either insincerity or bravado. "I suppose he didn't mention that Judith couldn't have told you about me asking for the aspirin tablet for the simple reason that she couldn't possibly have heard me do it?" Cornelia inquired, almost mockingly. "He didn't tell you that she and Joe never came to the box during the second entr'acte at all, that they just stayed in their orchestra—I mean their stall—seats?"

"No, he didn't tell me that."

"Well, he could have. And Lady Laura could tell you, if you asked her, that I didn't 'absent' myself at all. I sat in the box chewing the rag with her all through the second entr'acte. I didn't go to the john—I mean the lavatory—at all. De Valcourt sent an usher—I mean an attendant—to us with water when he found there weren't any glasses in the lavatory. Lady Laura wanted some water, too. De Valcourt gave her an aspirin tablet the same time he gave me one. The same kind, too. I suppose he didn't tell you that, either."

"No, he didn't."

"It looks to me like he left out most of what he might

have said," Cornelia went on, still scornfully. "But I'll say this for him: he gave me credit for being a lot smarter than I am, if he thought I could fancy-up an aspirin tablet with cyanide between two acts of a play—always supposing I was smart enough to have latched onto the cyanide to start with."

"He admitted the improbability of the situation, Mrs. Castle. He presented it only as a possibility."

"Well, if you thought you'd hurt my feelings asking a fool question like that one, you've got another guess coming, Inspector, that's all I can say."

For an instant Kirtland had the uncomfortable feeling that they had changed roles, and that Cornelia was now the accuser instead of the potentially accused. Her voice had become more and more scornful and she rose, as if taking it for granted that the interview was now at an end, that it would be merely a waste of time to prolong it. He raised a warning hand. "Just a minute, Mrs. Castle, I'm afraid I have to ask you one more question. Didn't it ever occur to you that if you were wealthy and independent, you might be able to do certain things that you hadn't been able to do in your husband's lifetime, not even when you had all the charge accounts that you wanted and all the petty cash you could possibly use? Things that you'd wanted to do more than you'd ever wanted to do anything else in this world?"

There was a long pause. Cornelia seated herself again and bowed her head. When she looked up again, Kirtland saw that the scorn was gone from her face, that her eyes were brimming and her lips trembling so that she could hardly frame the words.

"I guess I've got to come clean," she said at last. "Yes, it did."

CHAPTER XIV

The uncomfortable feeling which Cornelia had evoked a few minutes earlier returned in full force as Kirtland watched her leave the room. Not that the source of this feeling was still the same; he no longer had the vague impression that they had changed roles, that she was the accuser and he the accused. But he knew that he should keep his mental attitude no less than his spoken inquiries entirely objective; and somehow he could not suppress a pang of pity for this vulgar, disheveled woman who was obviously the most ignorant among the suspects he had questioned, who, indeed, could not claim even the rudiments of refinement and culture which formed an integral part of the very birthright of all the others. He sighed, and picked up the cigarette which had lain untouched beside him ever since De Valcourt's departure; but instead of smoking it reflectively, as he had intended, he tossed it aside and spoke with more curtness than was his habit when addressing his sergeant.

"We've got to get this business over sometime. Ask Miss Lester to come in here, will you?"

Nothing could have been more striking than the entrance of Janice. She had already gone to bed when she received Joe's summons, and her stage make-up had been carefully removed. She had not replaced it in any way, but, unlike poor Cornelia, she was even more attractive without it than with it. Her splendid eyes needed no mascara to magnify them, her mouth no lipstick to change its shape; there were no blemishes and no roughness in her skin to smooth out with powder, and its becoming pallor was tinged with natural rose. Her glorious hair had been brushed and braided for the night in two long plaits and she had wound them, quickly and deftly, about her head; the result was one which bespoke regality rather than simplicity, for the braids now had the effect of a coronet. She was wearing black velvet, cut long and straight and following the lines of her figure closely; it was finished at the throat and wrists with a deep-pointed collar and cuffs of fine lace and girdled around the waist with a heavy golden cord. Actually, it was the sort of robe into which any experienced woman could slip at a moment's notice; but worn by one with the face and figure of Janice, it, too, gave the effect of regality—regality in its more intimate moments, but still regality. The lace collar was fastened with a magnificent jeweled brooch and she wore one equally magnificent ring on each hand. Kirtland was not a learned man or one who would have glibly used the term *femme fatale;* but he had long experience in his profession and a natural proclivity for delving into history; while the superior education which he was stinting himself to give his sons had acquainted him with some of the world's best art and literature. The woman who now stood before him embodied his conception of a great princess of the Renaissance—a princess who might herself become a murderess upon occasion, but who was far more frequently provocative of murder, either her own or that of one lover too many. Again, he found it hard to speak or even think objectively; but he addressed her with admirable self-control.

"Miss Lester?"

"Yes."

"Won't you sit down?"

"Thank you."

"I believe you are now appearing in a play entitled *Gold of Pleasure* at the Terry Theater."

"Yes."

"As the star?"

"Yes.

"And in your professional capacity, you use your maiden name?"

"Yes.

"But you are married?"

"Yes.

"And your husband's name is–"

"Hugo Alban."

"Quite so. And is he also an actor?"

"No, he is my manager."

"He was never an actor?"

"No. He began his professional career as a magician. But that was before I knew him."

"I see. So there is no member of your family in the cast?"

"Yes, there's a young relative my husband and I adopted. Our own marriage has been childless."

"And the name of this young relative is–"

"Evan Neville. He plays the juvenile lead."

"You're being very helpful, Miss Lester, by answering my questions so clearly and briefly. Now I already know that you and Mr. Racina are old friends, because he told me so himself, and because of his good offices, in making all this sad and troublesome business as painless as he could. If I understood him correctly, he told me he thought that you and Mr. Castle were also old friends. Is that correct?"

"I knew Mr. Castle a long time ago, when I was very young. I hadn't seen him, or heard from him, in over twenty years, until tonight. I didn't think of him as an old friend. I'd practically forgotten him."

"But you and he were good friends once?"

"Yes."

"Where did you first meet him?"

"In New York."

"Under what circumstances?"

"At the theater."

"You mean you were members of the same theater party? Or that he saw you on the stage, admired your performance and sought your acquaintance?"

"Neither. We met at a moving picture show. Nobody introduced us. We were sitting side by side, quite by chance. And I was so struck–so excited–by a little detail of Dietrich's acting that I turned to the man beside me and exclaimed, 'Did you see how she moved her hands just then? Did you? *Did you*? Did it mean anything special to you?' I didn't realize until afterward that I'd hurled these questions at a total stranger. But after my outburst, we fell into conversation. I don't remember just how, but I do remember that it seemed entirely natural."

"And then it seemed entirely natural to continue this chance acquaintance?"

"Yes, entirely natural."

* * *

It seemed entirely natural that we should leave the motion picture show together. It seemed entirely natural that Win should suggest we might take a taxi to Columbus Circle, and then walk around in the park for a while, and by and by have dinner at a little place he'd just found the night before. Of course I had to tell him that I couldn't, that I had to hurry off because I was lucky enough to have a bit part in *Dusk in December,* and I had barely time to get to the theater; but it seemed entirely natural for *me* to suggest that, if he wanted to wait for me at the stage door after the play, I'd go out to supper with him. And then it seemed entirely natural that he'd see me home and that he'd want to come in for a while. Of course I had to tell him that he couldn't, because of my landlady, who was a regular dragon when it came to that sort of thing. But I didn't make any fuss when he tried to kiss me good night on the stoop. In fact, I kissed back. For a wonder, there wasn't anyone else in sight, but I don't know that it would have made any difference if there had been. It was a good long kiss and that seemed entirely natural, too . . . .

* * *

"You saw Mr. Castle frequently after that?"

"Yes."

"Quite frequently perhaps?"

"Yes."
"One might almost say–constantly?"
"Yes."
"For how long a period?"
"For about two months–perhaps a little more."

* * *

Of course I knew Win wouldn't be willing to let well enough alone after that kiss. I don't know that I would have, either. He was the best-looking man I've ever seen, before or since–big and blond–but not *too* big and blond. That is, he didn't have an ounce of fat on him, and there were red lights in his hair, and his eyelashes and eyebrows were darker and very thick. His skin wasn't pink and white, but tanned, with a sort of glow showing through, just on his cheeks; and when I put my hand on his face, it felt the least bit rough, even though he looked so clean shaven. When he put his arms around me, they felt hard and so did his chest; and when he kissed me, the kiss was hard, too, after the first minute or so while his lips were searching for just the best place on mine. I don't believe there ever was anyone who could pack as much into just one kiss as Win.

Anyhow, I was a lot more pleased than surprised when he turned up the next day and said he'd come to take me out to lunch, and afterward, what about that walk in the park? I said well, what about the Persian Room at the Plaza then, and afterward, instead of a walk, a ride in one of those old victorias ranged along outside? He thought that was a still better idea, and we had a wonderful lunch, and then we rode around the whole afternoon, until it was time for me to go back to the theater. We even forgot to go out to supper. It got dark early, so we had our arms around each other again, all through the latter part of the ride; and I was so afraid Win wouldn't be waiting for me again after the play that

I almost forgot my lines–almost, but not quite. Then I was so relieved because he *was* at the stage door, that when he said this was the last time he was going to stop with a kiss on the stoop, I didn't tell him he'd have to. I said well, we'd take a chance on the landlady. And he said, what would it matter if she did put me out the next morning, because, while I was still asleep, he was going to be looking around for an apartment, and that was where we'd both be the next night . . . .

He found a little apartment on Fourteenth Street, the sort I'd dreamed about, but that I'd never seen before and never expected to see. (The regular tenants were in Europe.) There was a living room with family portraits–good-looking people, too–and built-in bookcases crammed full of books, and an open fireplace with big easy chairs drawn up close to it. Win always lighted the fire before he went to get me at the theater, so the room was all warm and cosy when we came back to it together. Then, while I got out of my street clothes and into a dressing gown, he'd fix highballs for us, and I'd sit on his lap, in front of the fire, while we drank them. We wouldn't have any other light in the room, and sometimes I was so sleepy by the time we'd finished our drinks that Win would have to carry me to bed. Of course, he didn't *have* to really; but he liked to and I liked to have him.

We had a great big beautiful bed with high carved posts and a pink canopy that matched the spread. Of course we ought to have taken the spread off, and folded it up carefully, every night; we used to tell each other so, and laugh and say, well, to-morrow night. But somehow, we never did. We just threw it back. We did it together, except the nights I was extra sleepy. Then Win did it by himself. If I had my arms around his neck to steady myself a little, he could hold me in the crook of one arm and throw back all the bed coverings, including the spread, with his free hand. And then he'd take off my dressing gown and tuck me in. He liked to do that, too, and I liked to have him. So sometimes I pretended to be sleepier than I really was—for a few minutes. But I was never too sleepy for all the love-making he wanted. I wanted it, too.

Win offered to get a maid for me, but I wouldn't let him. I said she'd just be in the way, that I could do all the work in that little apartment with one hand tied behind me, everything was so convenient. The kitchen was as beautiful in its way as the bedroom and living room were in theirs and I loved cooking in it. Generally, Win made the morning coffee while I was still asleep and I drank mine in bed. Sometimes Win came back to bed and drank his there, too, and sometimes he fixed up a little table beside the bed and drank it there. I didn't have to rush about dressing and moving around; but by and by I got up and straightened things out—neither of us liked to have that lovely little place untidy—and cooked lunch, if we were staying in. The days I had no matinees we went to others and Win took me to the Plaza or the Ritz or some smart restaurant like Twenty One beforehand. We saw every play in town, good, bad and indifferent—not just because we both loved the theater, but because Win knew I wanted to learn everything about acting that I possibly could, and that one of the best ways to do that was to watch other actors and see how they handled themselves on the stage.

Sundays, when there weren't any plays on, we generally went to the movies in the evening, but in the daytime we went sight-seeing. I'd never seen many sights before I went to New York, just the sand dunes on the Indiana shore of Lake Michigan and things like that—well, I'd been skating along the Midway in winter and on boat trips, with dancing, to Milwaukee, but I wouldn't count the Midway and Milwaukee as real sights. Win had never spent much time in New York himself and he was keen on seeing everything he could—all kinds of things interested him and they all interested me, as long as I could see them with him. We went to Coney Island and the Statue of Liberty and the Aquarium and the Zoo and the Metropolitan Museum and the Asia Institute and the Public Library. We went down to Trinity Churchyard and out to Grant's Tomb and up to the top of the Woolworth Building. We rode on the Staten Island ferry and to the end of every bus line. It was fun sitting up high on those top-heavy old busses, not missing anything there was to see, but holding hands all the time, too. Everything was fun.

We did the marketing together, and Win taught me how to cook lamb and rice and other things the way it is done in Aristan, because he had learned to like it that way. I was terribly intrigued by all those weird dishes, quite aside from wanting very much to please him, and he said I caught on very quickly. He liked his tea made a special way, too, and he wanted afternoon tea every day, and lots of good things like English muffins and Scotch scones to eat with it. We always had that at home, in front of the fire. He had very lavish ideas about what it was all right to spend on food; it was a big change for me from the penny pinching I'd always had to do before then. The same way with clothes. He told me I didn't have any, not what you could really call clothes, and he went with me, to the very best shops, until I learned my way around and also learned the kind of clothes he liked. He wasn't the least bored, or embarrassed, going shopping with me–in fact, he told me that in Europe it was quite the usual thing for a man to go shopping with a girl, that is, if he were interested in her and in her clothes. He kept me gasping at first–he thought nothing of paying hundreds of dollars for a fur coat, or picking up a chiffon nightgown from a counter and draping it over me, right in the aisle, to see if he thought it would be becoming to me when I was in bed. He made me buy lingerie and silk stockings–

and dresses and tailored suits with blouses to match and a mink neckpiece. Of course, I didn't have much use for evening dresses, because I was acting every night, but he said every girl ought to have at least two, and one evening wrap, just for her own satisfaction, even if she kept them hanging up in the closet. He bought me those, too. The wrap was black velvet trimmed with ermine and lined with white brocade; one dress was white brocade, to match the lining of the wrap, and the other was black velvet, trimmed with ermine, to match the wrap itself.

He gave me jewelry, too. First, two rings–a square-cut emerald and a diamond circlet. The little velvet boxes were on my breakfast tray the morning after we moved into the apartment. I thought when I saw them that the emerald was a sort of engagement ring and that the diamond circlet was going to be a wedding ring. But, fortunately, I didn't say so before Win slipped the emerald on my finger and said it was one that had been given him in Aristan and that he'd had it set at the same time he bought the circlet and was giving it to me to show me how pleased he was because I'd taken a chance on the landlady and let him spend the night. Then he added that the diamond circlet was a guard, that the emerald was pretty valuable and that I mustn't take any risks about losing it. He showed me how to put the circlet on and I found out it was meant to wear over the other and not under it, like a wedding ring. Of course, I was a little disappointed; but how can a girl tell a man she's disappointed when he's given her a couple of beautiful rings along with her morning coffee?

Afterward, he gave me a diamond wrist watch, so that I'd never be late to the theater, and, for Christmas, a ruby brooch. (The rubies came from Aristan, too–they must throw precious stones around like pebbles in that country.) None of the jewelry that's been given me since has meant as much to me as *that* did, even though much of it's been a great deal more valuable—my pearls, for instance. Perhaps that's because a girl gets more of a thrill out of the first jewelry any man ever gives her, it's such a new experience, especially if she's been poor like I was, than she ever does out of any other; and perhaps the first man himself means more to her than any other, whatever he gives her or even if he never gives her anything. After all, there's nothing like first love, whatever the cynics say. I don't know. It doesn't matter anyhow.

Win kept right on giving me presents, but he never gave me any money, except just what I'd need to shop with, or rather, what he thought I'd need to shop with, and that was a good deal more than plenty. He knew I wouldn't have liked it if he had. He never did anything to make me feel I was bought and paid for. He just made me feel that I was a grand girl and that he meant me to have everything in this world any girl could possibly want. He never said how long he intended to keep on giving me all those things. I never asked him. I never thought about it at all. I suppose it was stupid of me. But I was so crazy about him, I was so terribly happy . . . .

* * *

"Now tell me, Miss Lester, did you stop seeing Mr. Castle at his suggestion or yours?"

"He never put it that way and neither did I. He felt he ought to get back to work. He'd telephoned his father when he first got to New York, to ask if it would be all right to stay there a while, and his father said sure, he had a fling coming to him before he settled down. But after a while his father started telephoning *him,* asking what about it, and the time came when Win couldn't stall any longer. He'd just come from London on his way home from the Near East, where he'd been representing the Perisphere Petroleum Corporation—one of his father's companies. He'd been recalled to the main office—the one in Oklahoma City—after pulling off some sort of a brilliant coup in Aristan. I never understood just what. Not that he wouldn't have been willing to tell me. But I couldn't seem to grasp what he was talking about."

* * *

He really did try to explain to me. He tried hard. But it was all Greek to me—or rather, it was all just that much Aristani. So at last he gave up. He wasn't disagreeable about it. He only said, "I don't see why it's so hard for a girl to understand what I'm talking about when I try to explain this situation—I mean a reasonably intelligent girl. I understand all right when you talk to me about the theater. And I've understood all right when other girls have talked to me about their interests. But you're the second I've talked to, without getting anywhere. I guess I might as well give up." I knew he hadn't seen any girls besides me since he'd been in New York, because he'd been with me night and day—in fact, neither of us had seen *anyone* else, male or female. We'd been too well satisfied with each other's company. So naturally I asked him, "Who was the first one?" and he said, "Oh, a girl I knew in England." Before I thought, I said, "You must have known her pretty well, to talk with her about your private affairs like that." I wasn't jealous, not really, I was just taken by surprise. But he answered back, quick as a flash, "Well, I didn't know her as well as I do you, if that's what you mean." Then I said, "Just what do *you* mean?" And he said, "She isn't the kind that goes to bed with a man the second time she sees him," and I said, "Oh, does she insist on waiting until the third time?" And the first thing I knew, I was crying and Win was swearing and we were both so angry we couldn't see straight.

Of course we patched it up. He even told me a little more about this English girl, and though he didn't say so, it was easy enough to guess that he'd been very hard hit, so hard that he'd asked her to marry him—because he was probably right; from what he said I knew she wasn't the kind who would have gone to bed with him unless they were married. I thought that, perhaps, he'd expected she *would* marry him and that it had been a big blow to him when he'd found he was mistaken or that she'd changed her mind or something. Anyhow, he'd left London sooner than he'd planned, feeling pretty sore, and then he'd had a very dull crossing. So when his father told him he didn't need to hurry back to Oklahoma, he decided to stay in New York a week or so and whoop it up, before he went on home. And then, just a few days after he'd got there, he met me. So he stayed longer than he first intended.

* * *

"But after all, Mr. Castle's stay in New York was really in the nature of a well-earned holiday?"

"Exactly. On the other hand, New York was my normal working center. I'd just scored my first real hit. I wasn't a star then, of course, or even a leading lady; but I'd already gone from my bit part to a supporting role, and nearly all the critics had praised my interpretation of a rather difficult character. One of the critics had even hinted that someday I might be a star. I couldn't have been if I'd left New York then to go anywhere."

"So it was quite logical that your friendship with Mr. Castle should be interrupted at this point?"

"Doesn't it seem so to you?"

"Excuse me, Miss Lester. Without wishing to be discourteous, I may perhaps remind you that, just now, it seems to be indicated that I should do the questioning."

"Of course. Yes, it seems to me that it was quite logical."

"It seems to you or it seemed to you?"

"It *seems* so now. I suppose it didn't then. I've told you I was very young. Young girls aren't especially good at logic. Naturally, I felt badly to have Baldwin Castle leave New York for Oklahoma City. We'd had a very good time together and I was sorry to have it come to an end."

* * *

He'd have left me sooner or later, of course it didn't take me long to realize that; but I don't believe he'd have left me so soon, or so casually, if we hadn't started talking about that English girl, let alone started quarreling because she was "good" and I wasn't. After that, he began thinking about her again—he didn't tell me so, but I knew it—and making comparisons between her and me, to my disadvantage. She'd gone back on him, and I'd have stood by him through thick and thin, not because he was rich, but because I loved him. He didn't think of that; all he could think of was that she was a lady and I was a tramp. And I guess he thought he was telling the truth when he said that he and I were too big for each other, that neither of us would be content in each other's shadow, that I would no more find my goal if I were Mrs. Baldwin Castle than he would find his as a sort of Mr. Janice Lester. He honestly didn't know I'd rather have been Mrs. Baldwin Castle than a second Sarah Bernhardt. He wasn't just talking, either, when he said he was sure that pretty soon I'd get a part that would kindle "instant recognition of my great talents." I can be fair about that now, I can admit it. I can be fair, too, about the arrangements he made —telling me the apartment was paid for through that month and that I could send any unpaid bills on to him in care of the Perisphere Petroleum Corporation, Oklahoma City. He must have known I never would, that I really didn't need to, because there was nothing the matter with the pay I was getting, now that I had a supporting role. He didn't even mention the clothes or the jewelry, and neither did I—not just because I knew he'd never miss what he'd spent on them and the time might come when I'd want cash more than emeralds and rubies, but because I knew I was welcome to them, that he'd really meant what he'd said when he told me I was a grand girl and that he'd wanted me to have them. He didn't leave a sheaf of bank notes in an envelope on my desk, either. I was grateful for that. He thanked me for being such a good companion, in a nice way, and said it was too bad that business had to interfere with pleasure. Then he kissed me on the cheek and picked up his bags and went off to catch his train. I felt that wonderful cool roughness his face had, but there wasn't any searching for my mouth or any pressure on it in that last kiss. It wasn't that kind at all.

After he'd gone, I saw that the fire was beginning to die down and I didn't put any more wood on it. The tea things were still on the table, so I took them into the kitchen and washed them and put them neatly away. Then I started packing. I couldn't finish, partly because I didn't have enough bags and trunks to put all my beautiful clothes in and partly because I didn't have time. I had to get on to the theater. But I left everything in order so that I could come back and finish in the morning, after I'd bought the baggage I needed. Then I called up the Commodore and found I could get a room there. I didn't want to go to any of those places where Win and I had lunched together so often, and I was glad a big, impersonal hotel like the Commodore could swallow me up until I could look around for another place to stay. I never could have slept in that beautiful bed alone; I'd have kept thinking of all the times Win had carried me to it, when I was half asleep, and undressed me himself, and made love to me. I'm glad I didn't try to be big and brave about it all, because that would have been a dismal failure. But as it turned out, I didn't sleep that night anyway. I was too excited about something else. That evening, after the show, Hugo Alban, the star's manager, came and told me she wanted them to try me out for her understudy.

* * *

"But you never tried to persuade Mr. Castle to come back to New York?"

"No, never. Very shortly after that I married. And I did become a star. I've been very happy and very successful."

"You never wrote to Mr. Castle at all?"

"No."

"And he never wrote to you?"

"No."

"And I did understand you to say, didn't I, that until tonight you'd never seen Mr. Castle again?"

"That is correct."

"And you saw him then in the presence of several other persons?"

"Yes, in the Royal Retiring Room."

"And nowhere else?"

"Yes, I also saw him afterward—at his request—in my dressing room backstage."

"Alone?"

"Yes, alone."

"Likewise at his request?"

"He didn't, in so many words, ask to see me alone. But I understood that was what he wanted. Hugo and Evan understood, too. Both of them came in, while he was there, for the sake of politeness—or for the sake of appearances, if you'd rather I put it that way. But neither of them stayed more than a minute."

"And the meeting was wholly amicable, I suppose?"

"Wholly. Mr. Castle and I talked about old times,

but very briefly. This was during the second interval and that's a short one."

"You talked about nothing except old times?"

"Mr. Castle told me he'd like to see me again and I said I'd let him know. I didn't feel too sure I wanted to, and on the other hand I felt perhaps it would be rather amusing. I wanted to think it over. He seemed perfectly satisfied to leave it at that."

"You didn't have anything to eat or drink, I suppose, during this brief period?"

"We'd just had a lot of champagne and lobster–during the first interval. Neither of us was hungry or thirsty."

"I'm sorry, but that doesn't answer my question, Miss Lester."

"Now that you speak of it, I think Mr. Castle drank a glass of water as he was leaving my dressing room. I keep a thermos bottle on a little table near the door."

"A thermos bottle? Then it contains ordinary drinking water? Not mineral water?"

"No, just water from the faucet–I mean tap water, with small pieces of ice in it. Like most Americans, I like my drinking water very cold."

"You didn't take a drink at the same time?"

"No. I've told you neither of us was hungry or thirsty. I think Mr. Castle took a drink, absent-mindedly, almost subconsciously. Americans often do that, too. I didn't notice that either Hugo or Evan took a drink as he went out, because I was talking to Mr. Castle at the time, but it's quite possible that one or both may have done so–just from force of habit, as I said."

"And you have no reason to suppose that anyone could have tampered with your ice water?"

"Certainly not. It's always put there for me by my personal maid. I've had the same one for years. If she'd wanted to poison me, she could have done it long ago."

"I quite see your point. I may want to question her later, however–though I doubt very much that this will be necessary. Thank you very much, Miss Lester. When you have read and signed Sergeant Griffin's notes that will be all for the present. But I hope you won't leave the suite without giving me a chance to talk with you again if I feel that's indicated. Meanwhile, I should like to talk with your husband."

CHAPTER XV

As Hugo Alban entered the sitting room, Inspector Kirtland looked up from the sheaf of notes he was shuffling almost as though arranging a newly dealt canasta hand. His swift appraisal took in the newcomer's stocky torso, the large nose and receding chin above a thick muscular neck, the sleek scanty locks brushed back from a high forehead.

"Please take a seat, Mr. Alban," he said pleasantly. "And just to put myself on record with you, as I have with all the others, let me say that you are under no compulsion to answer my questions. I have no authority to detain you. But you, like the others, did volunteer to help us get to the bottom of this very distressing occurrence. That is correct, isn't it?"

"Absolutely. I'll do anything I can to be of service. That's what I'm here for."

"You're Miss Lester's manager?"

"That's right."

"You and she have been associated how long?"

"Well now, about that 'associated.' We're married, you know."

Alban smiled, showing strong yellow teeth, and the smile was so wide and so curving that it completely transformed his face; it was not attractive, but it was persuasive—indeed, compelling. Kirtland noticed the change, in the same swift way that he had noticed the other details of the man's appearance.

"Oh, quite," he said easily. "If you'd rather not say how long you've been married—"

"Well, in confidence, you understand. In confidence. I mean an actress—a great star like Miss Lester—has to consider her position with the public. And the public's funny. Once they get the idea a star's too old for romantic parts, school's out."

The lips behind Kirtland's scrubby ginger mustache twitched slightly. "In confidence, of course," he agreed.

"Twenty-three years."

"And you were fellow actors when you met?"

"No, I was never what you'd call an actor. Sleight of hand stuff for a while, club dates, a few vaudeville spots. But managing was really my line. I was Maryse Verlaine's manager when I met Miss Lester. I know how to deal with producers, how to get decent billing and things like that. I had a knack for it. Miss Lester got a bit part in *Dusk in December* when someone in the cast ran off and got married—or something. Anyway, she ran off and they needed somebody for her spot. Miss Lester had been looking around for a chance and this happened to be it—they took her on. She had her Equity card by then."

* * *

You were a trouper right from the start. And right from the start, I could see you had it in you to get your name in all the lights there were. It's something a person can feel in show business, when a beginner is headed for Dressing Room A. You had it, whatever it is. One look, and I knew. Like that.

I waited a while, a couple of months or maybe three, just to make sure I hadn't flipped my wig. But meanwhile, you'd gone from the bit part to a supporting role, and I was surer than ever that I was right. Then I put a bug in Chet Dalton's ear, to try you out as Verlaine's understudy. He said I was nuts and asked if I thought he'd got to be director by following wild hunches. I let it go at that. If he wanted you to be his discovery, that was okay by me. So in about a week he called you in for a reading. Remember? Well, I do. I remembered that look in your eyes, half shining like glory hallelujah and at the same time half scared. That look had me stopped for a minute. I'd have understood fast enough if you'd looked scared in the beginning, but by then you had a right not to be scared. You walked straight past me without seeing me until I spoke. That was the first time you ever really saw me, to count; and for just one second the look was all scare. So I told you to stick your chin up, you were in like Flynn, nothing to worry about now. And you said wasn't it all too wonderful? But that scared look still didn't go clean away from those big eyes. It had me puzzled, for fair.

So then I got to giving you a little pep talk once in a while; and the few times we'd go out to supper between the mat and the night show, I'd tell you how Verlaine did this bit or that, or why she made one particular cross at a certain point, like she hated to go open the door where the baby was going to be found on the step and yet hated worse not to do it. I knew Verlaine was getting ready to quit the stage. This Count de Whosis was on the make for a long while, where she was concerned. I never did quite figure out whether it was because he finally agreed to come across with that wedding ring, or because she was afraid *Dusk in December* would be her last romantic starring vehicle that she finally decided to quit show business and go live in a castle with titles and butlers and stuff. Anyway, she had her mind—her mind, God forbid!—made up, and I knew it. I admit I was looking around for another star or coming star to manage when you showed up, and the minute I saw you, I knew that was it.

* * *

"Were you and Miss Lester married before or after you became her manager?" the Inspector inquired.

"Quite a while after. Eight–nine months, at least; maybe a year."

"But you had known her even before?"

"Not to say know. I could call her name and I would give her the big hello once in a while or something of the sort. But that was the crop."

The Inspector paused and rubbed the knuckle of his right fore-finger back and forth across his mustache. Finally, he shot Alban a look that had in it something akin to embarrassment.

"You realize it is sometimes necessary to ask questions one would a great deal rather not," he said at length. "And of course there's no need to answer if you don't choose. But after all, when one is investigating the death of–"

"If what you're getting at is had I ever in those days seen her with that no-good bastard Castle, the answer is yes," interrupted Alban in level tones. "I did. Almost every night for a month. Maybe two months."

"From the fact that you speak of him in such a way, even knowing that he is dead, I take it your feeling toward him was one of extreme dislike."

"Was and still is! When he was alive, he was a living no-good bastard, when he was sick, he was a sick no-good bastard, and now he's dead, he's a dead no-good bastard. That's all she wrote."

" 'All *she* wrote.' All *who* wrote?"

"Nobody. That's just the way we have of saying that's the long and short of it–that's all there is, there isn't any more."

* * *

> Of course it wasn't until quite a while after I stopped seeing the son of a bitch waiting at the stage door for you every night of the world that I got a sneaking hunch what that scared look in your eyes meant. Then I quit worrying about your future on the stage–I knew that wasn't what had you terrified. But I was all the more worried about

you as a person—a lonely little mixed-up kid with nobody to turn to, not even me . . . .

Sure I had you under my skin by then, and what a torch I was carrying! I'd have sawed off one arm and beat Castle to death using it for a club, if that would have done you any good. But how could I so much as offer to help, when I had to make out I wasn't even about to guess anything was wrong? That was a sweet spot to be in, wasn't it?

But finally, somehow or other, you tumbled to how things stood. The night I took you to dinner at that little spot in the Village, the one with candles stuck in bottles and red ink in the coffee cups, you blurted out that you'd have to leave the company; and when I said why didn't you leave everything to me, you asked what did I mean, and everything got itself told across both sides of that rickety little table. Everything except that I loved you . . . .

First off, I became your manager. Then I told Chet Dalton I was taking over your affairs, because Verlaine was fare-thee-welling anyway. He got kind of a funny look on his puss, and I asked him would he maybe want a kick in the teeth, because if so, he could get service, it was no trouble to show samples. He didn't make with any more funny looks after that, in fact he was a very good doggie. When I offered to bet that, within less than two years, your name would be a bigger draw than Maryse Verlaine's ever had been, he looked real interested, and said something about you, as understudy, jumping right into the part when Verlaine left.

I told him nothing doing, that I was sending you off for a complete physical checkup first, on account of I had heard you make with a couple of bad coughing spells, and I wasn't about to risk what could turn out to be the best property I'd ever managed. If the vet prescribed a rest in some sanatorium, that's where you'd go until you got the green light to come back. Meanwhile, he could find himself another girl. I even suggested Paula Standish.

After that, I found a nice place for you to stay, just off the Morristown road in Jersey, and asked you to marry me, so we could both stay there. I said I would never bother you, but you gave me the great big no and said marriage without love was even worse than love without marriage, and you didn't propose to have both of them on your conscience. You didn't know that for me it wouldn't have been without love. There was never anyone else for me but you and I didn't give a damn about the past; it was the future. When I tried to sell you that idea, you said I was just the kindest person in the whole world to lie like that, but I couldn't really be fond of any girl who had just gone off the deep end for another man. What's more, you wouldn't let me put up one copper cent for you. So maybe it was a good thing that louse had tossed all those furs and bracelets at you. They paid for everything.

Anybody'd have thought I was Chet's favorite rich uncle, the way he took on when I told him you were okay again. Of course, I knew the Standish chick didn't have what it takes, only just enough to get by with a total of nothing to spare. So when I told him you'd be coming back in a week or so, he did everything but kiss me. People were beginning to stay home from *Dusk in December* in bunches and those that came were sitting on their hands after they got there.

* * *

"And it was immediately after you became her manager that Miss Lester began to rise to her present eminence?" inquired the Inspector.

"No, I can't say that began right off. She'd gone from her bit part to a supporting role and then to understudy for the star before I took over. Then, just when she had a chance to step into the star's place for good, she had a breakdown and another girl filled in. If she'd been any good, Janice would have been out of luck, but she wasn't and the show was fast going on the rocks when Janice came back from her sanatorium, looking in the pink again. She was hustled right into the star's part and she was better from the beginning than the cluck that had been playing it—there never was a day when Janice Lester would give a really poor performance. But *Dusk in December* needed something more than a performance that wasn't bad and by and by the director got to talking with the owner about maybe carting the scenery off to Cain's and calling it no contest. And then, something gave her a lift and she was off."

* * *

That was where I stepped in again, because I knew the answer. That doll they were using as the foundling on the doorstep for an Act I curtain didn't mean a thing to you, not when you had your heart set on getting back to your own baby. Your heart, I said. Not your mind. Your mind was on the stage all right and giving a letter-perfect reading. But in show business mind alone won't do. You've got to have your heart there, too.

So it was on that account that I had the fake telegram sent to you from Toledo. Of course, I said I was just trying to protect my meal ticket, because you still wouldn't believe me when I made another try to sell you the idea that for me all dames were divided into two classes—you in one and the rest of them in another. This you wouldn't believe; but that I was out to see nothing happened to my meal ticket—*that* you went for hook, line and sinker.

So you got a telegram from Toledo, or wherever it was, saying that your cousin and her husband and their new baby had been in an auto when a train hit it at a grade crossing, and that the husband was killed instantly, but that your cousin had lived long enough to beg you to send for her baby and bring it up yourself, not put it in an asylum. And I made a pitch to Chet Dalton to use that baby instead of a Kewpie doll in the foundling scene.

I'll break down and admit it was me tipped off Winchell to catch a piece of *Dusk in December* the first night it was your own baby you found on the doorstep, after making that slow cross just before the Act I curtain. But the rave he put in his column next day, all about a new star in the sky, and how anybody that missed you in *Dusk in December* would pass up a chance to buy ten-dollar bills at three for a quarter—that was his idea. And instead of closing, *Dusk in December* ran to standees all the rest of the season, until the marquee went dark for the summer. By that time, Janice Lester was in.

* * *

"And do I understand that after that brief period in which you saw Miss Lester and Mr. Castle so constantly together you never saw him again until last night?"

"That's right."

"But you have just spoken of him in terms that signify great hatred."

"That's right, too. I hated his very hide."

"I'm not referring to the way you felt about him twenty-odd years ago. I'm referring now to the way you felt about him as recently as a few hours ago."

"I hated him then, too. I told you that before—when you said that even though he was dead it was evident from the way I talked that my feeling for him was one of 'extreme dislike.' Extreme dislike, hell! When he was alive, he was a living, no-good bas—"

"Yes, yes, I recall . . . . And on the other hand, I take it that you are devotedly attached to your wife?"

"You can put it that way if you want to. I'd say it was the understatement of the year."

* * *

Even after that marquee went down, you wouldn't believe I really thought about you as anything more than the answer to a manager's prayer. I tried to tell you. But it wasn't until I said that if we were married we could legally adopt the baby, and after that nothing could ever take him away from you, that you agreed. You married me, not because you thought I loved you, or because you loved me, which you didn't, but because you loved your baby. And after that, I was carrying a bigger torch than ever–carrying a torch for my wife!

I kept my word though. I didn't bother you, even if sometimes I wanted to rip out a piece of the wall between our rooms with my bare hands. And then that summer night in Provincetown, where you'd gone to play in a straw hat barn, and we'd left the baby and the nurse in Boston, and the moonlight was pouring down on the sea, and the surf was like a pulse beating and beating, it was you came to me, and that was when you knew it wasn't any meal ticket I had been trying to win, but just my own true love.

* * *

"Mr. Alban, I think you will admit that, knowing how you feel, it wouldn't be too farfetched a supposition for someone to suspect that–well, that you might have had –mind, I don't say that you did have–a hand in doing away with Mr. Castle. You are devotedly attached to your wife and you have nurtured a hatred against–an admirer of hers for more than twenty years. Inevitably it appears, on the face of things, as if there might be–well, some connection between the two feelings. Especially as you've spoken of him, repeatedly, in terms which show your hatred might be one of the most compelling motives for murder."

"All right, I had a motive. So what?"

"Well, you apparently also had an opportunity."

"I've followed you all right, Chief, so far. Now I don't seem to."

"You were once a conjurer and, though you have not engaged in sleight of hand, professionally, for many years, I understand you have continued to give exhibitions of it for the entertainment of your family and friends. I have been informed that you gave such an exhibition last evening."

Alban threw back his head and laughed. He was still smiling, and his yellow teeth seemed more prominent than ever, when he replied. "You mean the trick with the champagne glass?" he asked, chuckling. "You think I slipped a poison pill into the fizz? I could have, easy as shooting fish in a barrel–granted I'd had the poison, of course. But I'd never have poisoned the guy. Never in this world. Let him die without even knowing who did it to him or why? That wouldn't be my style." Alban, the smile gone, looked down at the hands he was flexing, so that the tendons and veins stood out from their backs. "Get my fingers around his throat when I could see the scare come into *his* eyes until they blanked out–that I could have done. I'll go far enough to say that many's the time I've thought about doing it. But slip the guy a pill so that he passes out without knowing who hit him, or what, or why . . . . Where'd be the percentage in that, Chief?"

"I was merely speaking of motives," the Inspector replied without answering the question. "As long as the motive is there and the opportunity is there–"

"All right, then. Here's your answer and it covers all three of us."

"All three of you?"

"Yes. Janice and Evan and me."

"Oh, I see. Mr. Neville is your adopted son, I believe?"

"That's right. His mother was my wife's cousin. That

makes him a first cousin, once removed, to my wife. He isn't actually related to me at all."

"And I take it his own mother is no longer living?"

"No. She and her husband were both fatally injured in an automobile accident. Janice wanted to adopt their baby and I was glad enough to have her. Out of charity, I mean, at first. We've been mighty glad for practical reasons, too, ever since. Talk about born actors! Evan's been a hit from the time he played the foundling in the basket at the end of Act I in *Dusk in December*. He's been in all Janice's plays and he's never once let us down. Of course, he's 'devotedly attached' to her, too, and he and I get along all right, though sometimes he's complained that I've kept his nose too close to the grindstone. He got exhausted a couple of years back, near the end of a run, and it was all he could do to go on the last few nights. Each time, he'd say he didn't think he could last through the third act. But he did. After we had closed, though, he'd slouch way down in the biggest chair he could find, and mope. He couldn't sleep or eat except at some odd hour. Janice and I were as patient with him as we knew how–it was hard when we were working on the next show–but just when we began to wonder whether some kind of a rest cure mightn't help, he snapped out of it. I don't know how we'd have managed right then if he hadn't. Anyway, I've always done my best for the kid, even at times like that, when he was difficult to handle. I've seen to it that he had the best possible training and that never does any harm, no matter how much talent a guy's got."

"Well, as you were saying–"

"Well, as I was saying, none of us had so much as a notion Castle was on our side of the ocean until we got that note in the middle of Act I, asking us to come to the Royal Box. You don't think that for twenty-four years we've been carrying around some kind of poison on the chance that one of those times we might run into the son of a bitch, do you? And finding out about him when we did, how could we have sent out and got poison in ten minutes, even if we could have found one of those drugstores that they call chemists' shops over here that wasn't already shut tighter than hell's hinges? And, on top of that, one that would have handed out cyanide right over the counter? You see, Chief, it just doesn't add up to make sense. So, no matter who's suspected, we three are bound to be in the clear."

CHAPTER XVI

IT CERTAINLY LOOKED that way, Kirtland said to himself, rather wearily; but it would have seemed even more self-evident if Alban had not stressed it as a fact instead of a probability. In any case, there were two more persons the Inspector must question before he would have interviewed all those who had been fellow guests of Castle's the previous evening, at one party or another: the young actor and the journalist. He had decided to leave Joe Racina until the last, partly because he believed this interview would involve less strain and stress than most of the others, and partly because he felt that Joe's experience in summing up character and circumstance might serve as a useful supplement to his own. Evan would be of less use and he might also be more trying; as in the case of Janice, though for very different causes, Kirtland decided that the sooner he was through with this petulant-looking boy, the better. For the very reason that he was not drawn toward the *jeune premier,* he made a greater effort than usual to be civil.

"Mr. Neville?"

"Yes."

"Mr. Evan Neville is, I believe, the full name?"

"Yes."

"Is that your real name or your stage name?"

"Well, actually it's my stage name, but I've used it so long I never think of myself as possessing any other."

"However, your real name does, I assume, appear on your passport and other official documents you may be called upon to sign and keep in your possession?"

"Yes."

"And it is–"

"Evan Alban. I was legally adopted by Hugo and Janice when I was a baby and given their surname. You know, of course, that in private life, as it's termed, Janice Lester is Mrs. Hugo Alban–not that she has much of any private life. She has to share everything she is and does with her adoring public."

* * *

Almost everything, but not quite everything. It's never leaked out, my dear Janice, that you had an affair with the man who's been murdered tonight. It's never leaked out that you had a child by him, who's been passed off for more than twenty years as your cousin. Even your son himself didn't know his true relationship to you until ten days ago. He wouldn't know it even now, if it hadn't been for what happened after that last curtain call.

* * *

"But since your stage name has seemed like your own for so long, doubtless you prefer that I should address you as Mr. Neville rather than as Mr. Alban."

"I sure do."

"That will be quite agreeable to me . . . . Won't you sit down, Mr. Neville?"

"Thanks. If it's up to me, I'd rather stand."

"Just as you wish. It should not be necessary to trouble you long in any case."

"Good deal!"

"Oh, no! Quite the contrary. Not a good deal at all. Just a little while."

"That's what I was getting at. Good deal with us

means that the deal is good. What you'd call top-hole, I expect."

"Oh, quite. I understand now . . . . It's the time element that interests me most at the moment, Mr. Neville. As I understand it, you had never met Mr. Castle until last night."

"That's correct."

"But you know him, no doubt, by reputation?"

* * *

By reputation! If I had, I'd have known he was a scoundrel. Or maybe not. Maybe it's less a case of having a scoundrel for a father than a fool for a mother. The more I mull it over, the more I'm inclined to believe it is. You could have written to him, you know, Janice. You had his business address—he'd told you that you could send him any unpaid bills. He hadn't asked you to write to him, but he hadn't told you that you mustn't—he'd parted from you very politely, by your own account. My God, *politely*! After you'd been living with him for a couple of months! He'd given you bushels of jewels and trunks full of clothes. He'd have given you money, too, all the money you asked for—probably more than you asked for. He hadn't given you any up to then because you'd have taken that as an insult. You weren't insulted because he climbed into bed with you the second time he saw you, but still you were so noble he couldn't insult you by attributing any mercenary motives to you. He would have given you money though—if he hadn't done it of his own free will, you could have blackmailed him easily enough, and then he'd have come across in a hurry. But you wouldn't have had to. He always spent money like a drunken sailor. The only difference is, drunken sailors don't have much and he had plenty. A lot more than plenty. More than he knew what to do with. He'd have had all your hospital bills paid, quick as a flash, and probably he'd have given you a big lump sum besides. He might even have married you—not for keeps, maybe, but long enough for you and me both to have his name and a right to some of his money. Even if he'd engineered a divorce afterward, he'd have arranged to have you live comfortably in some nice suburb; he'd have arranged to have me educated. I mean *educated*—sent to one of those swell New England prep schools, to a Grade A college, to Europe every so often, perhaps even on a trip around the world. I wouldn't have had a succession of hotels for my only home and a succession of bellhops for my only playmates. *Playmates*! They didn't play with me—they corrupted me, quick and plenty. I wouldn't have been kept cooped up in a greenroom with an actor for a tutor, a broken down old has-been, whose favorite textbooks were the stilted old dramas he'd played in when he was young. He couldn't get it through his head I wanted to learn much of anything that wasn't in them. And you weren't much better, Janice—you or your precious husband, either. You took it for granted I wanted to be an actor; you never gave me a chance to be anything else. And all because, at the age of three months, I happened to howl exactly when I should have, after I'd been shoved into a basket and put on the doorstep, at the end of Act I, scene 2, *Dusk in December*. That was twenty-three years ago, and in all those twenty-three years I've never escaped from you and the theater, never once, except when you sent me off for one of those so called "rest cures." You like quotations, how's this one? "You've made me what I am today, I hope you're satisfied." Not quite as classical as those you generally favor, but even more to the point. You made me into a child prodigy and then into a matinee idol and I've hated it every step of the way. I've tried to tell you so, but you wouldn't listen. Sometimes I've almost hated you, because you didn't or couldn't or wouldn't understand. But Baldwin Castle would have understood. If I'd been acknowledged as his son, I'd have been a man now, not a *jeune premier*. I could hate you for not telling him about me, not almost but good and plenty, if I hadn't found out about all that at the same time I found out about something else.

* * *

"I notice that you're hesitating, Mr. Neville. Quite natural, too. I should have put my question rather differently. When I said I thought you must know Mr. Castle by reputation, I wasn't referring to his moral qualities—in short, his personal character. I was referring to the public recognition which has been accorded him on account of his achievements. I understand he was a notable figure in the petroleum industry."

"That's correct, too. So I probably have seen his name in the papers and heard people talk about him as a big shot. But it wouldn't have made much of an impression on me. I'm not especially interested in the petroleum industry; I've never been brought into either direct or indirect contact with any of its top men. There must be dozens of people in the oil business whose names I wouldn't know. I couldn't tell you offhand, for example, who's president of Standard Oil or Shell or any of those outfits. Not if my life depended on it, which I certainly hope it doesn't, for ' 'tis a vile thing to die, my gracious lord, when men are unprepared and look not for it.' "

"That's very well put, Mr. Neville. I hope I can remember it. Would you mind saying it again, so I can copy it down? . . . . My younger boy would recognize that straight off," Kirtland said, as he finished writing. "Gets us to take him to the Old Vic every time they put on a different play there, and as if there weren't enough Shakespeare, nothing will do but that I must take my whole family to Stratford during my holidays. Well, that's neither here nor there. Now, to get back to the business in hand. When did you receive the invitation to join the

Castles in the Royal Retiring Room between the first and second acts of *Gold of Pleasure?*"

"Why, I can't say I ever did receive it, officially. I heard about it and was included in it, in a rather offhand way."

"Yes?"

"Yes. Janice keeps a thermos of ice water—I mean real ice water with chunks of ice in it—in her dressing room all the time. I know that may be hard to believe, but she actually does get it. After all, she's filling every seat from orchestra to peanut heaven—what you call the 'gods' over here—night after night."

"I don't quite see what—"

"Did you ever try to get ice water—I mean the real thing? No, I suppose not. But take my word for it, ice water is the hardest thing on earth to get in London. I've given up trying myself. But I drop into Janice's dressing room for a beaker from her thermos every so often. You know—drink to me only with thine ice. Brother! How corny can you get!"

"I'm afraid I didn't make myself clear. I wondered if you'd be good enough to tell me just when you learned you'd been invited to join the Castles."

"That's what I'm getting at. I wasn't and I hadn't any notion of going. I just wanted a drink of ice water, as I said. So I started for Janice's dressing room and while I was going down the corridor toward it, I heard a hell of a row going on about some note Mrs. Castle had sent backstage. From what I gathered, this billet-doux just about ordered Janice and Hugo to show up, and Janice was livid with rage. Said she wouldn't go, said Castle could . . . well, never mind. Anyway, Hugo kept telling her she had to go, that he never would be satisfied until he saw with his own eyes how she and Castle hit it off. And finally, she agreed."

"You think you heard pretty much all that was said by your cousins? Mr. Alban and Miss Lester are your cousins, aren't they? Or are they your aunt and uncle? She spoke of you as a 'young relative,' but she didn't say exactly—"

"Hugo's no relative of mine–he's just a guy who married into the family. Miss Lester's some sort of a third cousin of my mother's–or so I've always been told."

* * *

And so I've always believed, which shows what a fool I am. When I kissed you again, after that last curtain call, and you told me that was enough, the show was over now, I still didn't catch on. Not until you spelled everything right out for me.

* * *

"And Miss Lester and Mr. Alban came out of Miss Lester's dressing room together while you were still in the corridor?"

"Oh, no. Naturally I'd gathered that wasn't the best moment for me to intrude, so I hurried back to my own dressing room after I heard Janice agree to go to the Castles' party. She said maybe Hugo was right, maybe she even owed it to him to show that everything was over and done with."

"And have you any notion what she meant by that?"

The young actor's face went blank. He looked at the Inspector in wide-eyed bewilderment.

"Not the slightest, Mr. Kirtland. It must have referred to whatever it was they had been quarreling about when I got there."

"And what was it you did then?"

"I was still in my own dressing room when Hugo came there and told me Janice had been invited to the Royal Box by the Castles for an entr'acte collation, and had accepted not only for herself, but for Hugo and me, too. So I tagged along, of course. But that's why I say I wasn't really invited. They had only asked for Janice. Maybe they didn't know about Hugo, or me. Anyway, Mr. Castle didn't know about–me. I feel sure he didn't."

"In any case, you had no idea you were going to meet

Mr. Castle until Hugo Alban came to your dressing room, and between your first knowledge that you were going to see him and the time you did meet the interval was no longer than it took to walk from your dressing room to the Retiring Room of the Royal Box. Is that approximately correct?"

"Well, that's making a lot of stuff out of a big nothing, but that's the way it was."

Kirtland nodded, and jotted some notes on one of the sheets of paper before him.

"And after the theater, Mr. Neville?"

"After the show—if you've been there, you'll know how I can't get away earlier, because when I commit suicide that's the end of the last act—anyway, after the show, I carried the mail—meaning I hustled, you understand—right over to the hotel and grabbed myself an armful of that business that knits up the ravell'd sleeve of care. I mean sleep. When I get through my stint in the salt mines, I'm tired. I don't play around."

"And you were asleep in your hotel when Mr. Racina asked you if you'd accompany Mr. Alban and Miss Lester here?"

"You win the big Kewpie doll for a right answer."

"Thank you very much, Mr. Neville. You've been more helpful than you realize. You may go back to sleep now, if you like—in the next room. But before you doze off, you might just ask Mr. Racina to come along. After all, turnabout is fair play."

CHAPTER XVII

JOE SLOUCHED BACK into a deeply cushioned armchair, lighted a cigarette and snapped the match behind him in the general direction of the copper-faced electric grate.

"I hope you've been making as much progress as I have, Inspector," he said amiably.

"Meaning just what?"

"Well, you've talked with ten persons so far. By now, you must have found two or three clues and developed at least a few theories. Me, I've got the first chapter of my novel into rough draft."

"Your novel!"

"Yes. I got an idea for a novel while we were having supper downstairs last night. It's already got a title—'The Midnight Marriage'—and it's all about the royal Duke of York and the beautiful commoner Anne Hyde. Of course, the Duke's mother—in fact, all the Royal Family—opposed the marriage; and it wasn't just because Anne was a commoner; they were dead certain she wasn't the right kind of a girl for him. Funny how history repeats itself, isn't it? But this man took matters into his own hands, and by the time the rest of the tribe found out, it was too late to do anything to stop him. He did finally abdicate, but that was after he'd been married for years."

"Very interesting. I'd like to learn more about this midnight marriage myself—this is the first time I ever heard of it, though I'm something of a student of history. Just now, as you'll appreciate, I have other fish to fry."

"Sure enough. And if you'll ask questions, I'll try to answer them without any more rambling over the countryside."

"Well done. But before I ask any questions, perhaps

I ought to state, so that there won't be any misunderstanding, that I don't regard you as a suspect."

"Much obliged for those kind words. I guessed you'd figure out that Castle was a lot more use to me alive than dead. Of course, I've had to cable *This Month* that the series about him, as we planned it, is off. But the editor's a great guy; he'll pay me something besides my expenses, because I've put in quite a good deal of time, traveling, doing research and so on, and I could have earned something else while I was doing that. However, what I get for a consolation prize won't be anything like the tall money I'd have had for the series."

"Very interesting," Kirtland said again. "I know almost nothing about publishing procedure. Now, in regard to Mr. Thorpe, who is, I understand, a friend of yours–"

"Excuse me if I'm interrupting your train of thought. But I can't help reminding you that Hilary had just as many reasons for wanting to keep Castle alive as I did. It doesn't exactly help a career diplomat's prospects to have a newly appointed ambassador, who is his official guest at the time, murdered stone cold dead in the market place."

"Quite. Yet, I understand that Mr. Thorpe has persistently refused to discharge a cook whose record is, by no means, above suspicion."

"Well, as a matter of fact, Hilary and I've been talking about Lalisse," Joe volunteered. "We did it while De Valcourt was in here with you, and Alban and Neville were over on the other side of the bedroom, apparently absorbed in a game of cribbage, or something. We didn't think you'd object, as the conversation wasn't based on anything you and Hilary had discussed. It was prompted by the fact that I'd been very much struck by that gal when I saw her at Hilary's house and had told him I'd like to do a piece on her, too. Would you care to have me give you the gist of what he said to me?"

"I should indeed."

"He said De Valcourt had always suspected her of monkey business because he–I mean Jacques–had seen her stealing off to an assignation while he was hiding in the niche of a garden wall, waiting until it was dark enough for him to keep one himself. He swore he saw Lalisse give this swain of hers a basket, covered with a napkin, but with a bottle sticking out at one side."

"Well?"

"Well, Hilary says that's likely enough, that lots of the servants in the West Indies give food and drinks to their families and friends, besides taking it home themselves, just as they do in our own South to this day. I wouldn't know how it is in England. Hilary claims it's just a coincidence that this poor chap was found dead within twenty-four hours—if it actually was the same man. Hilary doesn't see how Jacques could be sure, even of that. After all, it was almost dark at the time Jacques saw Lalisse meet someone."

"Evidently the police felt there was reason to suspect her."

"Oh, there's no question that the fellow who was found dead was her boy friend! Also, that she had another boy friend and was playing one against the other! She went out with the other one that same night."

"And what's her story?"

"Her story is that if she'd only gone out with boy friend number one he wouldn't have done what he did that night."

"Which was—"

"Which was to go to some sort of a wild native party. She thinks she sent him to his death—in fact she's said so, in a frenzied way, over and over again. Because there's no question that he was dead the next day."

"Of poison?"

"Yes. That's why Lalisse was investigated. She *was* in the habit of giving him food to take home and, as I've said, he was known to be—well, shall we say, an admirer of hers. But there wasn't a trace of poison found in the house where he lived with his mother. And several of the celebrants at this wild native party were very, very sick the next day. An American army doctor Hilary got hold of handed down the opinion there was no doubt they'd all had ptomaine poisoning. After all, refrigeration in Martinique isn't all it might be. And pretty soon, the police got around to the doctor's way of thinking, as well as Hilary's, and De Valcourt stopped talking about what he thought he'd seen. Naturally, under the circumstances, he wasn't very keen on coming out publicly with too much information, because, in that case, he was bound to be asked how he happened to get it and he was afraid that might make things awkward for his own inamorata."

"But then why should he persist in offering a different opinion now? There must be some basis for it."

Joe hesitated. "I wouldn't know, and I hate to say what I'm going to when it's only guesswork. But there's an old saw that all's fair in love and war, and maybe it is. Jacques doesn't care a hoot in Hades about this dame in Martinique any more and now he and Hilary are in love with the same girl. I think that probably he had practically forgotten all about his first suspicions of Lalisse, which, no doubt, were sincere enough to start with, until–well, until it became just as convenient for him to remember them again now, as it was for him to dismiss them before."

"I understand why it would have been convenient for him to dismiss them before. I'm not sure I understand why it should be convenient for him to remember them now."

"Partly because they might serve to make poor Hilary indirectly responsible for Castle's murder. And partly because they would serve to divert suspicion from other quarters."

"I see."

"Besides," Joe went on, much encouraged, "how could Lalisse manage to poison one guest and still not cause any of the others so much as a twinge? That would take some doing."

"Quite. But it is not an utter impossibility."

Kirtland rubbed his mustache with his knuckle and consulted his notes. "You say that you and Mr. Thorpe had this conversation about Lalisse while the Colonel was in here with me," he observed eventually. "Did he, when he rejoined you, mention that I had spoken with him about Lalisse myself and informed him that she had disappeared?"

"He sure didn't. What do you mean, disappeared?"

"I decided, after talking with Mr. Thorpe, that I might like to talk with her later on, too, and so informed him. He relayed this information to his chauffeur Celestino, who, in turn, relayed it to Lalisse—which, of course, he should not have done before he was actually about to bring her here. No doubt, he succeeded in frightening her thoroughly."

"Possibly. Or possibly, Celestino had been bitten by the same bug as so many others. Possibly he was planning to take her out tonight—a plan which might have been upset by the party or by the weather. I imagine a gal from Martinique might be glad enough to use weather like this as an excuse for not going out with someone she didn't care much for anyway. And then, she might have slipped off with someone else to a neighborhood cinema. She may be sitting, cuddled up to a good-for-nothing Cockney, munching chocolates for all she's worth, at this very minute."

"Well, we'll let it go at that, at least for the present. Now I understand from what you said to me yourself that Miss Lester is also an old friend of yours. Is there anything about that friendship which would make you disinclined to talk about it or her?"

"I'm not sure just what you mean by that, but whatever it is, the answer would be the same—nothing. We were good friends when she was a girl—we are still. But we were never more than that. Even if we had been, it would all have been on the level—she was as straight as a string at the time I first knew her. And anything that could have happened since would still all be in the past anyway. I'm devoted to my wife and Janice is devoted to her husband. I'd take my Bible oath on it that she's been as faithful to Alban as I've been to Judith and that's as faithful as you can get."

Joe spoke not only with great sincerity, but with considerable vehemence. His obviously deep feeling made it harder for Kirtland to ask his next question.

"You say she was as straight as a string when you first knew her. Then it isn't conceivable to you that she might have had a love affair? I mean, before her marriage? One in which–well, in which marriage didn't enter the picture?"

"Yes, it's conceivable," Joe flashed back. "But I'd still say she was straight as a string–in my book, anyway. Because I don't believe for a moment she'd have had an affair with a man unless it really was a *love* affair. I can't imagine any mercenary motive entering into it. I'll go further than that. I can't imagine anything like that happening unless she thought marriage *was* in the picture–perhaps not as much in the foreground as it should have been, but certainly there somewhere. And it goes without saying that there never would have been but one such love affair. There couldn't have been."

"You have a very high opinion of Miss Lester, Mr. Racina."

"You're damn right, I have. And it won't be changed even if the next thing you ask is whether I don't think the man in such an affair couldn't have been Castle."

"Well, couldn't it?"

"I knew that would be next and the answer is yes, it could. I didn't know until last night that they'd ever laid eyes on each other before, but of course they had. Why, Janice didn't make the slightest attempt to pretend that they hadn't once known each other well–called him Win, asked if he'd feel like telling the rest of the crowd about the good times they used to have together–all that sort of thing. But no matter how far those good times went, I'd still put my hand on the block she didn't care whether he was rich or not. Also, that she must have believed he meant to marry her–until something happened to show her that he didn't."

"You wouldn't hazard a guess as to what that might have been, would you?"

Joe appeared to reflect. "Well, if they actually did have an affair," he said eventually, "of course, it must have been after she left Chicago for New York, but before she married Alban. And, if I'm not mistaken, that was just about the time Castle came back from Aristan. He'd been in England before he went out there and again on his way home. I know that from what he told me himself. He could have met some English girl and fallen for her hard and she could have turned him down. That could have made him mighty sore and it would have been easy for some other girl to get him on the rebound. Get him, but not hold him, especially if something happened to loosen her hold—a quarrel, or some unconscious reference to an unknown rival which happened to strike home, or anything else of the sort. We're supposing so much anyway that we might as well suppose that much more."

"Right. And since we're supposing so much, could we go a step further still and suppose that such a girl—the one who'd got a man on the rebound—would be as sore after he left her as he'd been when he found her?"

"No—not if the girl were Janice. She'd be terribly hurt, of course, probably terribly puzzled, too. But she wouldn't be crushed; she's got too much courage for that. And she wouldn't be bitter or vengeful; she'd probably blame herself for what had happened, as much as she blamed the man. And she wouldn't brood over it; she'd go on to the next thing—which, in her case, always supposing this is Janice we're talking about, was to get a better part on the stage than she'd ever had before, and to marry a man who could help her get better parts still, besides being crazy about her."

Joe spoke with conviction. It was only after he had done so that he remembered the impression he had had at the theater—that Janice had changed in some way which he could not analyze, but that the change was not one for the better. Momentarily, he wondered whether he should speak of this to the Inspector, in the interests of complete candor; but the honest belief that the change had nothing to do with the phase of the situation under discussion moved him to wait a little before mentioning it, especially as the Inspector did not put another direct question to him immediately, but made a favorable comment on his own initiative.

"I must confess that I was agreeably impressed with Miss Lester myself," he said, permitting himself the luxury of a slight smile. "I imagine she has a somewhat disarming effect on most of the persons with whom she comes in contact. I do not mean only on account of her—ah—pleasing appearance; I mean because she seems so singlehearted."

"You've hit the nail on the head, Inspector. Single-hearted—that's the right word for her!" Joe exclaimed, dismissing the doubts which had briefly arisen. "Kind-hearted, too—willing to take all kinds of trouble to give anyone else pleasure. Why, after I cabled her from the ship that Judith and I were on our way here, she telephoned the hotel, over and over again, to let us know we could have her house seats for last night! She must have had about a million other things to do, but she never stopped trying to get in touch with me until she'd succeeded in talking with me personally. And I don't know how many years it is since she's heard from me, let alone seen me."

Kirtland stared at Joe in silence for a moment, and then took off his glasses, wiping them carefully on his handkerchief, before he replaced them. "Do you happen to remember," he inquired at last, "whether you mentioned in the cable the purpose of your impending presence in London?"

"You mean the series about Castle? Yes, I did. I told her I'd like to do a piece about her, too. She seemed to be very much pleased with the idea. So, when we finally made connections, I told her that, of course, the work with Castle had to take precedence over anything else I did, but that we'd find time for the other, too. However, there's nothing about that which could have any bearing on what happened last night, is there?"

"I wish I could assure you that there isn't. However, I'm compelled to inform you that I was told, unequivocally, that neither Miss Lester nor Mr. Alban nor Mr. Neville had the slightest inkling that Mr. Castle was in

London until Miss Lester received Mrs. Castle's note inviting them to a collation."

"The hell you were! By Janice?"

"No, by Mr. Alban. I believe it is quite possible—quite probable even—that Mr. Neville did not know. But I think you will agree that, as her manager, Mr. Alban must attend to such matters as the distribution of seats for Miss Lester. Also, that, as her husband, he would have almost inevitably been present on at least one of those occasions when she telephoned you over and over again."

"Well, Alban may have lied; I wouldn't know. But Janice didn't. I'd take my Bible oath on that, too."

"As far as I can judge, Miss Lester answered all my questions truthfully. I didn't happen to ask her how long beforehand she knew that Castle was coming to London. As a matter of fact, I didn't ask Alban, either. He volunteered the information. And then he added, 'So, no matter who's suspected, we three are bound to be in the clear.' Which, of course, they're not. Because, if they knew beforehand that Castle was to be here, it would give them time to prepare such a potion as we feel quite sure was administered."

"But I tell you, Janice never would have poisoned anyone! Let alone a man she'd been so crazy about that she decided all for love and the world well lost—if that's what she did do."

"You may be right and you may not. You seem to be very sure she isn't vengeful by nature and I'm inclined to agree with you. But that doesn't mean I can discount the possibility that she might have planned this murder, now that I know she was aware, several days in advance, of Castle's presence in London. And, as far as her husband's concerned—"

"I guess I'll have to grant you there's more of a possibility there. Still, I don't believe he did it—if for no other reason than that he's had more than twenty years to accomplish such a purpose, if he wanted to, and I don't believe he'd choose such a painless process as the one that was selected, if he did decide to do it."

"He pointed all that out himself . . . . Well, let's dismiss that phase of the situation for the time being, too—which doesn't mean I'm dismissing it permanently, you understand. Now suppose we look at another aspect of the case: has it occurred to you that this murder might be in the line of a political assassination?"

"Sure it has."

"Could you prove it?"

"Hell on the housetops, no! I'm only agreeing it's a possibility. Maybe even a probability. Politics are politics the world over, and east of Suez there ain't no Ten Commandments, according to Kipling and some others. The way to get rid of political opponents, in such places, isn't usually through the ballot box or an appeal to the people. Quite often it's through liquidation, as you just suggested."

"Liquidation? I don't remember—"

"Merely the modern word for assassination, Inspector."

"Power politics are rather out of my line. If you'd be good enough to explain what you mean in words of one syllable, so to speak—"

"Wherever any administration is in office, someone is trying to oust it. Caesar brought Rome to her greatest glory—and was assassinated for it. Your Winston Churchill was overthrown, after guiding Britain through history's greatest war. Ballots or bullets, the outs are always trying to replace the ins."

"But in Aristan—"

"It's the same difference. Old Suleiman was a good ruler, as autocrats go, I suppose. He did provide schools, hospitals, and so on for his people and he lived a rather Spartan life, according to Oriental standards, at least. But they were getting ready to rebel against him, just the same, until Castle came along and put him in the chips."

"That was a long time ago."

"Right; but now, instead of being opposed by disgruntled politicians only, Izzet ibn Hamis has turned most of the decent Aristanians against him. They're outraged by his extravagance and his loose ways of living. The professional outs have joined them. That forms a pretty big bloc. Opposing them, you've got the professional ins, the Izzet ibn Hamis crowd of pay roll patriots. Castle had all that blueprinted for him before he agreed to take the post."

"And he took it anyway?"

"From what he told me, the President put it up to him as a patriotic duty."

"Granted that's so–and we haven't any reason to assume it isn't–who would have anything to gain by Castle's death?"

"Politically, you mean, Inspector?"

"Politically, of course. The personal motives can be disregarded for the moment."

"The answer is quote everybody unquote. Everybody in Aristan, that is. Offhand, one would think Izzet, the playboy sultan, would be waiting for Castle with a red carpet from here to yonder, on the theory that the man who had redeemed his pappy's throne would do it again for sonny boy. But that wasn't the case."

"You're sure of that?"

"I only know what Castle himself told me during the course of our talks–that it might be necessary to get rid of Izzet as a first step toward making a new treaty that would safeguard American interests for the immediate future. Get him to abdicate in favor of one of his younger brothers, who was cast more nearly in the old Sultan Suleiman's mold."

"If that were the case, wouldn't the anti-Izzet bloc–the decent people–have been anxious for Castle to succeed?"

"Had they known about it, certainly. But they didn't. Even Castle didn't 'know' it, for that matter; he merely mentioned it to me one day as one possible course of action he might have to take in trying to do the job the President had turned over to him. So far as the good people in Aristan who opposed Izzet knew, Castle was on his way to save Izzet's regime just as he had once saved Suleiman's."

"They must have thought he could do anything he wanted."

"That figures, too, Inspector. They thought of him as a sort of Genghis Khan, or Kitchener, who does the impossible. They could very well have figured that the necessary first step to getting rid of Izzet would be to do away with Castle. Both sides had a believable reason for doing away with the man."

"Granted again. Then the next step would be to find out whether both sides had advocates among Mr. Castle's fellow guests last night."

"Well, on the face of it, Ahani should certainly be pro-Izzet. He represents the present government. But there might very well be wheels within wheels. In fact, Castle himself told me that he was suspicious of Ahani's brother-in-law. This was off the record, of course—just background information. But I don't see why I shouldn't tell you now."

"I appreciate your doing so. However, as far as Ahani is concerned—" Kirtland broke off, rummaged among his papers and again brought from its hiding place the jeweled box which had already figured in his conversations with Thorpe and Ahani. "I expect you've seen this trinket already," he remarked.

"Yes. I saw Ahani give it to Castle during the first entr'acte and Hilary told me it had been found in the car. I've been wondering when you'd get around to mentioning it."

"I should have done so sooner, if I had received a different report from the laboratory. But a large part of its contents have now been examined and, in every case, the specimens have proven entirely innocuous. They are exactly what Ahani claimed: fragments of salted walnuts, nothing more, nothing less. As you yourself pointed out, it would have been difficult for Lalisse to find a way of poisoning one guest, while leaving half a dozen others unharmed. It is equally improbable that

Castle, in selecting a nut, could have accidentally chosen the only one which was poisoned."

"But Castle didn't select the nut himself! Ahani extracted one from the box and handed it to him as a sample of the kind that was considered such a delicacy. And, up to that time, Ahani's wife had the box concealed somewhere on her person. It wouldn't be so highly improbable, would it, that the one poisoned fragment in the box was carefully marked—possibly shaped or colored differently from the others—before being secreted? And that Ahani chose an opportune moment, for which he'd been waiting, and knew exactly what he was doing when he offered the nut to Castle?"

"No, that wouldn't be so highly improbable. Thank you, Mr. Racina. This is the second time you've given me a very enlightening piece of information that was hitherto lacking."

"But they lead in entirely different directions! And you must admit that the second lead is a lot better than the first."

"I'll admit it *appears* to be. But, even supposing that Ahani was secretly anti-Izzet, I don't believe De Valcourt is."

"De Valcourt! Why on earth should he care who rules in Aristan?"

"Because it so happens that he and Izzet are boon companions or, if not actually that, at least on very friendly terms and with very kindred tastes. They both enjoy the Côte d'Azur, where De Valcourt has a villa and Izzet keeps a yacht anchored by his private beach. They both find congenial company in the locality of Monte Carlo and they both consider the casino an agreeable place to while away an otherwise dull evening. As I have just said, you have given me two very valuable pieces of information, Mr. Racina. Perhaps now I have given you one which will show you that I am not yet through investigating leads."

"I'll say you have. De Valcourt probably doesn't care who rules in Aristan, but you're right. It wouldn't be at all surprising if he cared a good deal about keeping his relationship with the royal playboy of the Riviera on an even keel. And I can see that, as far as you're concerned, whether he is or not, is, at the moment, the sixty-four-dollar question."

Part III

CHAPTER XVIII

KIRTLAND WAS USED to working long hours under pressure, but he was beginning to feel very tired and he showed it. The lines from the sides of his nostrils to the ends of his scrubby mustache were deeply etched and the puckered frown tightened the skin of his forehead above the bridge of his tortoise-shell glasses. He took them off, polished them and laid them down on his notes.

"I could do with a cup of coffee, Sergeant," he said wearily. "How about you?"

"It's been hard for me to keep my mind on anything else, this last half hour," Griffin confessed with alacrity.

"Very well. Suppose you ask for some to be sent up—coffee and sandwiches both. To us and, also, to the ladies and gentlemen who are assisting us, of course."

The refreshments arrived with the commendable promptitude characteristic of Savoy service. As Kirtland and Griffin sat gratefully but silently consuming their share of them, Big Ben struck three. Kirtland drained his cup for the third time and set it down conclusively.

"I don't need to tell you that it isn't our custom to talk with two persons at the same time, Sergeant. But the man who doesn't know when to depart from custom, as well as when to keep to it, wouldn't be much good as an inspector or anything else. As that young man we had in here awhile back would probably remind us, some are more honored in the breach than in the observance. It's getting pretty late, and I've a notion that we might speed things up a little and also be helped in other ways if we had Lady Laura and her daughter in here together. How does the idea strike you?"

"An excellent idea, sir," Griffin said emphatically, after hastily swallowing a final morsel of sandwich.

"Then suppose you inquire whether the ladies would be good enough to return here–after they've finished their own snack, of course."

The ladies were just finishing, Griffin informed Kirtland, after suitable inquiry; they would be glad to return to the sitting room almost immediately. Indeed, the sergeant had hardly finished reporting when the bedroom door opened again and Lady Laura and Althea came out. They had both been somewhat revived by their coffee and appeared less exhausted than the Inspector had anticipated. Lady Laura was still the personification of daintiness; not a hair of her elaborate coiffure was out of place, not a wrinkle visible in her elegant dress. As for Althea, her color seemed as fresh as before, her expression even more cheerful and candid. Nothing in the attitude of either suggested resentment.

"I have asked you two ladies to come here together this time because I find, on consulting Sergeant Griffin's notes and my own, that there seems to be a slight discrepancy between the statements which were made when I saw you separately," Mr. Kirtland said civilly. "I realize that it is getting very late and I should like to spare you as much fatigue as I can. This joint conference may mean a saving of time no less than of effort–especially as I feel sure it will enable us to reconcile these slight discrepancies very quickly."

"Of course it will," Lady Laura agreed instantly.

The Inspector inclined his head in her direction, but turned at once to her daughter. "Now, Miss Whitford," he said, "if I understood you correctly, you told me you were quite sure your mother had never met Mr. Castle before last evening . . . . I beg your pardon, Lady Laura, but it is your daughter whom I am questioning just now. I must ask you to wait until she has answered before saying anything yourself."

Althea cast a perplexed glance at Lady Laura, who had risen hastily and was trying to make herself heard above the Inspector's calm but determined voice.

"Why–why, yes, I did," the girl answered hesitantly, her bewilderment now tinged with concern.

"And you based that statement not only on the fact that she had never spoken to you about him, though your relationship has always been exceptionally close and she has seemed to enjoy telling you, in great detail, about her pleasant youth and happy married life. You also based it on the fact that she greeted him as a complete stranger—I think those were your exact words, a complete stranger—when he came into the dining room of Mr. Thorpe's house yesterday evening. Is that correct?"

Again Althea glanced at her mother, but this time Lady Laura sat stonily silent, her head averted.

"Y-e-e-s," Althea answered, still more hesitantly.

The Inspector consulted his notes. "And, after that, according to you, she said she knew almost nothing about the Middle East and that she had never received a letter from there—the statement was somewhat more detailed than this, but I believe that was the gist of it. Am I wrong?"

"No, you're not wrong. That is what I said. And I was telling the truth, too." For the second time, Althea was beginning to feel that her fears had been groundless. She *had* told the truth. Then why should she be afraid, either for her mother or for herself? There was something she did not understand, something that had troubled her for a moment; but presently it would be explained and then everything would be all right. Meanwhile, though she did not understand, she would go straight on telling the truth. That was not only what she knew in her own mind was right to do; it was what Hilary would count on her to do, even if she were frightened; and Hilary meant more to her than anyone else in the world, more even than her mother. She had just realized this; and with the realization had come the consciousness that she need not be frightened any more. She could answer anything the Inspector asked her, looking him straight in the face. But it appeared he did not intend to ask her anything more.

"Thank you very much, Miss Whitford," he said in the kindly impersonal way he had spoken before. "I would like you to remain here, but I shall ask you no more questions for the present . . . . Now, Lady Laura, of course there is a chance that my memory may be playing me false or that Sergeant Griffin may have made a mistake which you did not catch. But I have consulted my notes and his and I find in them both quotations from a series of statements you made to the effect that you met Baldwin Castle the year you came out; that you saw him frequently at the social gatherings you both attended; and that you still retained a very definite memory of the first actual conversation you and he had together. Is it possible that Sergeant Griffin and I could have misunderstood any of your statements?"

"Yes, of course it is possible," Lady Laura answered icily.

"Let me put my question a different way: Do you honestly think Sergeant Griffin and I did misunderstand?"

There was a long pause which the Inspector made no effort to interrupt. He sat with his hands resting quietly on his notes and looked out of the window, following the progress of a small, softly lighted boat as it clove through the water between Westminster Bridge and Waterloo Bridge. There was only one way in which Lady Laura could answer this question truthfully and he was prepared to wait until she did so. Although she was not under oath, he did not think she would dare to add to her many evasions by telling an outright lie, even if she did not realize that he had recognized the evasions as such.

"No," she said at last.

"Thank you. Now after this, you told us about several other meetings with Mr. Castle that stood out in your memory–one in the Royal Enclosure at Ascot, one at a tea party given by your parents at Haverford House, one at a Garden Party. Then you told us about your final meeting, a year or more later, in the presence of your fiancé Sir Guy Whitford. But you also told us that in the meantime, while Mr. Castle was in Aristan, he had written you frequently. It is difficult for me to reconcile this statement, and those which preceded it, with the one made by your daughter to the effect that you greeted Mr. Castle as a total stranger when he entered Mr. Thorpe's dining room, and that you said quite positively you had never received a letter from anyone living in the Middle East. Can you reconcile these statements?"

There was another pause, less lengthy than the previous one, but still sufficiently protracted to make itself felt. Eventually, however, Lady Laura again said no.

"Then do you accuse your daughter of telling a deliberate lie?"

"No, only of incredible stupidity."

"Oh, Mother!"

"Miss Whitford, a few minutes ago I reminded your mother that I was questioning you. Now I must remind you that I am questioning her. In fact, I can excuse you, if she would prefer to have me do so."

"It's quite immaterial to me whether my daughter stays or goes. She's already done all the damage she can."

"You mean, Lady Laura, that you think she misinterpreted your manner and misunderstood your words?"

"No. I mean that she needn't have blurted all that out. She might perfectly well have said that, *as far as she knew,* I had no previous acquaintance with Mr. Castle. That should have been convincing to you—no woman tells her daughter everything, and any girl who wasn's a simpleton would realize that."

"Mother!"

"As the Inspector has reminded you, Althea, he wants me to do the talking now. And as *I* said, Mr. Kirtland, such a statement should have been convincing and it would have been perfectly true."

"But it wouldn't have been the complete truth, now, would it?"

"This is the first I've heard about the *complete* truth. And you've said yourself you didn't expect us to remember everything."

"Not to remember everything, but certainly to relate with complete accuracy everything you do remember and relate—which is exactly what your daughter did do and what, apparently, you did not do, Lady Laura. It is quite true that you are not under oath. But it is also true that you, and everyone else connected with the present unfortunate circumstances, agreed to be as helpful as possible. And you have not done that, either. How deliberately you have interfered with the course of justice, I do not know. But I can see that, so far, you have not furthered it to the best of your ability. It is quite true that, under normal circumstances, it is not usual for a mother to tell her daughter everything connected with her youth. There is no reason why she should. But we are not dealing with normal circumstances now. We are dealing with a murder. And, under these conditions, it is your duty to tell me everything which may lead to the discovery of the guilty person."

The Inspector's voice, hitherto so quiet and kindly, had become stern. "We will now go back to the point where you admitted that you could not reconcile your statements with your daughter's," he went on. "I gather that there must have been some reason why, in her presence and that of Mr. Thorpe's other guests, you preferred to have it appear that you had never known Mr. Castle or corresponded with him."

"Yes, there was. I had no reason to recall, with any pleasure, my last meeting with him. In fact, I had every reason to recall it with such displeasure that I preferred to forget it–and not only that meeting, but all previous ones."

"Not only to prefer, but to pretend."

"Yes."

"Yet, sometime after that last meeting, when he was a widower and you were a widow, you wrote to him twice and he answered both times. It seems to me rather strange that you should have done this, if you preferred to forget not only your last meeting with Mr. Castle, but all previous ones."

Lady Laura did not reply.

"I will not press that point for the moment, Lady Laura, though I may revert to it later. Instead, I should like to refer to something else your daughter said to me and, in that connection, to question her again for a moment . . . . You told me, Miss Whitford, I think, that your mother did not like Americans very much on general principles. In fact, I believe you said she had a queer prejudice against them."

"Yes, I did."

There was not the slightest hesitancy in Althea's voice now. She was holding her head high and she was not glancing toward her mother any more.

"Did she ever give you any reason for this prejudice?"

"No. It's always puzzled me, it's so inclusive. As I said, she dislikes them on general principles, even the nicest ones, like Hilary Thorpe."

"Did you ever try to find out why?"

"Yes, but I never got anywhere. She always put me off when I asked questions about it."

"Then didn't it occur to you that perhaps there was some special reason for this prejudice? Perhaps some very grave reason?"

"Yes, it did. I've often wondered about it. So has Hilary."

"Without ever finding any clue to it?"

"Not before tonight. Now I think it's evident that something happened between my mother and Mr. Castle which she couldn't get over. And that then she brooded about it until the fear or the hurt or the resentment or whatever it was grew and grew. It wasn't confined to Mr. Castle any more; it included all Americans. Even Hilary. I think now the reason she doesn't want me to marry him is because she didn't marry Baldwin Castle."

"Althea!"

It was Lady Laura's turn to cry out. Althea turned toward her again, not in loving bewilderment any more, but in righteous anger.

"Well, I do. And I'll keep on believing so until you show me those letters."

"They were destroyed, long ago."

"I don't believe it. I shan't believe it until you let me rummage through your desk and your dressing table and everything else you keep so carefully locked. I don't think you were telling even the partial truth that time.

I think you were telling a downright lie. And I'm not going to let you stop me marrying the man I love unless I find out I'm mistaken. I'm not going to give up Hilary just to let you have your revenge on Baldwin Castle."

"If my own daughter has turned against me in this ghastly way, I do not suppose there is anything I can say in self-defense."

The theatrical manner in which Lady Laura pronounced these words robbed them of all genuine appeal. For the first time, the Inspector smiled; but he did so rather ruefully.

"You haven't been called upon yet, Lady Laura, to defend yourself of any accusation except that of prevarication. But, like your daughter, I should be very much interested in seeing those letters. Like her, I am inclined to believe that they still exist—and that you would be wise to produce them. If we are mistaken, and you cannot, then I believe it would be wise to tell us what was in them—and, in this instance, to give us, *and yourself*, the benefit of the *complete* truth." He waited for a moment, as if to make her feel the full impact of his words and then he went on, "If you would prefer not to do so now, I shall not insist. But I must warn you that, in this case, I may find it necessary to recall you for a third questioning."

"It will not be necessary to question me a third time. As I just told you, in my anguish, I do not suppose there is anything I can say in the way of self-defense, since my own daughter has turned against me. And it will not be necessary, either, for you to see the letters, unless you refuse to take my word for what is in them. You will recall that the first of the two about which you were so curious was sent in acknowledgment of a note of condolence that I wrote after hearing that Mr. Castle's wife had died. It was merely a black-bordered card engraved with the inscription:

BALDWIN CASTLE
DEEPLY APPRECIATES
YOUR KIND EXPRESSION OF SYMPATHY

"I see. To quote your own words, rather formal but quite correct . . . . And the second–the one which 'recalled something that happened in the course of your previous acquaintance'–something, I believe, which you had not told me?"

"It recalled that the last time we had met, Mr. Castle had told me he was through–and added that he had meant this literally."

"Ah–on the one occasion, which was in the presence of your fiancé, when you saw Mr. Castle after his return from Aristan, he told you he was 'through'–indicating, no doubt, that he wished to bring his acquaintance with you to an end?"

"Yes."

"And you had said nothing to indicate that you yourself wished this acquaintance to terminate?"

"I'd become engaged to Sir Guy Whitford during Mr. Castle's absence. The engagement was already announced, though the news hadn't reached the Middle East. I naturally wasn't receiving other callers as I had before."

"By other callers, I assume you mean other suitors?"

"If you wish to put it that way."

"So Mr. Castle had been a suitor of yours?"

"One of several."

"But you had never encouraged him to believe he might be an accepted suitor?"

"He had more or less taken it for granted. He took a great deal for granted. He was a very presumptuous young man."

"But it was something of a surprise–something of a shock–to him when he found you were engaged to someone else?"

"Evidently."

"Well, I think I can now understand why he told you he was 'through' when he called upon you so inopportunely. But I do not yet understand why he should have reiterated that rather brusque statement some years later. When I asked you whether there was any special reason why you wrote him at that time, you said, 'One might put it that way,' and your answers to my next questions were rather vague. Do you think you could be a little more definite now?"

"The special reason for my writing to Baldwin Castle was that I was in great need–in great want. My husband had passed for a very rich man; actually, he had lived far beyond his means and he died deeply in debt. Even after I had sold everything that was salable, I did not have enough left to live on, much less to give my little daughter a good home, a good education–other normal advantages."

Lady Laura cast a withering glance at Althea who tried, unsuccessfully, to interrupt her. "I humbled myself for the sake of my child," Lady Laura went on vehemently. "There was no question about Mr. Castle's finances. All the world knew beyond a shadow of a doubt that he was enormously wealthy. And you are quite right. He had been my suitor–my declared worshiper. He had told me over and over again, in person and in writing, that there was nothing he would not do for me, nothing he would not give me. Yet, when I appealed to him for help in my extremity, his answer was a pitiless refusal which took the form of saying for the second time that he was through."

"Oh, Mother, I'm sorry, terribly sorry for what I've forced you to tell! I understand everything now! And I don't blame you for your bitterness–your resentment–your hatred!"

Althea had gone impetuously toward her mother and attempted to embrace her. Lady Laura freed herself and spoke with icy detachment.

"It's a little late for you to think of that, now that you have been responsible for baring my sad secrets in such a way that you have convinced Mr. Kirtland my bitterness and my resentment and my hatred might drive me to any lengths–even to the lengths of committing murder."

"Your daughter hasn't convinced me of that, Lady Laura," the Inspector said quietly. "But it is my duty to probe all possibilities and the records I've been reading for a good many years now, in addition to the cases which have come within my own experience, prove that, from the earliest ages, the desire for vengeance has been one of the most compelling of all known motives for murder. No doubt you've heard that in my work we are guided by three *M*'s in framing our questions under circumstances like the present one: What was the *M*otive? What was the *Me*thod? And was there a propitious *Mo*ment? Whatever you may choose to say in denial, you had the Motive. You also had knowledge of the means to accomplish your end, partly through your work with your husband, and partly through your acquaintance with Colonel de Valcourt–you knew that cyanide was used in the treatment of butterflies and you knew that it could be coated in tablets, like aspirin. So poison of course would have been your Method. As for the propitious Moment–why, you prepared the tea which Mr. Castle drank at Mr. Thorpe's party and you poured it into his cup! Moreover, you knew, at least an hour beforehand, that you were going to this party; nothing could have been simpler for you than to prepare the deadly tablet and slip it into your victim's tea!"

Althea gave an exclamation of horror. "I don't believe it!" she cried. "I don't believe a word of it!"

"My dear young lady, I didn't say your mother had done all this. I merely said she *could* have and that I must look into the possibilities. If you think the matter over, I believe you will realize this is so."

"But she didn't do it!"

"I presume you would make the same denial, even more forcibly, Lady Laura?"

"Of course I should. Of course I *do*."

"Very well. Then I will excuse you both for the time being. But I should like you both to stay in the bedroom a little longer."

He rose and opened the door for them to pass through. Then he glanced in a questioning manner toward Sergeant Griffin, much as he had done when he had first finished interrogating the mother and daughter. Again, the sergeant seemed to be completely absorbed in his notes.

But again he looked up to meet his chief's eye with understanding.

"The most powerful of all motives is indeed proven to be the desire for vengeance," Kirtland repeated, and paused. "But the most frequent is still what our French friends call 'the *crime passionnel.*' Before we press this other matter any more, I think we had better probe the further possibilities of that."

"I couldn't agree with you more, sir," Sergeant Griffin answered heartily.

CHAPTER XIX

DESPITE THE HEARTY support of his sergeant, the Inspector did not instantly act on his own suggestion. Instead, he sent for Judith and asked her to give him a brief outline of what Cornelia had told her, which she did with a brevity and clarity that increased his already high opinion of her. Then he resumed the study of his notes and remained for a long while obviously deep in thought. Griffin, who was by this time very drowsy, permitted himself to doze, unobserved by his superior.

"*Mo*ment, *Me*thod, and *Mo*tive," Kirtland was saying to himself. "Well, Moment puts an accusing finger on all of them except perhaps the Albans and Evan Neville. Hugo Alban said none of them knew, an hour before they saw him, that Castle was on this side of the ocean. That can't be wholly true, because Janice Lester did know beforehand, from Racina's cable, that he was coming to London with the Castles. But it's quite likely, all things considered, that she didn't mention the Castles' proximity in speaking to her husband and more than likely that she didn't mention it to her cousin. However, all of them had been with Castle at some time during the evening when he met his death, and all of them, except the Albans and Neville, knew well in advance that they were going to be. I should say that Neville had less than a few minutes' foreknowledge of the fact that he would meet Mr. Castle and also that he was not with the party for more than ten minutes at most, perhaps less. That is an almost perfect alibi, as such things go, unless we assume that Neville was or could have been the accomplice of one of the others. On the matter of Moment, Miss Lester and Mr. Alban assuredly had more time to plan an act than Evan Neville, but they had less than any of the others. Everyone else had opportunity and time to plan and execute this or any other similar deed. Time and to spare. The only one we can disregard in this connection is, I think, Neville.

"Well then, which of the M's should be considered next? Method or Motive? Let me have a go at Motive and start eliminating a few of the group at this point—Mr. and Mrs. Racina and Mr. Thorpe. No known Motive appears in their cases, not even a farfetched one. But for each of the rest, there is at least a possible Motive, some of them way out in the blue and some of them melodramatic. But others are among the most compelling urges to crime in all the records of police experience.

"Ahani's might be one of those that seem pretty farfetched. But it's been made all too plain, from what Thorpe and Racina have told me, that at least two of the major parties in certain Middle Eastern countries would have stopped at almost nothing to keep someone like Castle from carrying out the mission he had undertaken. In addition to that, though the nuts in the box which were tumbled all over the car were apparently harmless, the one Ahani handed to Castle before the gift was made may have been very carefully prepared and selected. I have Racina's word for just how that was done; and Ahani did make insistent efforts to draw Castle away from the company of his friends. Once persuaded to go off with Ahani, no one except the chauffeur saw him alive again. The political motive may or may not be farfetched; but the attendant circumstances make it credible.

"The same is true of De Valcourt. I don't feel at all sure that his financial status is as satisfactory as he makes out; and I don't feel sure, either, that both he and Izzet are above striking some sort of a bargain which might involve politics, as well as money. Perhaps only a few words passed between them: 'Look, Jacques, I'm not so pleased at this probable appointment of Castle as American Ambassador to Aristan. He's bound to regard me as a playboy—which, praise be, I am! He's also bound to support me, and Allah knows I need support—I can feel the props wobbling underneath me all right. But the support would have a price. And the price would very likely be that I give up night life on the Riviera and devote my time to good works in Aristan, as my father did, with this same man's help. I'd be a lot easier if the appointment were only part of the spoils system, which flourishes in the United States as well as in Aristan, no matter how vehemently Americans try to deny it—if the man they were sending were rolling in dollars, but didn't even know where Aristan was on the map and didn't care, or if he couldn't talk anything but Brooklynese or Dixie dialect, or if he understood his role to be something like that of a court jester. There have been several such sent out from the Land of the Free and the Home of the Brave and you know it as well as I do. Now you see a good deal of Ahani in London and if you could just tip him off—' . . . . 'Are you suggesting that I have my price, too?' . . . 'My dear fellow, of course not! But I do have a short memory—for money as well as women. I'm quite likely to forget all about those pleasant evenings at the casino, when I came off better than you did. On the other hand, I think I could patch up the slight difficulty you're having about getting rid of one of our pretty little companions.' . . . Not just those words perhaps, but something to their effect."

"Well, of course, that's all supposition, so far; still I don't think it's too farfetched, either. At all events, I'm not ready to dismiss it. On the other hand, I'm not ready to talk to either Ahani or De Valcourt again, as yet, so now for Mrs. Castle. She didn't attempt to deny she knew that, through her husband's death, she would become a very wealthy woman. She went further than that. She admitted there were certain things she wanted to do, more than she'd ever wanted anything before, and that she couldn't do them in her husband's lifetime. In view of the shock she's sustained and her indisposition, I hate to labor the point. But I expect there's no help for it . . . . Griffin!"

"Yes, sir!" Griffin answered dazedly, getting to his feet with a start.

"Ask Mrs. Castle to come back here for a few minutes, will you?"

"Yes, sir!" said Griffin again, blinking and rubbing his eyes as he went across the floor.

Kirtland had fully expected that Cornelia, who had looked disheveled before, would look actually bedraggled by this time. Therefore, her appearance was a source of considerable relief. Through some miracle, for which he had no doubt Judith was largely responsible, Mrs. Castle was now clad in the "nice plain black dress" for which she so logically felt the occasion called. Her hair was brushed smoothly back from her brow and temples and rolled into a neat bun at the nape of her neck; the sprinkling of gray so revealed had the effect of softening a face which was still innocent of make-up and somewhat haggard of expression, but which was clean and composed. Evidently she realized how greatly this transformation had improved her mentally and spiritually, as well as physically, and felt the better for it.

"I've taken a bath," she announced. "Judith thought I'd have time, before you called me again, and I did. And she telephoned the housekeeper and asked if someone on the staff wouldn't have clothes they'd be willing to lend. They found two dresses and sent them for me to choose between and the housekeeper loaned me some of her own undies. Nylon stockings, too, and she can't have many of those. Then, after I was all nice and clean again, along came that good strong coffee and those sandwiches. I'll say everyone's been mighty kind and thoughtful. You, too, Inspector."

"I'm glad you feel that way, Mrs. Castle, and I'm also glad to see you looking so much better. As perhaps Mrs. Racina's told you, I've had another talk with her and she's given me the gist of her various conversations with you. Perhaps now you'd feel you could tell me yourself–"

"What I couldn't before? About what I wanted to do?"

"Yes, that's it."

"Well, I'll try. I do feel better and if you'll give me a minute to think how I put it to Judith and how she answered, maybe I can. She did tell me she'd had another talk with you, and when she came back to the bedroom afterward, I did tell her what it was I wanted to do. I hadn't, before."

"Take all the time you need to, Mrs. Castle."

* * *

"I had some good neighbors when I lived on the farm, Judith. Of course some of them–most of them –sided with Sam, my husband. But there were a few who thought he'd been too harsh and hasty, that he might have given me a second chance. One of them was a woman who lived on the next place to us–Abby Blaker. She'd never married–ran her farm herself then and still does–and she's never thought much of men. Not that she's a sour old maid, either. She's just the type that has no nonsense about her, if you know what I mean–plain and bossy and strong as an ox. Well, Abby came right out and quoted Scripture about it profiteth a man nothing if he hath not charity and forgiving seventy times seven and neither do I condemn thee, go and sin no more. Not that it did any good. But she kept track of my address and, come hell or high water, she sat down every Sunday just as soon as she got back from church and wrote me a great long letter."

"I have a feeling that I'd like Abby Blaker."

"Sure you would and she'd like you, too. Well, it seems that after Sam divorced me, things didn't go too well on our farm–his farm. His mother came and stayed awhile, but she never was much of a cook, and it was so long since she'd had a young one of her own that she was terribly unhandy with Barney. I hadn't told you my baby's name before, had I? Well, it was Barney. So then Sam tried having housekeepers, but either they were so old and feeble they just crept around, letting half the work go, or else they were so young and flighty that they were out every night until all hours, he didn't know where, or if he did that was worse still. He had to do more and more himself around the house and helping to look after Barney, and of course that meant he had to let some things go outside. Just the same, I'll never believe it was really his fault that the herd was condemned."

"Condemned?"

"Yes, for t.b. Every last one of his cows."

"That was hard luck. I've known the same thing to happen where I come from and it can just about ruin a farmer."

"It just about ruined Sam. But he put a heavy mortgage on the place and bought some more cows. He had confidence in the dealer he got them from–in fact, the man was an old friend, or at least he and Sam had known each other all their lives and Sam thought of him as a friend. But he didn't mention the fact that abortion was running through the stock he sold, just like wildfire. Sam lost nearly all the new cows, too."

"Oh, I'm sorry, I'm very sorry!"

"You can't help but be sorry, can you? I was so sorry, when I got Abby's letter telling me about it, that I sat right down and cried. I wrote back and said if there were any way I could send Sam a little money, without his knowing where it came from, I'd scrape it up some way. But she wrote back, saying she didn't see how it could be managed. And then the worst thing of all happened. Barney got polio."

"Cornelia–"

"Yes. I guess it looked pretty bad for a while. But he pulled through. Only he's got a bad arm–his right arm. He'd grown up into a very husky little boy, good looking, too, Abby said, and was a great help to his father. But then he couldn't help any for a long while, even after he was out of danger and there were no more doctors' bills and hospital bills to meet. He won't ever be able to help like he could if he was able-bodied. It was all Sam could do, by selling his hay crop and working in another dairy for wages, to scrape together enough, each year, for taxes, interest on his notes and the bare necessities. There was never enough left over for a fresh start and, since everything on the place was already mortgaged to the hilt, he couldn't borrow enough. Naturally, each year, the house, the barns, the fences and the whole farm would be a little more rundown than the year before. So there is Sam, struggling along with a heavy mortgage he can't pay off and no one with him on the farm but a semicripple. And there's Barney, penned up in this forlorn place, without a prayer of getting out and doing something else. And, according to Abby, he's just as smart as a steel trap. Leads all his classes, has ever since he was in the first grade. And now he's almost ready to graduate from high school–think of that, *graduate*!–and is crazy to go to college. And there isn't a red cent for a college education, even if he could leave his father–what help he can give is better than none.

"So what I thought was this: if I was a widow, a real, respectable sod widow, instead of a grass one, with money of my own that I'd come by fair and square, maybe I could find a way of helping. I don't know just how, but if I studied on it, I bet I could find out. Even if Sam wouldn't take anything for himself, he ought to be willing to give Barney a chance, if it were put to him the right way, by the minister or someone. My money would send Barney to college, and hire someone to help Sam, and repair the house and the barns, and buy a new herd. That way, Barney would have something to come back to afterward, if he decided that farming was what he wanted to do; if he didn't think he *had* to, he'd be a lot more likely to *want* to. He wouldn't have to scratch for a living, the way his father has. He could be someone in the community, right from the start. He could be prosperous himself and he could do a lot of good. He'd probably be the president of the village improvement society and a deacon in the church and a director in the bank. He might even go to Congress after a while—to the state legislature, anyway. And he'd marry the right girl, not the wrong kind like his father did. She'd be a credit to him and the community, too, she'd bring up her kids right and she'd look after her father-in-law, too. Sam would be provided for, in his old age. He wouldn't be wondering, every time he drew his rocker up to the stove, whether the next winter he'd own so much as a rocker or have a stove to draw it up to."

"You've thought it all out very carefully, Cornelia."

"Yes, I have. And honest, Judith, don't you think that maybe it might work?"

"I certainly do. And I hope you'll tell the Inspector yourself, just as soon as you can, what it was you had in mind when you said there was something you'd do if you had money of your own. Because I'm sure he had no idea you meant anything like this. And when he finds out—well, I believe he'll have a very different feeling about you, Cornelia."

* * *

"I've thought over what Judith and I said to each other, Inspector. I think I could tell you now."

"Well done. I'm listening."

She faltered occasionally in the course of her recital. Once she bowed her head again, as she had when she first talked to Kirtland, and twice she looked toward him, obviously seeking encouragement. Each time, he spoke to her so gently that she was reassured. When she finally finished, her voice breaking, he took off his glasses and wiped them carefully. Then he cleared his throat before speaking.

"Mrs. Racina was quite right," he said. "This isn't the kind of story I expected you to tell me. And I don't need your assurance that it's a true story. There's only one thing I don't quite understand: I don't see why you didn't tell it to your husband–that is, to Mr. Castle–as you've told it to Mrs. Racina and me–I mean the part about the bad luck with the herds and the little lad's misfortune. I don't understand why you felt you had to be a widow before you could help that little lad –your own son. Surely, Mr. Castle wouldn't have begrudged the money that would have helped a child of yours get a decent start in life! Why, he never would have missed it, a wealthy man like that!"

"Oh, he wouldn't have begrudged the *money* and of course he wouldn't have missed it! But he wouldn't have liked to have me talking about a child I'd had by another man–not when he wanted one of his own so much! And he wouldn't have liked to hear about my–slip-up. He didn't mind my being sort of ignorant and common–you see, his first wife was so *very* well educated and so *terribly,* terribly refined that he'd got sort of tired of that, if you know what I mean. He liked belly laughs and rough and ready love-making and I could fall right in with all that. I guess it was a welcome change, though he never said so. At the same time, he thought I was straight. I hadn't given him any reason to think different. Perhaps I ought to have told him, but I didn't. I'd found out, you see, early in the game, that he didn't forgive and forget so easy. In fact, he bragged that he wouldn't and couldn't. He told me there was some dame who played a dirty trick on him once, and he just bided his time, until years later he had a chance to get back at her. Then he did, good and plenty. I don't know who it was and it doesn't matter; but I always hoped that dame wasn't biding *her* time now; I wouldn't be surprised but what she thought murder wasn't good enough for him. Baldwin Castle was a fine man, one of the best; but we all have our faults and vengefulness was one of his."

"Well, but–"

"If I'd asked for help with Barney, I'd have had to tell Baldwin Castle why I lost Barney in the first place. And then he'd have thought I wasn't fit to be his wife, let alone an ambassadress–why, he thought so just last night, seeing me once under the influence, when he'd been led to believe I never drank at all! If he'd heard about that shotgun wedding, and all the reasons why it *was* a shotgun wedding, he'd have walked out on me. I wouldn't have blamed him, either."

"But he did know you'd been married before?"

"Yes, he knew that. But he didn't ask me many questions and I didn't volunteer any information he didn't ask for. I never even told him I'd had a child."

Again she looked at Kirtland as if beseeching his understanding. "It's all sad, isn't it?" she said. "And one of the saddest things of all–well, I don't know as I ought to tell you this, Inspector–"

"Please tell me everything you will and can."

Cornelia glanced toward the sergeant and lowered her voice. "Then don't have him write this down," she said. "It doesn't have anything to do with–with what happened last night. But I've been talking to Judith again, like I told you, and she's been asking me more questions about–well, about me being so seasick and all. And she doesn't think it's just because the Atlantic is rougher in October than the Pacific is in August. She thinks—well, she thinks I might be in the family way. And I sort of think so, too. I sure hope so. But isn't it just the damnedest luck that Baldy shouldn't know it?"

CHAPTER XX

WHEN KIRTLAND TOLD De Valcourt that his list of suspects had as yet no top and no bottom, he had spoken the truth. But soon after his conversation with Cornelia, it was so provided, and her name was at the end of it. Next to the end was that of Lalisse, for Kirtland had received a telephone call which proved that Racina's assumption was correct. Lalisse, on waking from her bad dreams, had decided that the easiest way to forget them would be in the company of her latest admirer, and had gone off with him to the cinema. But she had now returned to Devonshire Mews and had expressed willingness, even eagerness, to accompany Celestino to the Savoy. In the face of this attitude, Kirtland decided that her contribution would be negligible.

The names of four of the persons with whom he had talked—Hilary, Joe, Judith and Althea—did not appear on the list at all. Joe had put into words the reasons why he and Hilary were almost automatically eliminated and Kirtland had found no reason to differ with him. Neither Judith nor Althea had expressed herself similarly; but Kirtland had needed no such declaration to regard them as ineligible for consideration. True, Judith, a highly trained nurse with army combat experience in her field, was incontestably more familiar with the administration of drugs than anyone else who had been in Castle's company; and this familiarity inevitably embraced the effects of poisons, including cyanide. But she had no conceivable motive for killing Castle—in fact, she had almost as much reason as her husband for wishing him to remain alive, since the fortunes of a devoted married couple were essentially interwoven; and even if she had been animated by a credible motive, she would have had more and better opportunities to act upon it during a fairly protracted voyage than in the course of a single evening's festive outing. Besides, it required hardly more than one swift glance to realize that hers was not the nature of a poisoner. Althea's candor and inexperience were almost equally obvious. Briefly—very briefly—the Inspector had considered that, as a devoted daughter, she might abet her mother in some evil design and shield the latter from the consequences; but the girl's instinctive recoil from falsehood and her courageous refusal to be intimidated or shamed into changing her straightforward story had convinced him that he need not give the possibility a second thought. Even her firm belief in her mother's innocence and her sturdy defense of Lady Laura had not been strong enough to swerve her. But, despite his complete exoneration of Althea, Kirtland's list, as it stood after his second conference with Cornelia, was headed by Lady Laura Whitford.

She was familiar with cyanide and its employment. She had accompanied her husband, a noteworthy collector of butterflies, on many of his expeditions; over and over again, she must have seen a "cyanide jar" in use. Though the butterfly collection had been sold, it was quite conceivable that there had been no similar disposal of all the apparatus connected with it. De Valcourt was a suitor of her daughter's and she would have had time, between the announcement of the Castles' presence in London and her departure for Thorpe's house, to prepare a pellet in accordance with the Frenchman's methods; and, while her hands were fluttering over the teacups, nothing would have been simpler than to slip such a pellet into one of them, quite unobserved. She had nurtured a bitter grievance against Castle for years, and the more she had brooded over this, the more it had become intensified; in the course of her brooding, she might very well have pictured to herself the various ways in which she could be avenged for a wrong she would never forgive, and then she might seize upon one which seemed relatively simple. As Kirtland himself had told her, without equivocation, the desire for vengeance had been proven, over and over again, the most compelling cause for murder . . . .

Nevertheless, turning from his notes with her name at the head of his list, Kirtland did not send for her to return and charge her with the crime. With so many arrows pointing to her guilt, there was still one that pointed another way: that she had wanted to commit murder, that she had pondered the matter for years and that she had the means of doing so ready at hand—all this was not possible, but probable. However, nothing about her suggested daring or even decisiveness. She had been afraid to marry a man who was "different," even though greatly drawn to him; she had actually been afraid to tell him she had changed her mind about considering him as a suitor; she had allowed herself to slip from her once proud position without venturing on any experiment which might have improved her lot; and she was fastidious and vapid, as well as vacillating and timorous. She would have instinctively recoiled from violence in the same way that her daughter recoiled from falsehood; and, at the very moment of preparing to strike, she might well have faltered, not because she was overwhelmed by a sense of guilt, but because she envisioned a scaffold prepared for her.

All this, Kirtland took into careful consideration. Besides, he still was not wholly ready to dismiss either De Valcourt or Ahani from suspicion, though he had not yet decided which he would put in second place and which in third. Indubitably, De Valcourt belonged second when it came to method; it was through his familiarity with enteric-coated poison that unnumbered Nazi officers had met their death; to bring about one more death would have required no ingenuity, not even any special preparation on his part. But granting the possibility of a political motive, Kirtland did not believe it would be as strong in the case of De Valcourt, even if money entered the picture, as it well might be in the case of Ahani. And he still had not delved, as deeply as he felt impelled to do, in other directions. He bracketed the names of De Valcourt and Ahani and pushed his papers aside.

"For a man who's always supported the theory that the *crime passionnel* is the most frequent motive of all," he muttered, "I certainly am a long while getting around to it."

"I beg your pardon, sir?"

Kirtland gave a slight start. "I must have been thinking out loud, Griffin," he said.

"Yes, sir. Was there anything you wanted?"

"No, just to go on thinking."

"Very good, sir."

Griffin, who was momentarily wide awake, continued to look at his superior attentively for a few minutes, in the hope that more of Kirtland's thoughts might be put into words. The sergeant was, however, doomed to disappointment. The Inspector was now going over the notes he had taken on Janice, Hugo and Evan and he was doing so silently. Griffin relapsed into comfortable somnolence.

The more the Inspector reflected on Janice, the less inclined he was to consider her guilty of Castle's murder. This was not only because of the apparent lack of opportunity for preparation; it was also because, as he had said to himself when he first saw her, she seemed more the type that inspired murder than the type which committed it; and getting down to cases, rather than dealing in generalities, he believed she had spoken the truth when she said she had not thought of Castle for years, that she had been happy with her husband and successful in her art. There was nothing to indicate that there was rancor mingled with her memories of her early affair; she had asked nothing of her lover because she had wanted nothing from him. If she had wanted anything, unquestionably she could have got it—a renewal of their intimacy, indefinite financial assistance, even honorable if belated marriage. She must have preferred that their relationship should be a closed chapter, since a woman like her had few unfulfilled desires.

Hugo then was a much more logical suspect: he made no bones of his hatred for Castle; and wholeheartedly as he loved his wife, this passionate devotion could not be untinged by normal male resentment that he had not been the first to possess her, and equally normal resentment because her only child was not his; for that Evan was Janice's son, and Castle's, Kirtland had very little doubt; the accounts of a baby, orphaned in an automobile accident, had been quite unconvincing to him. But while Hugo's glib description of Evan's adoption had lacked the ring of authenticity, there was no question of lacking sincerity when he described the ease with which he could have eliminated Castle, under the protection of legerdemain, had he chosen to rid himself of a hated rival in such a painless manner. The motive for murder had certainly been present for years; but nothing pointed to the probability that he had committed it the previous evening.

When it came to Evan, the motive as well as the moment was apparently lacking. Even supposing that he had found the story of his adoption unconvincing, as his answer to Kirtland's question about the relationship had seemed to indicate, and had first suspected and later ascertained that Castle was his father, there would apparently have been nothing in this knowledge to motivate sudden patricide, even if there had been time to arrange it–which, quite conclusively, it appeared that there had not. Besides, Kirtland reminded himself, he must hew to the line; it was the possibility of the *crime passionnel* he was considering now, and not patricide. Well, there was no help for it, he must begin all over again with Janice. Something was eluding him, something of which he had not even thought so far; both his instinct and his experience told him this much. He must go on searching until he found it . . . .

Janice was looking even more beautiful than before, if possible, when she entered the sitting room a second time. True, there were now dark circles of fatigue under her eyes, but the result was that they appeared larger and more magnificent than ever. She moved less rapidly, but her lassitude seemed to accentuate the lovely lines of her figure. When she had seated herself, she raised one arm and rested her cheek lightly on her hand; her slender white fingers, faintly tipped with rose, formed a delicate support for the pale oval of her face. Her grace, like her charm, was inescapable. For more reasons than one, Kirtland decided that the coming interview must be kept as brief as possible.

"Miss Lester," he said, without preamble, "when you talked with me before, you answered all my questions promptly and, I believe, truthfully. Yet I cannot help thinking you did not answer them as fully as you might have. I felt so at the time, and I have felt so increasingly as the night has gone on–partly because of my own deductions and partly because of what others have told me. Don't misunderstand me–nothing disparaging has been said about you. It is obvious that you enjoy the loyal friendship of Mr. Racina and the devoted attachment of Mr. Alban and that you merit both. Nevertheless–"

"Nevertheless, Inspector?"

"Nevertheless, I should like to have you tell me a little more about your association with Mr. Castle. Unless I warn you to the contrary, everything you say to me will be held in confidence–that is, no one who is not already in possession of any facts you may reveal will be told them by me."

"Thank you."

"With that clear understanding, would you be willing to tell me whether this association was merely one of friendship–or whether it was closer than that? Believe me, I ask this question reluctantly."

"And you know that I cannot help answering it reluctantly. But since you do ask it, and since I am sure I must answer it sooner or later, that might as well be now. The association was considerably closer than friendship."

"Yet when it ended, you did not blame him?"

"No, I felt I was as much to blame as he was. I still feel so."

"So you have never entertained any feelings of rancor toward Mr. Castle?"

"Never."

"Yet, from something your–'young relative'–said to me, I gathered you were averse to meeting Mr. Castle again last evening."

"That is true. But several factors entered into my aversion. As you must know, it is not customary for actors to go to box parties during the intervals. Acting is a great strain, and the persons who wish to see actors generally realize this and do not insist upon doing so until after a play is over. Then visitors come to the dressing rooms—considerate friends do not demand that actors visit them. I felt that Mrs. Castle's summons was not only inconsiderate, but arrogant. My first impulse was indeed to refuse the invitation, if such it may be called; actually, it was more like a command. But my resentment was primarily against her presumption."

"Your husband understood this?"

"I think he did; but I believe he thought the others might not understand–that Baldwin Castle would think I was afraid to see him again, or that he would assume I was harboring resentment. I have never been afraid of anything or anyone since my marriage and I have never harbored resentment at any time during my life. Hugo was very eager that I should make this clear and I know now that he was right. I did not feel that way about it at first, and we came nearer to quarreling than we ever had before. It must have been fragments of this dispute that Evan overheard and which, apparently, he reported to you. I do not blame him for doing so, if you asked him questions which indicated such a report. But I am sure you will not take it amiss if I remind you that he could not have heard very clearly, because he was in the corridor. He did not come into my dressing room at all."

"Not then, I know. However, I understand that he did come in later in the evening."

"That is so. But this later and very brief call had no bearing on the discussion between my husband and me, or on my feeling toward Baldwin Castle, who was in my dressing room at the time, as I told you myself and as Evan has probably told you, too. Evan came in partly out of civility, because I had asked him to; just as I asked Hugo to—"

"Yes, I understood that."

"—and partly to get a drink of ice water, which he does practically every night."

"Yes, I understood that, too."

For a few moments the Inspector was silent. He was still convinced that Janice was telling him the truth, but he was also convinced that something was still eluding him. Speaking even more hesitantly than he had before, he framed another question.

"Miss Lester, you referred to Mr. Neville, when you were speaking with me before, as 'a young relative.' I mentioned this—ah—slight ambiguity to your husband and he explained that Mr. Neville was a distant cousin—or so I understood him. In order to be quite sure I *had* understood, I mentioned the matter again to Mr. Neville, and his answer was also slightly ambiguous. He said, 'So I've always been told.' I could not help feeling from the way he spoke that for some reason he doubted the—shall we say, the complete accuracy?—of what he had been told. Do you know of any reason why he should?"

"Yes. And I think you do, too."

She turned her splendid eyes full upon him and he found himself unable to meet them, just as earlier in the night, he had found himself momentarily unable to meet Judith's. He waited, not only to give Janice breathing space; but to seek it himself.

"Evan Neville is your son?" he said at last.

"Yes, of course. You guessed that hours ago."

"Castle's son?"

"You guessed that, too."

"But Castle never knew it?"

"No."

"And how long has Evan Neville known it?"

"That I was his mother or that Baldwin Castle was his father?"

"I want answers to both those questions, of course."

"He has known I was his mother for about ten days. He has not known that Baldwin Castle was his father quite so long."

"And did something precipitate this knowledge?"

For the first time, Janice made no immediate reply, but looked away in her turn. Kirtland found it harder than ever to go on.

"I'm sorry if that question distresses you," he said. "But after all, when a secret has been successfully kept for more than twenty years, it does not often come to light, except in some fairly significant way."

"Do I have to answer?"

"No, but if you do not, I shall have to ask someone else, because I cannot help feeling very strongly that the answer may be important."

"You might ask Evan?"

"He would be the most natural person, under the circumstances, wouldn't he?"

"I suppose so. And in that case, I would rather tell you myself."

She was no longer sitting with her cheek supported by her fingers, but had clasped both hands in her lap, not lightly and elegantly, as Lady Laura had done, but closely and convulsively, as if at any moment she might wring them, should she lose control of herself. And when she spoke it was without eloquence, with pitiful repetitions, hurriedly, almost breathlessly, as if she must say what had to be said as quickly as possible and have done with it.

"In *Gold of Pleasure,* Evan plays the part of my stepson–a grown stepson with a young stepmother. He falls in love with her–in the play, I mean. He plays it wonderfully, so wonderfully that it doesn't seem like acting. It seems real. I mean, it seems real to the audience. It has from the beginning. And finally, it began to seem real to him. I mean, he began to imagine he was in love with me. At first, I just made fun of him. And then, one night after the curtain had gone down, he started making violent love to me. So I had to tell him. I mean, I had to tell him I was his mother."

The words ended in a long convulsive sob. Janice's hands were now so tightly clenched that the knuckles looked white, just as her husband's had, hours before, and her bright head was bent, so that Kirtland could no longer see her enormous black-ringed eyes. He was thankful for that, at least. He felt he could not have stood their gaze.

"I'm glad you told me yourself," he said, struggling to speak calmly. "Believe me, it is better that you should have done so than that I should have learned it otherwise. Now I have only two or three more questions to ask, and then you will be free to go. And I do not think these questions will seem painful to you, compared to that last one. When you told Evan Neville that you were his mother, what was his reaction? Was it one of horror?"

"No. Not–not as much as I should have expected. It was one of extreme anger."

"Against his unknown father?"

"No, against me."

"And so you tried to tell him the circumstances of your love affair, because, when you have thought of it at all, you have done so without anger or resentment and you hoped he might feel the same way?"

"Yes."

"With the result?"

"That he was angrier with me than ever, because I had not told Baldwin Castle I expected a child. Because he–Evan–had not been recognized as Castle's son, and given the advantages such recognition would have meant, instead of being brought up as an actor. It seems he's always hated being an actor–that he'll never forgive me for making him one."

Again the words ended in a sob, and this time Janice rose and turned her back on Kirtland, so that he would not see her face disfigured by weeping. He rose, too.

"That is all, Miss Lester. I am sorry, more sorry than

I can tell you, that I have caused you so much distress."

"It wouldn't matter how much distress you caused me, if I could only convince you that Evan couldn't possibly have meant or even wanted to kill Baldwin Castle."

"You have convinced me of that."

She wheeled around suddenly, no longer afraid to have him see her face, for now it was transfigured with joy.

"I have?"

"Yes–completely."

"And you believe the same thing about me?"

"I do."

"And about Hugo?"

"Yes."

"Then–"

"Then I think you had better go home and rest," he said, speaking with great compassion.

Sadly, Kirtland watched her out of sight. She was walking swiftly again now, her head, with its coronet of braids, held high. Her velvet robe swept out behind her in a sumptuous train. She had regained her regality, and she was a triumphant, not a tragic, queen. He shook his head and sighed, for, though he felt sure he had at last found the factor which had so long eluded him, the conviction brought him no gladness, not even the satisfaction of a difficult job well done. Then, with a rapidity equal to hers, he crossed to the bedroom where the men were waiting. Up to now, he had sent Griffin to summon them, one by one. This summons was his to give.

"I have just suggested to your wife that she should go home and rest," he said, addressing himself to Hugo. "I now suggest that you should go with her. I think it is most unlikely that I shall need either of you any more tonight–this morning, rather." He gazed in the direction of the wide window, which framed a scene in which the city lights were dim against the reluctant autumn dawn. "Suppose you leave this room by the door leading directly into the corridor and knock on the door leading from the corridor to the other bedroom" Kirtland went on. "I believe you will find Miss Lester ready and waiting. And I am sure you and she will wish to be together."

Hugo needed no second bidding. He leaped up and bolted in the direction indicated, flinging a hasty "good-by" over his shoulder. His departure occasioned a slight stir. Hilary and Jacques, who had been sitting near the window talking together, rose and came toward Kirtland. Joe, who had been writing busily at the ornate kidney-shaped desk, threw down his pen and looked up expectantly. Only Evan, who was seated by a reading lamp, seemed unaffected by Kirtland's presence in their midst and the announcement he had just made. To all appearances, he was still buried in his book.

"And now, Mr. Neville, if you will come with me, please."

Kirtland was obliged to repeat the request before Evan looked at him. Hilary and Jacques exchanged glances and Joe, though he picked up the pen he had tossed aside, did not begin to use it again, but regarded Kirtland with redoubled intentness. Only Evan continued to appear oblivious to what was happening.

"Mr. Neville–"

"Oh–were you speaking to me, Inspector? I was under the impression that I was dismissed with my–relatives. But, as I think you observed yourself, they doubtless wanted to be by themselves–such a devoted couple! So I thought I would sit here quietly and finish my chapter before I went 'home'–by which I suppose you mean our grim hotel. There is nothing about London at this season and this hour that tempts me to plunge headlong into the street."

"I did not dismiss you at the same time as Miss Lester and Mr. Alban. And I have told you twice now that I should like to have you come into the other room with me."

Evan rose slowly, still holding his book and with his finger marking the place where he had been interrupted. Then he bowed formally in the direction of Hilary,

Jacques and Joe, who acknowledged this salutation with noticeable brevity, and sauntered out of the room in Kirtland's wake. This time, the Inspector did not invite him to be seated.

CHAPTER XXI

"MR. NEVILLE," the Inspector said without preamble, "when I questioned you before, you made some reference to a lot of stuff about a big nothing. Remember?"

"Yes. That's the way it seemed to me then and that's the way it still seems to me."

"Well, you might feel the same definition applies to my next questions. Therefore, I must warn you that you are not obliged to say anything, but anything you say may be given in evidence."

Evan shrugged his shoulders. "All right by me," he said casually.

"Very well. Do you remember just when you and Miss Lester and Mr. Alban went to a garden party at Colonel de Valcourt's place in Chiswick?"

"About ten days ago."

"Quite so. And do you remember telling me you often went to Miss Lester's dressing room, merely to get a glass of ice water?"

"Sure I do."

"In fact, that was the only reason you started to go there when you heard some sort of an altercation going on between Miss Lester and Mr. Alban?"

"Yes."

"And you changed your mind and didn't go at all then?"

"Right again."

"But, if I understood Miss Lester correctly, you did go to her dressing room later in the evening."

"That's right. She asked both Hugo and me to come in to give Castle the glad hand–for the sake of appearances. She always does that when she has some male caller who insists on butting in. She's very careful of her reputation. 'Who steals my purse steals trash, but he that filches from me my good name,' etc."

"A very praiseworthy attitude. Now Miss Lester had also told me, and before you did, that she always kept a thermos of ice water in her dressing room, though she hadn't mentioned your habit of coming there to help yourself from it, when you couldn't get it served otherwise–a most natural habit, if I may say so, considering the American predilection for ice water. Nevertheless, she did tell me that as Mr. Castle was leaving, he stopped and helped himself to a drink–quite mechanically, almost subconsciously, because it is most unlikely that he would have been thirsty."

"Sounds reasonable to me."

"Entirely reasonable, in view of the predilection I've just mentioned. However, Miss Lester could not seem to recall whether you and Mr. Alban also helped yourselves to ice water–mechanically, almost subconsciously–as you were leaving the dressing room. In fact, she said she did not notice, because she was talking to Mr. Castle at the time."

"Right once more. She was."

"So she couldn't tell me. But perhaps you can."

"Tell you what?"

"I realize that I didn't put that very clearly, Mr. Neville. Suppose you begin by telling me whether you and Mr. Alban went out together."

"No, we're not great buddies."

"Did he go before you did?"

"Yes."

"And did he stop to take a drink at the little table by the door?"

"I don't think so. I wasn't noticing him particularly, any more than Miss Lester was."

"You were, perhaps, more interested in watching Mr. Castle and Miss Lester?"

"Well, it did strike me that Mr. Castle might be an interesting man—a good deal more interesting than Hugo. But he and Janice weren't saying anything particular to each other. At least they didn't as long as I stayed there."

"Perhaps you had the feeling that you were slightly in the way? I mean, that they might feel freer to talk about old times if they were by themselves?"

Evan shrugged his shoulders. Without pressing him for a reply to this, Kirtland asked another question.

"At all events, you did not stay long?"

"No."

"And when you went out did you take a drink of water?"

"Yes. I told you before that I was thirsty and, as you know, I didn't get my drink the first time I went to the dressing room."

"So you stopped for a moment by the little table near the door?"

"Naturally, since that is where the thermos and tumblers are always kept—another thing I've told you already."

"And when you stopped, you had your back to Miss Lester and Mr. Castle, didn't you?"

"Naturally, since I was on my way out of the room and not into it."

"And by this time I gather Miss Lester and Mr. Castle were more or less absorbed in conversation, since Miss Lester—to refer again to things which I've been told already—said she did not notice whether you took a drink or not."

"Then I suppose they must have been."

"And *I* suppose in that case, after you had taken a drink, unobserved, while you were standing for a moment by the little table near the door, you might have done something else—unobserved?"

"Such as—"

"Such as putting a very tiny tablet into a water glass."

Evan threw back his head and laughed.

"Really, Inspector! And where would I have secured this tiny tablet?"

"You would have secured cyanide from Colonel de Valcourt's greenhouse, when you visited it ten days ago, and you would have inserted it in a pellet, after hearing of the Colonel's ingenuity along those lines and having experimented with doing the same thing."

Evan laughed again. "And having shown all that ingenuity, I would then cap it with the extreme non-chalance of dropping such a tablet into the water glass from which my dear cousin habitually drank on the chance that her caller, whom I had never seen before and who was completely unknown to me, might drink out of it before she did?"

"There is nothing about this that suggests extreme nonchalance to me. I think you might have taken a chance—the very slim chance—that Mr. Castle, who could not possibly have been thirsty and who would, in all probability, pass by the little table without even noticing the thermos and the glasses, might drink from one of them first. But I think the little tablet was deliberately put there in the belief—I may say the hope—that Miss Lester might be the first one to pour herself a drink of water from the thermos habitually placed there by a faithful maid. I believe that you, Evan Neville, are responsible for attempted matricide and successful patricide. And I, therefore, arrest you for the murder of Baldwin Castle."

EPILOGUE

I

JOE AND JUDITH

As an active newspaperman, Joe had always taken his writing more or less in his stride; he had done an enormous amount of work, at lightning speed, and he had been able to go long hours without sleep, to eat irregularly and inadequately, to support sudden changes of climatic conditions and editorial policy–all without suffering either physically or mentally. The material he turned out, whatever the circumstances under which it was written, was uniformly accurate, timely and readable and, occasionally, extremely brilliant; and though his temper sometimes snapped under extreme pressure, he recovered his good nature almost as quickly as he lost it and, on the whole, was respectful to his employers, genial with his associates and helpful to the newcomers who had not yet learned the ropes which he knew so well. When his primary field of action shifted gradually from newspaper writing to magazine writing, he began to compose somewhat more slowly and carefully, but only with the result that his style gained in finish what it lacked in dash; and he still never missed a deadline or minded when, where and under what handicaps he wrote. He occasionally argued with his editors to prove a point about which he felt very strongly, and he nearly always won both the point itself and the more or less grudging admission that he had been right; he was more and more inclined to shut himself away from other writers, though this habit could easily be laid to his happy married life and his natural predilection for his home, his wife and his children. Essentially, he was altered very little, either in his own character or in the character of his work; it was only when he started his first novel that the picture changed completely.

He consented to remain in London until he had become acquainted with everyone who, in his opinion, could help him ferret out more facts about the dramatis personae of his story, particularly about Anne Hyde, who intrigued him more than any other. But he was enraged when he found that what seemed to be a promising source led only to a blind alley. A certain Mr. Singleton Cooling was highly recommended to him as one of the greatest living authorities on English history; however, when this eminent gentleman consented to receive him, Joe was rather abruptly informed that Mr. Cooling considered anyone later than the Plantagenets or—after them —earlier than the Windsors outside his scope. From then on, Joe refused to waste his time, as he put it, with so-called historians; instead, he haunted the British Museum, the Warburg Institite and other notable seats of information, and he bought reference books by the dozen, advertising for works that were out of print and paying exorbitant prices for many of them; but except when he was off on some hunt connected with his work, he remained stubbornly secluded in the sitting room of the service flat he and Judith had taken, strewing the table provided for their meals with his material and refusing, almost savagely, to have it disturbed. He was surly at interruptions from outsiders and short even with Judith when she attempted, however quietly and tactfully, to divert him from the furious flow of his work.

"No, I don't want to see anything of the beautiful English countryside," he told her, in response to her mild questioning. "No, I don't care whether I get to Dublin or Edinburgh at all. No, I don't want to run over to Paris for the week end. I've been sold short on those Castle articles, but I'm going to get something out of this trip, if it kills me."

"You'd probably come across some other subject just as good as the one about Castle, if you poked around a little. I never knew you to go out for a story yet and come up with nothing. And even if you're in a mood for suicide, I'd prefer to have you go on living."

Joe growled, without showing any signs of gratitude for this sentiment, and resumed his pounding on the typewriter.

"You've always said you'd like to see some of the Shakespearean plays that aren't given so often," Judith went on, undefeated. "There's a revival at the Old Vic of—"

"Oh, Ju, for Christ's sake! I would like to see them *sometime*! But have you known me all these years without finding out that I like to do first things first?"

"No. But I've seen you show a better sense of proportion in deciding which thing were first things."

She did not speak unpleasantly, but she left the room and, eventually, he realized that she had been gone for a long while, and that her absence constituted a lack. Even if he did not speak to her for hours, he liked to know she was there. Finally, he became concerned; it was not in character for her to go off like that and stay away, without a word of warning. Unable to write any more, he paced restlessly up and down the room, which was too small to allow much leeway for a man of his size, imagining all sorts of motor accidents and robberies. When at last he heard her key turning in the latch, he rushed out into the cold little corridor to meet her.

"Where in hell have you been all this time?" he inquired angrily.

Judith inserted a shilling into the meter by the front door, turned the knob which permitted the coin to sink noisily to the base of the box, where its presence would do some good, and laid a row of other shillings on top of the apparatus. "We had to have more of these if we were to get any heat," she said calmly, "and the porter's supply was exhausted, so I went to get some. Then, as I was out anyway, I thought I might as well see a little of London—I haven't seen much so far, you know. Now I've been for a walk through the park, I've spent an hour at the National Gallery, I've bought two dress lengths and some scarves at Liberty's, and I've had a cocktail at Claridge's. That isn't bad for a start, but after all, it's only a start. Perhaps you've forgotten I've never been here before and–"

"No, I hadn't forgotten, but perhaps *you* haven't noticed I've been pretty busy."

"Joe, I think we're beginning to get on each other's nerves, and it's the first time that's ever happened; so I think we'd better do something about it. I'm going out sight-seeing every day from now on and tomorrow I'm going to buy some theater tickets and make inquiries about reservations on the 'Golden Arrow.' If you don't want to go to the Old Vic or to Paris, maybe Althea would go with me. Anyway, I can ask her. When it comes to that, I don't much mind going alone, though, all things being equal, of course I'd rather have company —agreeable company. What I do mind is sitting here, day after day, doing nothing. I never was very good at that."

Joe growled again, but though he would not have been driven to admit it, he knew that Judith's attitude was justifiable and he was correspondingly remorseful. He went docilely to the theater the following evening and, without significant protest, to Paris a week later. But it was plain to Judith that his mind was on his book all the time he was away from the flat, and she did not raise the subject of interruptions again. She noticed, however, that Joe ceased to miss her when she went out herself. She had never needed to worry about a rival before; now she recognized one in Anne Hyde.

Only two topics served to divert Joe from his labors —that of De Valcourt's impending departure for Indo-China and that of Evan's trial. Until he realized that even his visits were regarded by Joe as an intrusion, Hilary had dropped in from time to time, and it was he who brought the news of Jacques's decision to ask for relief from his London post and reassignment in the Far East.

"I know you look on Jacques as more or less of a playboy," Hilary said earnestly. "I can see how you would. But he's really a good deal of a person. I've always known that he'd never consider this London appointment as anything more than an interlude—a breathing space—between real jobs. He's counting the days until his resignation can take effect."

"I don't suppose the announcement of Althea's engagement to you had anything to do with this noble decision," Joe said dryly.

"No, of course not," Hilary protested loyally. But he flushed as he spoke and, after a moment, he added, "Jacques was awfully hard hit, though—you're right there. He's just as crazy about Althea as I am and it must be awfully hard for him to stand by, knowing she's going to marry me in a few months, and that there's nothing he can do to stop it."

"Especially as he didn't regard you as a really serious rival. He was the one who had all the requisite qualifications."

"Except that Althea wasn't in love with him!"

"Ah, but that didn't count very heavily—against the château and the title and all the rest of it! I don't mean with Althea, I mean with her lady mother. And he thought Althea was pretty well under that lady mother's thumb. I thought so myself when I first saw them together. The way that girl shook off the shackles really was something."

"Yes, wasn't it?" Hilary flushed again and beamed with pride. "But I do wish you'd be fair to Jacques, Joe. It isn't like you—"

"Not to give the devil his due? All right, I'll try to. Especially when I hear he's really prepared to make the supreme sacrifice."

"Joe, you shouldn't say such things, even in jest."

It was Judith who spoke this time; and when Joe turned back toward his littered table, indicating unmistakably that he wanted to stop talking about De Valcourt and get back to work, she went to the front door with their caller and continued to talk with him, in a lowered voice.

"Joe's bark is ever so much worse than his bite, Hilary. Tonight, when he gets to what he calls a 'good stopping place' or is too bushed to write another word, he'll bring up the subject of Jacques on his own initiative and do it understandingly, too. This book has him down, though. I've never known him to act this way before. I thought when he got the letter from Brooks and Bernstein, saying they liked the first three chapters and the outline immensely, that afterward he'd take things easier. Up to then, he didn't feel too sure he was equal to novel technique. But the letter only acted as a spur. Now that Joe's convinced he *can* write a novel, he wants to find out how fast he can write it. I suppose it's a hang-over from the days when he wanted to get out spot news in record time."

"Well, probably it is," Hilary agreed pleasantly.

"And then, of course he's terribly troubled about Evan's trial. He doesn't mention it much, but I know he is. Not on Evan's account; on Janice's. He's afraid she'll break under it."

"Well, I can understand that feeling, too. Her courage has been simply phenomenal. It's all very well to talk about the theater tradition that the show must go on and take it for granted for a night or two; but Janice has gone on for weeks, and I'm afraid she can stand just so much, especially playing every performance opposite Evan's understudy."

Neither spoke again instantly. Following Evan's arrest, he had been taken to the Bow Street police station, where Inspector Kirtland had acquainted the Charge Officer with that night's events. A charge of murder had been formulated and read to Evan, who had stubbornly refused to say anything and had, thereupon, been led away to a cell. By the time, later the same morning, that he had been brought before the Bow Street magistrate, Janice and Hugo had persuaded the famous Sir Reginald Larson to represent Evan. Sir Reginald and the Crown had joined in requesting a preliminary remand, and later a second one, as both needed time for investigation and preparation. Now, the actual trial was due in a few days. Judith sighed and then smiled.

"Maybe if she can stand the play, Janice can stand

the trial," she suggested, trying to inject some optimism.

"Especially with the psychiatric help of our good friend, Dr. Clayspoon," returned Hilary.

"I hope so," said Judith, "but it's all you can do to persuade one of these experts on mental cases to make a positive statement about anything."

Hilary chuckled. "We'll have trouble enough," he predicted, "being positive ourselves, once we're on the witness stand. And this applies to smooth-spoken Jack just as much as it does to outspoken Joe. In fact, Ahani's the only one who isn't in trouble—at the moment! He certainly succeeded in working diplomatic immunity for all it's worth."

When the trial was over, the verdict was still in doubt. At nine in the evening, the jury was still out. Hilary had returned to the Chancery, to attack his interrupted tasks; Jacques had gone to a dinner given at the Marlborough Club by one of its highly titled members; Cornelia had taken the advice of her physician in regard to early bedtime; and Lady Laura and Althea, after a pick-up supper, had needed no medical advice to follow her example; Hugo and Janice, as usual, had persevered in going to the theater. Joe and Judith took refuge in a Pilgrim Restaurant for fish, tea and toast.

"You have to hand it to these people," observed Joe, spreading jam on his toast, "they certainly have a more mature attitude in court than we do. Can you imagine a judge in the States excluding evidence without any objection having been made, just flicking his nose with his handkerchief and saying, 'Oh, come, now, it won't do, you know; it just won't do'?"

"No, I can't," answered Judith, "but I don't think it's very 'mature' to stick to the same old rules on insanity that somebody dreamed up more than a century ago."

"They weren't dreamed up, dear. The Judges laid them down for the Lords in McNaghten's Case—if I heard right."

"They laid them down all right, and they've stayed there ever since. Wouldn't you think these people would wake up to modern psychiatry?"

"The psychiatrists are wide awake—it's the law that has stayed put, and won't recognize the 'irresistible impulse' doctrine I guess they use in some of the states, at least. But you couldn't ask for anybody more modern than Dr. Clayspoon with his manic depressives."

"Yes, I could, Joe. He's a great man, no doubt, and I hand it to him for digging out of Hugo the fact that those so-called 'rest cures' Evan took from time to time were actually treatments at sanatoria. But I'm afraid he confused the jury by using too many technical words. Why did he have to say it was *not* paranoia, and that the Oedipus complex which Evan might have had earlier was unresolved, and a lot more stuff I can't remember myself, before he got around to saying Evan was a manic depressive. Why didn't he just say what the trouble was, as clearly as that?"

"Well, the Attorney-General did try to restrict him, as you suggest; but maybe it impresses a jury to hear that kind of talk. Maybe it takes care of some half-baked idea that some juryman may have about such things. Once Dr. Clayspoon had more or less surveyed the possibilities, he had a better foundation for showing that Evan really was in such an emotional state that he didn't know what he was doing. It *was* erratic of Evan, to say the least, as Clayspoon pointed out, to put that pill in the glass and just hope his 'object of hate' would be the one who'd drink out of it, and not somebody else—or that no one would."

Judith sipped her tea, looking cautiously at the people at nearby tables, to see if any were trying to overhear. None appeared to be eavesdropping, but she lowered her voice.

"For my part, I like the prison doctor," she said. "He was a good sport, and I think the Crown was none too pleased with the way he agreed that Evan's conduct while he was being held for trial was far from normal and was at least consistent with a severe depression. But I think his talk about the difference between neurosis and psychosis must have been baffling to some members of the jury."

"Perhaps it was, dear; perhaps. But if all anybody did was get across the idea that Evan was in a fog, McNaghten or no McNaghten, Evan has a chance—and if the jury convicts him, the Home Secretary might have him reprieved."

The jury's verdict of "Guilty but Insane" was brought in so early the next morning that only Joe and Judith, Hugo and Janice, among the former witnesses, were in the courtroom at the time. They were all seated together, and, despite the general commotion, Janice remained perfectly still, staring into space, for some moments. She did not look at Evan, still standing in the prisoner's dock, or return the pressure of Hugo's hand. At first she did not even seem to hear the Judge when he ordered that the prisoner should be kept in custody as a Broadmoor patient until His Majesty's pleasure should be known. It was not until her son had been led away, and the courtroom was nearly empty, that she turned to her husband and whispered, "What is Broadmoor?"

"The institution maintained by the British Government for patients who are—criminally insane."

"Is that what the verdict of 'Guilty but Insane' really means?"

"I guess so."

"But whatever happens, they won't hang him?"

"No, lover."

She drew a deep breath. "Let's go home and get some rest," she said. "We'll need it, before the matinee."

It did not seem to occur to her that she should say anything to Joe and Judith and they did not try to force themselves upon her consciousness, nor did they speak to each other until they were out in the street again. Then Judith asked one question.

"There isn't any reason now, is there, why we shouldn't go home for Christmas?"

"There doesn't seem to be," Joe answered. "I can finish the book all right in New Orleans."

II

CORNELIA

EVERYTHING TURNED OUT exactly as Cornelia had hoped it would—well, not *exactly* as she had hoped, but that was only because it was better . . . .

It began that way the very first afternoon. She was driving quietly along, taking in everything she saw—the greatly improved highways, the herds of cattle so much larger than she remembered, the one-storied houses so much smaller and so much farther apart—when she saw a boy trudging along on the road in front of her. He was bareheaded, with thick tousled light hair, and he was wearing blue jeans and a red sweater, like most of the boys and many of the girls she had seen. Though his clothes were somewhat dingier than the majority, the difference was not really noticeable; apparently, during her absence from American rural regions, blue jeans and red sweaters had become a species of national uniform among teen-agers in the country, the well to do and the poverty stricken alike. The boy was carrying a big bundle of books, tied together with a leather strap, which was considerably the worse for wear; and he seemed to be having some difficulty with this bundle because, though occasionally he shifted it from one arm to another, he shifted it quickly back from the right arm to the left one; obviously, that was the stronger of the two and yet not strong enough to support such a burden indefinitely. He turned, as the car drew close to him, and looked at it appraisingly and approvingly; then, as it slowed down to a stop, he glanced up at the driver with a smile that disclosed even white teeth between lips that parted generously. His eyes were very blue, and there were a few freckles on his nose, which was his most nondescript feature; but even the least partial observer would have pronounced him an unusually attractive boy. He did not jerk a thumb upward, in the manner that was becoming increasingly familiar to Cornelia, or mumble something about wanting a ride the worst way. He only said, "Hi!" grinning more broadly than ever. Then he added admiringly, "That's a mighty fine car you've got there, ma'am."

"Well, I like it," Cornelia admitted. "I hesitated for a while between a Nash and a Pontiac, but I finally decided on the Nash."

"You couldn't go wrong on that," the boy told her approvingly. "This is the new model that's just out, isn't it?"

"Yes. I've never had a car of my own before, so buying it–I mean making the choice–was quite a responsibility."

"You've never . . . . Oh, I suppose your husband's always picked them out for you before."

He was looking her over now, not rudely, not with the effect of staring, but nevertheless with a surprise he could not wholly conceal and–she was pleased and proud to realize–with the same degree of admiration that he had viewed the car. Obviously, he was astonished because a lady like her, wearing such fine store clothes, should never have had a car of her own–until he figured that her husband had selected her cars for her. But it was also plain that he liked her looks: the beautifully cut black broadcloth coat, with its collar and cuffs of black Persian lamb; the small black veiled hat, which obviously was meant to go with the coat, since it was trimmed with Persian lamb, too; the black suède gloves, loose enough to allow easy play for the fingers, but buttoned closely and neatly around the wrists. And it was not just her clothes, either, or the way she wore them that he liked; he would have no idea, of course, how expensive they were or how well suited to her. He would only know that she looked "nice" in them; and he was thinking that she was pretty and pleasant and friendly and easy to talk to, that it would be fun to have a ride with her in her nice new car . . . .

"Couldn't I give you a lift?" she asked, as he had

hoped she would. "We seem to be going the same way."

"Well, that's mighty kind of you. I've got a motor bike; usually I don't have to hoof it. But the bike's in the repair shop right now. I bought it secondhand, and I reckon, before I got it, it hadn't had the kind of care I give it. You sure I wouldn't put you out any? I'm heading for Sam Martin's farm. I'm his son Barney."

She had known it, she had known it from the first instant she looked at him, and her heart was so overflowing with gladness that it was all she could do to keep her eyes from overflowing, also. For this was not only Sam Martin's son; it was Cornelia Castle's son, too. Everything about him proclaimed this: the tousled head of hair was exactly the same color hers had been at the same age; that smile was the same that had helped to win her the first little part in a chorus and, years afterward, to decide hesitant customers that a thousand dollars was not too much to pay for a dress after all; those blue eyes were the same whose sparkle had caused Sam Martin to cast aside his strait-laced principles for a while and Herb Styles to try the lure of liquor and Baldwin Castle to forget his age and his importance. They were eyes that could be too bright for their own good, but they were honest eyes; and the only difference Cornelia could see between those now meeting hers, and the ones she had seen reflected so many times in her own mirror and in the gaze of captivated men, was that their shining quality came more from an illuminated mind and less from a primitive urge to attract. And for this difference she was duly thankful.

"Why, climb right in, Barney," she said, struggling to keep her voice steady, and succeeding surprisingly well. "I'm on my way to Abby Blaker's. That's just beyond the Martin farm, isn't it?"

"Yes, the next place. You're not a stranger here then, ma'am? I don't seem to remember—"

"It's more than fifteen years since I've been here—well, to be exact, nearly seventeen. So of course you couldn't remember. You're not much more than that, are you?"

"I'll be eighteen, come May."

Yes, that was it, May. Barney had been born in May, on an unseasonably cold, blustery night; and though Cornelia had been young and strong, it had been a hard birth, for there had been only an ignorant midwife to see her through, though Sam had helped as much as he could; the overworked general practitioner, who served the entire region, had been out of reach until it was too late for him to do any good. This coming May everything would be different: Cornelia could go to a good hospital, if she wanted to, though, all things being equal, she'd rather stay at Abby's—provided, of course, that Abby didn't mind; and, in any case, there would be a competent physician in readiness and a competent professional nurse. Besides, Judith had said that if everything were all right at home, she would gladly come over for a few days—New Orleans was really no distance away, the plane service was so good. Cornelia would rather have Judith with her than anyone else in the world—except, of course, Sam and Barney. And it wouldn't be fair to ask Sam to stay with her even—well, even if things went on turning out the way she'd hoped. This new baby wasn't his. And Barney was too young for anything like that yet. Though she supposed, living on a farm, he'd seen animals. . . .

"You've got quite a walk to school, haven't you, Barney?" she inquired, resolutely closing her mind to May and concentrating on December. She had told herself sensibly, right along, that this was one of those situations that you had to cover a step at a time, and she didn't mean to forget it. "You must miss your motor bike when you don't have it. Do you think the repairs will take long?"

"No, just a couple of days, most likely. And there's a school bus. I didn't take it going home tonight, because I stopped at the garage to see if I couldn't hurry things up. I do need that bike for my paper route."

"Your paper route!"

"Yes, I've got one that brings me in twenty-four dollars a month, cash money; prizes, too, for getting new subscribers. I told Miss Abby, when she loaned me enough to snatch up the bike at a bargain, before anyone else could, that I'd be able to pay her back, out of the paper route, so quick she'd never miss the money. I did, too."

"So you and Miss Abby are friends?"

"I'll say we are. Of course, she didn't loan me all the money I needed to buy the bike. She isn't the sort that would do that. She's kind, but she's cautious, too, and she only likes to help people who help themselves. She knew I was trying to do that. We're passing the field right now where I earned my first cash money, picking cotton in September and October, three years ago. Maybe you remember, seeing that you've been here before—school lets out early those months, a-purpose so it's not just the older ones can help get in the crop."

"Yes, I remember."

"Well, *I* remember the first day my pick came to more than a hundred pounds and I got paid three dollars and eighty-five cents come nightfall. Of course, that was a Saturday. I hadn't picked just from midday; I'd begun from soon in the morning. That three eighty-five started the fund for my bike."

"And then it kept on growing?"

"Yes. See that looping line of trees over yonder? They're on the edge of Shawnee Creek. And Shawnee Creek's full of carp. My dad taught me how to make dough bait out of flour and corn meal and loose cotton and just a bit of sugar. Then he started me fishing. I sold all the fish I could catch and it wasn't hard to catch 'em—carp are fat and slow moving. I got five cents a pound for them. And this came in mighty handy, because the best fishing's when there isn't any cotton to pick. Just the same, I never could have got enough out of fishing and cotton picking to get that bike when the getting was good, if it hadn't been for Miss Abby." Barney paused and, for the first time, showed signs of embarrassment. "I don't know how I come to be telling you all this, ma'am," he said, apologetically. "You haven't got any cause to be interested in how I make money or whether I do make any or not."

"But I *am* interested! And I asked you questions—I'd like to ask you a lot more . . . but I'll have to ask them some other time, I guess," she added, bringing the car to a stop. "This is your place, isn't it?"

"Why, yes, ma'am, it is." Surprise had now supplanted embarrassment in his voice: surprise because it was evident to him that this nice lady, driving around in her nice car, really was interested in a boy who was a total stranger to her; and surprised that she should have known where he lived, without being told. "Don't bother to turn in," he said, climbing hastily out of the car and slinging his books into the crook of his left arm. "The road's rough and there isn't much room to turn around. Thanks a lot for the ride. I hope I see you again sometime, and I reckon I will, if you're going to be staying with Miss Abby. I visit her myself, real often. So long!"

"So long!" Cornelia called back.

She started the car again, because Barney might have wondered why, if she didn't, but, by keeping in low gear, she managed to watch him out of sight, to see how well built he was, and how tall. It was not only her vivid coloring and the sparkle in her eyes that he had inherited; it was a virile version of her fine figure and easy carriage, a shapely head above wide shoulders, narrow hips above long straight legs. The sleeve of the shabby sweater effectually concealed the shrinkage in girth of the right arm, and it was as long as the other; moreover, the right hand was in no way deformed. Again, Cornelia's heart swelled with pride and this time she did not have to set herself the difficult task of keeping her eyes from overflowing. But her vision was not so much blurred that she failed to take in the bedraggled appearance of the buildings before her: the peeling paint, the sagging doorsteps, the missing blinds, the broken windowpanes, the doors half off their hinges, the general betrayal of both insufficient care and insufficient funds. She did not mind the barns so much. They were often a sorry sight, thereabouts. But the house! Of course she knew that it had been run up by the village carpenter, who had never seen anything more tasteful and commodious himself, and who could not benefit by the advice of someone who had. Of course she knew that the space underneath it, between the short ugly brick posts which supported it and raised it above the ground just enough to keep out the dampness, was inevitably the dumping ground for every sort of rusty utensil and miscellaneous rubbish. But still . . . it could have been reasonably trim, it could have looked cosy and comfortable, as if a hard-working, contented family lived there. In fact, it *had.* Well, it would look that way again—or not that house, maybe, but the one she would have built and used in its stead. Nothing pretentious, nothing oversized, nothing out of keeping with the tone of the countryside; just a one-story house, like all the others, but a *good* one, in the modern ranch style. It would be better than Abby's, which was the best around there, so far; but it wouldn't have a parlor, like Abby's, with Nottingham lace curtains and an upright piano, and a marble-topped center table, surrounded with black walnut rocking chairs—a parlor that was closed most of the time. It would have a big living room with a fireplace and a picture window and lots of bookcases and television and a radio—that really was lived in by the whole family. It would have a gun room especially for the men, and that would have a fireplace in it, too, and maybe more bookcases and an extra radio. It would have a kitchen with all the latest gadgets and a utility room besides, and they would both be as bright and cheerful as any other room in the house —the deep freeze and the electric dishwasher and the ironer would all harmonize, and there would be frilled yellow curtains at the windows and yellow bowls on the shelves, and the snack bar would be painted yellow. And the bedrooms—at least three, maybe four—would have adjoining bathrooms, complete with showers, and a different color scheme for each. And there would be a big linen closet and big clothes closets and the loft upstairs would be finished off for a rumpus room. . . .

She was still visualizing all this, when the sagging door of Sam's kitchen creaked and then slammed, and Barney disappeared, calling out a greeting to someone whom Cornelia could not see, but who, she felt quite sure, must be Sam. She shifted gears and went speedily on to Abby's, where she was engulfed in a warm welcome. Abby had made quite an occasion of her arrival: the parlor had been opened up and the gas heater there turned on; the table had been laid in the dining room —which was furnished in quartered golden oak, exactly as it had been when Cornelia last saw it—instead of in the kitchen, which was also still the same as it had been fifteen years earlier—no more convenient, no more attractive. Abby had got in Neb, one of the Negro women from the settlement across the tracks, to serve supper; and a yellow-legged rooster had been killed, so there was fricassee with rice, instead of just pork and white beans. Cornelia appreciated all these outward and visible signs of unvoiced affection, for she knew what they represented; but it made her happier still that after supper had been cleared away, Abby was willing to draw up two of the rocking chairs nearer the marble-topped center table and discuss hopes and plans, ways and means, instead of urging Cornelia to go straight to bed and conserve her strength, like that doctor in London.

"You did have good luck, running into Barney, straight off, that way," she agreed. "And like as not, he'll be over here, tomorrow or the next day—he's kind of got the habit of visiting me. Probably he'll tell Sam about the lift you gave him, because he was interested in the car and all; but Sam hasn't got the least notion you was coming home—at any rate, I don't think he has. I haven't said a word to a living soul about it and I don't know who else could. So I don't know how Sam could see any connection between his former wife, come back where she belongs, and the prosperous-looking lady that gave Barney a lift. But you know how news spreads around here. Neb will be telling everyone over at the settlement that I got company, and even if she didn't hear the 'Castle' part, she must have heard me calling you Cornelia; so, presently, everyone will be putting two and two together, and it won't be long before the word gets to Sam. If it did, he might try to keep the boy at home. So, before he has a chance to interfere, I'd start paving the way to let Barney know who you are, whenever the right moment comes. I think if you go about it the proper way, Sam'll have hard work to stop Barney coming to see you whenever the boy's in the mood."

Cornelia lost no time in acting on Abby's advice. True to this faithful friend's prediction, Barney turned up late the following afternoon, driving a dilapidated jalopy, which, it appeared, he had borrowed from the mechanic who had not yet succeeded in getting the motor bike into running order. He sat down sociably in the kitchen, accepted the milk and cookies that Abby offered him and settled himself for a leisurely visit. It did not seem to occur to him to go into the parlor, though this was still open and warm, or even into the dining room, where the cloth was still laid; and neither Cornelia nor Abby liked to suggest this, for fear of upsetting the calm pattern of his customary routine. So Abby muttered something about seeing to a calf and, declining Barney's prompt offer to help, left the mother and son together. Cornelia promptly took advantage of the opportunity so offered.

"I'm ever so glad you dropped in," she said. "You know, I told you yesterday I was very much interested in everything you'd been telling me and that I'd like to ask you some more questions. That is, if you wouldn't mind, when we've been acquainted such a short while."

"No, of course not. Shoot!"

"You said you earned twenty-four dollars a month, besides prizes, on your paper route, and before that, you told me you saved what you earned from picking cotton and from fishing carp to get your bike. I couldn't help wondering whether you were saving the paper money to get something else and, if you were, what it was."

For the first time, Barney flushed and hesitated. "No, I'm not saving it," he said at last. "But I'd like to."

"Then why—"

"Well, ma'am, it's this way: I go out cotton picking on any plantation where they need an extra hand. That's all right. Most of my gang does the same. But when it comes to older men, mostly it's those who don't own their farms who do that. And my dad's managed to hang onto his, so far, by selling his hay crop, and working in other people's dairies. But he couldn't have hung on much longer–not and paid his taxes and the interest on the mortgage when they're due. So my paper money goes to help with those. He's had a lot of hard luck and I don't want him to be shamed when he's hung on this long. It's more important he should be easy in his mind than that I should be saving."

"I think you're right. Just the same, if I'm not too curious, I'd like to know what you'd be saving for."

"I'd like to go to college in the *worst* way."

"Then why shouldn't you? After all, there must be scholarships a boy like you could get, even if your money savings are used to help out your father."

Barney shrugged his right shoulder and nodded his head toward the weak arm, smiling ruefully.

"The only scholarships they give for full free are the ones to the Military Academy at Claremore, and you got to pass a physical examination before they'll take you at that place."

"There are no scholarships to the State University or the agricultural colleges?"

"Just working scholarships for fifty cents an hour; and if I take one of those my dad won't have what I might make doing day-work and running my paper route here. That'd be nearabout the same thing as using my savings for agricultural college instead of helping him."

"And you'd be satisfied to go to an agricultural college? You think you want to be a farmer?"

Again Barney flushed and hesitated. "I'm not sure. I'm not satisfied with things the way they are now. But I don't believe that's a sign I mightn't like farming if it could be done right. And maybe it could–well, if I learned *how*, better than I have so far. Anyway, I'd like a chance to find out."

Isn't that just what I told Judith, Cornelia said to herself. Aloud, she remarked, hesitating a little in her turn, "So you'd like to go to Norman and then give what you learned there a trial? That's what you'd do, if you had the money?"

"Yes, and if I could be sure everything was all right with Dad. I told you he'd had hard luck. But it wasn't just with the farm, like you might have thought. It was with me. I'm not as much help to him as I could be if I hadn't had polio. You wouldn't have noticed, but my right arm—" With a sudden gesture, he pushed up the right sleeve of his sweater, revealing the withered member in all its ugliness and then, as quickly, pulled the sweater into place again. "And that isn't all. He doesn't have a wife to help him, either. I haven't any mother."

Oh, but you have, Barney, you have! Again it was all she could do to keep from voicing the cry that rose from her heart. But somehow she bit back the words. She must not risk failure now, by giving this long-lost son, at last miraculously near recovery, a surprise so sudden that it would be a shock. Unconsciously, Barney helped her by going on before she made a potentially fatal mistake.

"She isn't dead. That is, I don't think she is. I think if she was, Dad would have heard and would have said something about it. Maybe married again. But she left him—when I was just a baby."

"Left him?"

"Yes, that's all he's ever said. Of course, I've heard stories about it from other people—you know how those things are. Abby's told me one kind of a story and my grandmother—Dad's mother—has told me another and the kids at school—"

"Why don't you ask your father to tell you his story? Whether his wife wanted to leave him or whether he wanted to have her? If she wanted to leave him, why? If he wanted her to leave him, why?"

"Well, I've heard enough from other people to know it was him who wanted her to leave—and why. I don't know as it would prove anything to ask him questions. He doesn't want to talk about it. If he had, he'd have done it, before now."

"Ask him this much anyway: Didn't your mother ever

tell him she was sorry for what she'd done? Didn't she ever beg him to give her one more chance? Didn't she say she wanted more than anything in the world to come back?"

This time Cornelia could not keep the surge of longing that sprang from her heart out of her voice. And when she had said this much, she neither knew nor cared what would happen if she said more.

"Ask him and then come back and ask me. Maybe this'll be another time when you'll hear different stories from different people!"

After he had left, rather abruptly, and looking both startled and bewildered, she was terrified. Abby, coming in from the barn, where she had thoughtfully lingered until she heard the jalopy taking its noisy departure, found Cornelia sitting at the kitchen table with her head buried in her arms and shaking with sobs. Abby stood over her, putting a steadying hand on the quivering shoulder.

"Don't you start worrying now," she said consolingly and sensibly. "In the first place, it won't do any good. What's going to be is going to be. But, in my opinion, it's going to be all right. Barney'll do just what you told him to, if I know him—and I think I do, pretty well. And Sam will be cornered. By this time, he's sure to have found out I have a visitor, and I wouldn't put it past him to have found out who the visitor is. If he tells Barney the story as if he was the Almighty, qualified to pass judgment on the sins of others, acting stern and storming while he does it, then it's likely to be a boomerang. And if he tells it in a way that's even halfway fair and forgiving, Barney'll see you have a side, right off. Either way, you'll have him with you, or I miss my guess.

"I ain't superstitious," she went on after a moment, giving a reassuring pat on the shoulder, which was now not shaking quite so much. "And I ain't pious, either—at least, not the way Sam is. Just the same, sometimes I think there's a kind of pattern and it don't seem to me impossible that there's answers to prayers. Maybe 'God moves in a mysterious way, His wonders to perform,' like it says in the old hymn. I don't know as it matters much which way you say it. I reckon you know what I'm driving at. Anyway, I don't think it was just an accident that you met Barney on the road and that he wasn't on his bike that day, so that it come natural for you to give him a lift. I don't think it was an accident that you and he took to each other right away and that he come back here to see you, more'n he come to see me, of his own free will. I think it had to do with some will a sight more powerful than yours or his—or mine. Of course, he's in for a surprise and a shock, like you say. But he can take it. He's taken a good deal already—as much as his father has, if you ask me. As much as you have, Cornelia. It ain't easy for a boy to grow up the way he has, in a ramshackle place that's getting more rundown every year, and be half crippled and not have any mother."

Cornelia began to sob again, more violently this time. Abby stopped patting her shoulder and sat down beside her.

"You listen to me now, Cornelia Castle," she said. "You listen *good*. Barney may not come over again for a day or two, if it takes him time to get over the shock and think things through. But when he does come, it'll be of his own free will again—because he wants to come. He may not see everything just the way you do, but that won't matter—he won't see everything the way his father does, either. He'll see things his own way and it won't be a bad way. I don't know a young one that sees things any straighter than Barney does or that is any straighter. If there'd been anyone like him hereabouts when I was growing up, maybe I wouldn't be a sour, old maid today."

"You're not a sour old maid," Cornelia lifted her head to protest. "You're just the best and the kindest and the—"

"Now, now, don't let your tongue run away with you, Cornelia. You go on listening to me. Barney'll be back and you and he'll get to be good friends—why, you're good friends already, when it comes to that! Friendship isn't always a matter of time. It can come fast or slow or not at all, just as things happen, or according to God's will. And presently, you'll tell Barney about the new house and the new barns you're planning to build on my land right where it adjoins his father's. You needn't tell him you hope to see the day he and his father'll be living in that house with you and looking after the cattle in those barns, and that the ramshackle old place where they're living now will be torn down, so there'll be one less eyesore on the road. And before you get to showing it, I'd tell him you're going to have a baby. I don't believe you'll need to remind him that baby'll be his brother—he'll think of that himself after a while anyway, and neither of you'll ever need to say anything about it's being a half brother. That part isn't important. The baby's father's dead, and for all he'll ever know, Sam'll be the same as his father, if things work out the way you hope they will."

"It may be a half sister," Cornelia said, wiping her eyes, which were now nearly dry anyway.

"That part ain't important, either. What's important is that there's going to be a new *family,* living in a new house, a new way—that there's going to be a fresh start all the way around. Sam can't hold out forever, not with Barney against him—as Barney's going to be. And after you and Sam are remarried, and living in that new house with the new baby, and Barney's coming home from Norman for his vacations, Sam and Barney will both be so happy they won't think about being beholden to you for money. They'll be beholden to you for so many other things going into making that fresh start, one won't matter more than another."

"What's that noise?" Cornelia asked suddenly, springing to her feet.

"My land! It sounds like Barney's bike! It must have got mended and been brought back to the farm after all. If it hadn't been, I don't see how he could have got here so quick."

"What does that matter? What matters is that Barney's back!"

The words were hardly out of her mouth before the

kitchen door was flung open and Barney came into the room. He closed the door to keep out the chill air and then he stood in front of it, looking at Cornelia, but not advancing toward her or, apparently, expecting her to advance toward him. But the two pairs of blue eyes gazed into each other steadily, with mutual understanding and affection; and eventually Barney took the one step forward that made it easy for Cornelia to take one, too, and spoke the words that made it easy for her to say everything that should come next.

"I asked Dad what you told me to," Barney said, "and he answered all my questions. He said yes, his wife had told him she was sorry for what she'd done; yes, she did beg him to give her one more chance; yes, she did say it would mean more to her than anything else in the world if he'd take her back. And then he told me two things without my asking: he told me his wife never wanted to go off and leave her baby and that he knew he'd done wrong to harden his heart against her all these years. And finally, he said he'd been punished for it and that that was what he knew he deserved. He didn't say any of this because he thought he knew who'd come to visit Miss Abby and wanted to get word to you in a roundabout way. He said it because he wanted to unburden himself of something that had bothered him a long time. He'd heard Miss Abby had a visitor, and that was all. It didn't even interest him. But I think I know who you are. So now I've come back to tell you what he said. And you don't need to tell me anything unless you want to, ma'am–I mean, Mother."

III

DE VALCOURT

THE HEAT OF a moonless tropic night bore down upon the blacked-out command post with almost physical weight. Haiphong was somewhere to the east, Laos across the tumbled mountains to the west. Between them, ever growing in extent, lay the territory fallen to Viet Minh arms. There was just enough starlight to show the airstrip as a less ponderable black than the pervading darkness. The dispersal bays where the helicopters and transports waited were hidden by tall canes of Tonkin bamboo. Their polished nodes clattered woodenly against one another with every vagrant puff of wind. By contrast, the rustle of knife-bladed elephant grass was a metallic tinkle.

Within the command post, Colonel de Valcourt, wearing half-sleeved tunic, shorts and a fatigue cap, rakishly tilted upon his tumbled black hair, addressed a group of officers gathered in close attention about a map.

"You understand what it is that confronts us," he said, tapping a long, slim forefinger upon the outspread paper. "It is of the essence that the Ve-Quoc and Tuh-Ve and their bandit allies be checked from raiding the rice bowl in the western mountain valleys. For the last seven years they have waited each summer for the grain to ripen. Then they have swooped out of the hills upon those still loyal to us, and have harvested the crop in their own particular fashion."

Heavy drops of perspiration, falling from his brow, spattered down upon the open map. He brushed the moisture from his forehead with an impatient gesture.

"To halt these enemies, we must have an airstrip somewhere within the territory they control. General Navarre and his staff have selected a point near the Laos border for this operation. Our Regiment–and more specifically our battalion–has been honored. We are to lead the way in!"

An inarticulate murmur rumbled through the oppressive little room. De Valcourt nodded as though it had been put into clear words.

"I know, I know," he agreed. "But there is no other way. The Yankees demonstrated it when they were leapfrogging along the island chains of the Pacific. One airstrip, well held, on a single island, could immobilize an entire hostile archipelago."

"True enough, Colonel," a swarthy, heavily mustached major broke in. "But they had clouds of airplanes, oceans of essence and mountains of bombs at their disposal. What have we?"

"We have French soldiers," De Valcourt replied quietly.

"With a few airplanes and old patched parachutes," the Major retorted obstinately. "Instead of descending upon the rebels in a swarm like locusts from the sky, we must make five or six drops, each with but a battalion or two, which the enemy can cut up before the next reinforcements arrive."

"What do you demand of combat, Jeannot? The *guerre en dentelles* of our ancestors, and the one some of those journalists and politicians prattle about at home, as though a lace-trimmed war were always the portion of France's soldiers? Have you forgotten the taxicab army that left Paris for the Marne in 1918? And the message from Foch: 'My center is giving way, my right is pushed back—excellent! I'll attack.' It is true our supplies are scanty, our parachutes old and worn, our transport infirm—so, *bien*! We shall attack!"

A deep-voiced chorus of approval greeted the declaration. The group broke up in a mood of exhilaration. France had been on the defensive, engaged in a holding action and without too much success. Now the *Corps Expéditionnaire Français Extrême-Orient* was about to attack. And the Colonel would show the enemy what a lace-trimmed war could be like. A man well salted, the Colonel . . . . Some of his fellow officers tried earnestly to dissuade him from leading the first drop. His place was aloft, they assured him, watching the progress of operations and directing their further course as he saw the action develop beneath him. He brushed the objection aside.

"A leader leads. Otherwise, he isn't a leader, but a follower. I will make the drop that is to trigger the assault."

Eventually it was decided that since they would number not more than a dozen, his group would take one of the smaller transports. The large planes were not to follow until this cadre signaled what the ground situation was. With one exception, he had chosen personally those who were to companion him in the venture: young Antoine Magniard had volunteered of his own accord—an eighteen-year-old *sous-lieutenant,* heir to one of Burgundy's fabulous vineyards, slim as an arrow and, under proper direction, just as deadly.

Others in the select patrol included De Catinat, who had graduated as little more than a boy from the rum fleets off St.-Pierre et Miquelon during the American insanity of prohibition. He could crack a foe's neck with as little compunction as another man might swat a fly. Then there was Meyer, who had been De Valcourt's orderly in Martinique; Girardeau, the bearded scholar who, beyond question, would one day have been elevated to the Academy as a historian of world-wide renown had he not embezzled funds to retain the favor of a blowzy trollop he should have sent back to the sewers that spawned her; Audusson, the cleverly gifted little stonecutter from somewhere in the Ardennes.

De Valcourt had hesitated long before agreeing, reluctantly, to take Magniard.

"I could order you back, you know," he reminded the slender hothead.

"Certainly I know it," laughed Magniard. "I also know you won't."

"What makes you so sure?"

"Perhaps I am like that mind reader in the music halls, Mlle. Zaza, the girl with a thousand eyes. Who knows?"

"Don't be absurd, *mon petit.*"

"Then consider this: You need at least one you can trust to carry on the operation if—well, if you should happen to be listed *tombé en combat.* You know I can lead, too, if need be and, moreover, you need me because I know what this foolhardy venture is all about."

"Then suppose you enlighten a thickheaded old man, *mon petit.*"

"To the devil with that old and young business, *mon colonel*! Of course I know we are to drop first in a small group, so that if the Viets are watching they will think it is a raid, nothing more, and will surround our little band, intent on killing us all, which they could do, of course, in time. Then, while all their attention is on us, the other drops will come raining down out of the sky to secure a position from which the *salaupards* can never oust them. Eh, then! Do I not have reason?"

For once, De Valcourt's red lips did not part in a smile.

"You have reason, my little–I mean, my friend," he said, after a pause. "But you have not stated the full case, no? For we must select our spot with special care. Major Vuillemot, who follows us, understands that our drop will not be on the exact spot where the real operation is to take place and that, regardless of where we step out into the blue, he is to strike the target area full into the black. Yet, if we have luck on our side, we will be as safe as in the bosom of God. To that end, it needs that we make certain preparations, after we board our plane."

"After?"

"To avoid useless explanations. We must have some luminous tape, adhesive tape with phosphorus paint is the right thing. A cross of such tape must be gummed down upon the front and back of each man's helmet."

"But our drop is scheduled for dawn."

"*The* drop; not ours. Though the sky above us will be gray, when we get to earth it will still be dark there. We will come down into a great patch of elephant grass, thick as the hair on a poodle's mane, where the Viets must search us out one at a time. We will drop from as low an altitude as possible, so that their outposts are certain to be on the *qui vive*. In that dark jungle, we will merely be noises and darker bodies to one another and to them. So we must have luminous crosses on our helmets, before and behind, lest we kill one another, or permit a Viet to go unharmed."

"And while they are trying to comb us out of the poodle's mane one at a time, we will be the fleas who skip and nip, skip and nip," cried the slim *sous-lieutenant* gleefully. "And, if we are nimble and keep them busy until the others come, all may yet march for us."

"On the master map that went forward to headquarters, I have called our island of elephant grass, at the edge of some rice paddies, the Place Pigalle. I have told Colonel Bauman to look us up in the Place Pigalle, assuring him he will find each of us there in the arms of a woman, or vice versa."

The two-motored transport, its propellers idling, stood at one end of the almost invisible runway, while a supply major checked equipment with a pocket electric torch as each man stepped up into the plane. He halted De Valcourt, the last to enter so that he might be the first to leave.

"I suggest a different parachute, *mon colonel,"* the Major said, peering at the number scrawled in indelible ink upon a linen tab. "That is one of our oldest. If we did not need every stitch of equipment we can lay hands on, it would have been condemned long ago."

"C'est la guerre!" De Valcourt shrugged lightly. "Someone must use this parachute today. Why should I be favored over another? *Au 'voir.* Once I knew a very young man, very briefly, though it was through a period that was to change my life. He was fond of quotations. Were he here in my place, he would declaim from Shakespeare something like this:

" 'And if we meet again, why we shall smile; if not, this parting was well made.'

"I say the same."

De Valcourt waved his hand and stepped aboard the transport.

The pitch of the idling motors became a full-throated roar that seemed to fill the black bowl of the sky. Blue flames leaped back along the metal wing surfaces from the cowlings, and the propellers began to scream. The plane lumbered forward, then tore off into the night, heading toward the invisible western horizon.

All but the brightest stars had faded from the crisp, graying sky when it reached its designated area. In the rice paddies, separated by hedgerows, the grayness was reflected; beyond them, the jungle was still shrouded in the black of night. De Valcourt walked the length of the cabin, motioning the men to rise from their bucket seats and make the final adjustments of harness and gear. Returning, he clapped each member of his party on the shoulder, until he reached the door, already opened. He motioned to the pilot to make another traverse over the far-flung patch of elephant grass before rising a bit for the jump. Then he called back into the fuselage, before stepping out into the void: "*Au revoir, mes enfants! Place Pigalle!*"

He counted to ten, pulled his rip cord, clenched his fists and pressed them tightly against his chest pack, bracing himself against the shock with which his free fall would be halted, his head bent forward, his feet outthrust and close together. The harness clawed at his shoulders and thighs and, for an instant, he was suspended without motion. Then the slow drift toward the dark jungle began. Above him the gray sky was brightening—and brightness also showed through a slit that had opened beside a dark square of patchwork in the nylon canopy from which he hung suspended. The line of cleavage lengthened as he looked up at it in startled fascination; its edges pulled apart and more and more air rushed through it. In a single run, the rip spread to the parachute's rim and blew open, the ragged sides of the tear fluttering like lace along the edge of a woman's dress.

"*La guerre en dentelles,*" De Valcourt murmured. And crashed to the unyielding ground.

Antoine Magniard and four other survivors of the first jump team brought him in that afternoon, when a detail assigned to pick up discarded parachutes found him still fast in his harness. A grave had already been dug at the foot of a great boulder. His comrades wrapped the broken body into the patched parachute for a shroud. While they covered it silently with the rich dark jungle loam, parachutes of the day's last drop were floating safely groundward.

IV

LADY LAURA

IT HAD BEEN an extremely successful luncheon.

Naturally, Lady Laura preferred giving dinners. A more relaxed atmosphere always prevailed in the evening—at luncheons, there were apt to be surreptitious glances toward wrist watches and murmurs about impending appointments, right in the midst of some intriguing discussion, or even before everyone had finished coffee and liqueurs. This was very upsetting to a hostess who liked to impart an air of accomplished leisure to her entertaining. Besides, it went without saying that dinners were more elegant. Even in these days, when men persisted in claiming that black ties were appropriate for all but the most formal functions and many women wore short evening frocks, a group of carefully selected guests presented a more distinguished appearance at eight than at one. Candlelight helped, too. It gave a gleam to old silver and old mahogany; it softened old portraits in a way which harsh daylight could never do. Of course the silver and the mahogany and the portraits were great assets at any time; Lady Laura never ceased to regard, with gratification, the results of her patient search through antique shops for the treasures she had sold, many of which she had been able to retrieve, thanks to the lack of appreciation—or the lack of funds—on the part of the purchasing public. But some of them still showed the effects of their exile and neglect, despite careful restoration, and candlelight was very kind to them. Incidentally, it was also kind to Lady Laura herself. She went to the best dressmakers again now; she took beauty treatments at the soothing and skillful hands of experts twice a week; her skin and her hair and her figure were all remarkable for a woman of her age. But by daylight she knew she looked at least thirty-five, whereas by candlelight she might have passed among strangers for twenty-five; and there was no getting away from the fact that actually she was forty-five and that she was not ready to admit it. With Althea safely on the other side of the Atlantic, it was easy not to, in some cases; on the other hand, the nucleus of her present circle was naturally made up of early acquaintances, and these had inconveniently long memories for dates.

It was because of a recent and welcome addition to this circle that the party today had been a luncheon and not a dinner. Don Augustín de Piedras Negras, the suave Spanish marqués who always spent the greater part of the Season in London, was so bespoken socially that it was almost impossible to find him free, even for tea. Dinner was quite out of the question and it was a great triumph to have secured him for luncheon. But after all, everything had worked out very well, for the weather was so atrocious that candlelight was appropriate, even at midday, to relieve the gloom, and open fires had been welcome to remove the chill. All the guests had arrived warmly clad and had been amazed to find fires lighted, in July, and Lady Laura had laughingly quoted Althea's father-in-law Abner Thorpe.

"You know it was cold and rainy like this at the time of the wedding," she said, "and Mr. Thorpe went around saying he didn't propose to freeze just because the English heated by season instead of by temperature —provided they heated at all. Of course, he couldn't get *central* heating, whatever he said or did. But he wouldn't dine or lunch out unless his hostess would promise beforehand to have an open fire, if she had a grate in working order; and he made the hotel management install electric heaters everywhere in his suite, even the bathroom, though there was quite a scene about that. However, Mr. Thorpe won the day. He said he'd broken the ice in his water pitcher many a time when he was a boy, but that he'd never pretended to enjoy it and that his days for doing it ended when he made his first hundred; now that he had plenty, he didn't propose to go back to shivering while he stripped and washed. He'd been brought up to believe that cleanliness was next to godliness and a man wasn't likely to get clean or feel godly, either, when his teeth were chattering and he was covered with goose flesh."

"Really? He is a peculiar man, now, isn't he?" inquired Lady Violet, whose daughter Rose had never succeeded in capturing Hilary Thorpe's attention, though she and Althea had enjoyed much the same opportunities for doing so.

"He does have a rather original way of expressing himself," Lady Laura agreed. "But *such* a dry sense of humor! He enlivens every gathering. I found him delightful."

There was a vague but pleasant murmur of assent, followed by a momentary pause. Everyone at the table, including Don Augustín, whom no one could rival in his talent for picking up stray bits of information, was well aware that Lady Laura must indeed have found Hilary Thorpe's father delightful; for it was immediately after Abner Thorpe's visit to London that her fallen fortunes had begun their upward trend, and it was inevitable that some connection between the two should be suspected. The tenants of her ground-floor and first-floor flats had been informed that their leases would not be renewed, and Lady Laura was now reoccupying them in greater style than ever before, for they had been made into a maisonette; a general renovation of the premises had taken place, so skillfully as to retain their essential character, yet so thoroughly as to remove all signs of wear and tear. The tenants on the second and third floors were still in residence, but it was understood that when these leases expired, the occupants would have to leave, because Mr. and Mrs. Hilary Thorpe and Mr. Abner Thorpe would require just such space when they visited London in the future. The lower ground floor, where Lady Laura and Althea had lived prior to the Thorpe era, was now empty; but that was being renovated for occupancy by Lady Laura's cousin Julia, who was in reduced circumstances and to whom Lady Laura let it be known she was greatly indebted, though she did not say for what. She did, however, say that of course dear Cousin Julia would not pay rent; Lady Laura was only too glad to provide her with a suitable home and the lower ground floor was really *most* suitable.

The gossips were partly right and partly wrong in their surmises about Lady Laura's mended fortunes; they had guessed right as to the source of them, but wrong as to the reasons and to the charitable extent. Abner Thorpe had not fallen a victim to Lady Laura's charms and sought to make reparation by extreme generosity. It would have been contrary to his principles to feel that a respectable man could compensate, with money, for straying from the straight and narrow path; and such straying would have been rare, even under extreme provocation. As a matter of fact, in this instance there had been no provocation; he was not at all attracted by Lady Laura, much less attracted irresistibly. In talking confidentially with his son, he had unhesitatingly described her as a shallow woman.

"Just the same," he had told Hilary, "she's Althea's mother, and Althea's as fine a girl as I'd expect to find in a month of Sundays. It isn't fitting that her mother should be living down cellar like that. We've got to study on how to get her out of that cellar."

"They don't call it a cellar over here, Father. They call it the lower ground floor."

"I know what they call it. And they call gasoline petrol and the hood of a car the bonnet and the trunk the boot. But I aim to go on calling them just what I've always called them, same as I'm going right on calling a spade a spade. Now I'm not in straitened circumstances any more, as you know. In fact, you might go as far as to say I'm in fairly comfortable circumstances. Not that I'm a wealthy man; the Democrats have been in power too long for that. But I've been careful. I can spare something if I go on being careful and I guess I shall–it isn't easy to change habits of a lifetime at my age. So as long as I've got the money laid by, I'd just as lieve as not that part of what I can spare was used to get Althea's mother out of that cellar."

Abner Thorpe's "studying" had taken the highly practical form of consultation with a prominent Boston lawyer who, almost inevitably, suggested the establishment of a trust fund, from which Lady Laura should derive the income for life, but from which the proceeds should eventually go to Althea's children. There was also the stipulation that the house in Belgrave Square should forthwith be deeded to Althea, and that she should control the property, though her mother would continue to live there. Far from planning to evict the tenants on the second and third floors, Althea, acting on the sound advice of her father-in-law's attorney, was planning to raise their rent sufficiently to compensate more than liberally for the loss of revenue from the lower floors; and there had been a further stipulation that any heirlooms or other valuables purchased with money from the trust fund should, in due course, revert to Althea. These canny provisions, which converted an act of apparent prodigality into a sound investment, were naturally not broadcast in London society; and Lady Laura herself did nothing to dispel the legend that a hard-bitten old Yankee had succumbed to her spell.

During the pause that had followed her pronouncement that Abner Thorpe was delightful, Lady Laura signaled to General Sir Arnold Marwood, who was acting as her host, that they would now proceed to the drawing room for coffee, and turned to Don Augustín with her most winning smile.

"I'm afraid the soufflé brought our simple little luncheon to an end," she said with a slight deprecatory shrug of her pretty shoulders. "I was disappointed in my Stilton—or possibly it was the port we put in it. As for the pineapple and the peaches, I never should have dared offer those to a Spaniard—it is simply incredible what the fruiterers expect one to put up with these days! I do hope you will forgive such a meager meal!"

"Lady Laura, it was superb! To eat anything after

that dream of a soufflé would have been a crime, as you well know. But do tell me–is it possible that your chef is an Englishman?"

"No, of course not. He is an Italian. I should have preferred a Spaniard–but you Spaniards are so selfish! You keep all your best products in your own country. Take sherry, for instance–it never tastes the same outside of Spain! And as for *gazpacho* and *paella*–one does not get so much as a glimpse of them in this country."

"If you really want Spanish wines and Spanish dishes and a Spanish cook in Belgrave Square, I shall be delighted to see what I can do for you. But I have a much better suggestion to make."

"Yes? What is it?"

"That you should come to Spain and enjoy our products there–in the course of an indefinite sojourn."

"What a tempting suggestion! If only I dared to take it as an invitation!"

She was moving toward the drawing room, her hand resting lightly on Don Augustín's arm. Lady Violet, outdistancing the M.P. who was her own escort, had caught up with her hostess and gave a little cry of surprise as they came, in the passageway, to the glowing portrait of a woman with flat ringlets, tapering fingers and a beautiful bosom.

"My dear! Don't tell me you've got the Lely back!"

"Yes, just this last week, by the greatest good fortune. You'd never guess where I found it! But there, I'll tell you while we're having coffee." She swept ahead, her hand still on Don Augustín's arm. "Of course, what I really want is the Zurbarán," she murmured. "Shall we talk about that some other time?"

"By all means," he answered, smiling. "But the sooner, the better."

V

HILARY AND ALTHEA

FROM THE VERY beginning, Althea loved Vermont. Hilary had teased her a little, asking if she were sure it wasn't just that she loved him, and that therefore she was willing to make the best of things, wherever he took her. And she had denied this indignantly—not that she loved him, of course, but that this love had anything—or at least much—to do with the way she felt about his native state.

She had seen it first when it was at its most beautiful—when one still, sunny day succeeded another and the hillsides were aflame with scarlet and gold. Even when the early mornings and late evenings grew crisp and cool and the scarlet leaves fell to the frosty ground, she said that it was more beautiful than ever; for then there was mist at daybreak and nightfall, and where the yellow leaves, which still clung to the trees, shone through this mist, the world seemed a magic realm of gold and silver, such as she had never envisioned before. She said that she could not have imagined that the world could be such a wonderful place. She said the same when the harvest moon came up, huge and copper colored, over the New Hampshire mountains which were snow sprinkled beyond the Connecticut River, dividing the Twin States, where the water ran bright between fertile meadows that were still verdant with a deep autumnal green. But when Hilary drew her outdoors, late one starlit night, without telling her beforehand what he wanted to show her, and, for the first time, she saw the heavens transfigured with northern lights, she said nothing at all. She stood gazing speechlessly at the flamboyant tracery of flames ascending from behind the hills and meeting to form a fiery diadem; and when she turned to look at her husband and reach for his hand, her eyes were full of tears.

"I've thought sometimes there might be something like that in heaven," she said. "I mean, that you might find it there after—well, after you had died. I didn't know you could see it right here on earth, with all the rest."

Eventually, the crystalline atmosphere engulfed the silvery mists and the weather grew colder and colder. The golden leaves fell in the wake of the scarlet ones, and the rustling carpets they formed on the chilly ground were either quickly swirled away by the wind or patiently raked into neat piles which, in due time, became bonfires that sent a fragrant blue smoke curling signal-like upward to mark the places where they were tended with such care. The trees were stark and the fields dun colored, and Hilary was afraid that Althea might soon find the dormant countryside depressing. But an early snowfall mantled not only the distant mountains and the near-by landscape, but covered the bare branches and clung to them so closely that their brilliant coating seemed part of every limb and twig. Back of Abner Thorpe's house, which stood on a slight rise of ground, the lawns sloped down toward the meadows and made an ideal slide. Hilary got the Flexible Flyer—which had been the pride of his boyhood—out of the old carriage house where it had long been stored, and initiated Althea into the thrill of coasting. He also resurrected an ancient sleigh, took it in a truck "out back" where the snowplows still did not penetrate and, hitching up one of the few available horses in the neighborhood, explored with her the almost disused woodland roads. When they returned to the house, it was with glowing cheeks and ravenous appetites.

"It's a satisfaction for me to see you eat," Abner observed approvingly, as Althea held out her plate for a second helping of homemade sausage and pancakes. "Anything I despise is one of those folks that goes visiting and moves vittles around on a plate, without ever tasting anything, as if they were trying hard to find something to please them and not succeeding. Help yourself to a little more of that cucumber pickle, too, Althea. It's Bertha's best. And while you're about it, help yourself to another biscuit. No point in letting them set there, just cooling off."

Abner had "taken a liking" to Althea the first time he saw her. He had received the news of his son's engagement to an English girl with tempered enthusiasm, and it had been difficult to persuade him to go to London for the wedding. But, as he did not hesitate to tell Hilary, Althea had given him a pleasant surprise; in fact, if he had been picking out a daughter-in-law himself, he doubted if he could have done much better. It was he who suggested that, since Hilary had accumulated leave coming to him, he and his bride should have them a nice trip before they settled down; so they had spent a rapturous month in Italy. Shortly after their return to London, Hilary had been recalled to Washington for consultation at the State Department and their stay had been of months' instead of weeks' duration, as they had expected; but now they were at his father's home, while Hilary awaited reassignment. Every day when the mail came in, he expected to receive the fateful tidings which would send him and Althea to some remote region; every day they breathed a sigh of relief when the letter did not come.

One of Abner's main causes for concern beforehand had sprung from his doubt as to whether Althea would get on with Bertha Randall, the "widow woman" who had ministered to his household needs for many years. Bertha's deceased husband had left her with numerous progeny, now all full grown, and at need Beulah or Eben or Jessie came in to help her out, and at all times Harvey did the heavy chores. But Bertha reigned supreme and neither Abner nor her children disputed her authority. Bertha herself had been quite prepared to give notice, if Hilary's wife tried to force foreign ways down her throat. But it did not occur to Althea that anyone expected her to set foot in the kitchen or to run the vacuum cleaner and the washing machine; and she accepted the lack of formality in table service as a logical part of the pleasing Vermont picture. Her one source of solicitude lay in the fact that Lalisse and Celestino were both still in the Devonshire Mews, patiently awaiting instructions as to where they were to go next. This did not trouble Hilary; he was accustomed, by this time, to telling his staff what to do and when, and it did not seem to him important how long they had to wait to find all that out. But it troubled Althea increasingly; and one day when Hilary had gone to the talc mine to see the manager about some minor emergency which had arisen, and she was alone with Abner, she spoke to her father-in-law about it, encouraged by the fact he had told her Bertha had taken a liking to her, too.

"I'm ever so glad, Father." (She had called Abner Father, quite naturally, from the outset, and that was another thing which pleased him.) "But I can't help wondering . . . isn't she quite an elderly woman? Why, some of her grandchildren are almost grown up! And I wouldn't like to think it was making things too hard for her, having Hilary and me here so long."

"Well," Abner admitted, "she does get tuckered out faster than she did once. And of course this idea of having tea and supper both–seperate meals–is new to her. There used to be just one or the other, and we called it whichever we had a mind to and had it anywhere from five o'clock on. Not that Bertha's breathed a word about minding the work. She's so thankful you don't tell her about some rule of your own for making gold and silver cake, or something of the sort, she isn't liable to."

"But, Father, I never heard of a gold and silver cake until I came to Vermont, any more than I heard about golden leaves and silver mists! And I haven't got any rules for anything."

"Maybe you call them receipts or recipes or something of the kind where you come from. It don't matter. What I was aiming to tell you was, Bertha likes to do things her own way and anyone who tries to tell her to do different gets her dander up. And she's still spry. But you're right, Althea. She's getting on in years. And Beulah and Jessie have got their own families to look after, and it's natural they shouldn't want to be at their mother's beck and call all the time, whether she realizes it or not. And Harvey needs more help from Eben than he gets when Beulah's forever sending him to the store for some trifling thing she forgot the last time; when you get right down to it, two hired men aren't any too many around a place of this size anyway. I don't want you should worry though, Althea. Bertha can rest up after you and Hilary's gone to Tibet or Patagonia or whatever godforsaken place the State Department sees fit to send him to next. If you were going to be here any length of time–"

"But Hilary says we may be here quite a length of time! He has a friend who's been sitting around on some western ranch for seven weeks now and hasn't heard a word about reassignment. On the other hand, he has a friend who left Haiti on a few days' notice, though his wife had a brand-new baby, and started for Helsinki. They were barely settled there, and recovering from pneumonia after the change, when he was ordered to Cuba."

Abner snorted. "Don't talk to me about the State Department and its way of doing things," he said. "I wouldn't have any hired help left, at the mine or the nursery or on this place, either, if I treated them the way the State Department treats its hired help. But then mine are mostly Vermonters; they know how to stand up for their rights . . . . Well, as we were saying, if you were going to be here any length of time–and by that, I meant more or less for good–maybe you and Hilary wouldn't be content to stay here with me. Maybe you'd want a home of your own."

"Why, Father, I thought this was our home! Isn't it?"

Abner cleared his throat. "As far as I'm concerned, it can be," he said. "It's big enough to allow for large families–six rooms to a floor in the main part and two to a floor in the ell, besides the attic and the part that isn't finished off over the woodshed. It's a good substantial house, too, built when they were meant to last. And antique dealers come pestering me all the time, trying to strip it bare of everything that's in it. I'm not a wealthy man, don't make any mistake about that, Althea; but I'm not in straitened circumstances, either. I don't expect I'll live to see the day when I'll need to let my forebears' belongings be sold for junk."

"Of course you won't, Father. And your belongings are so beautiful! The house is just full of museum pieces."

"Well, I don't aim to have them end up in any museum, any more than I aim to have them end up in some antique shop, getting parceled off to some woman with more money than sense. And I'm glad you like them. But I know young folks enjoy being by themselves, doing things their own way—womenfolk especially. Now menfolk don't care whether there's tidies on the chairs or not, or whether a certain picture hangs over the mantelpiece or between the windows and which corner the tall clock stands in. Half the time they don't notice whether the china you're using is the wedding ring or the moss rose pattern. But womenfolk set store by those things. For all I know, you may be hankering to move around every piece of furniture there is in this house and hesitating to say so on account of Bertha."

"But I'm not! I like it all just the way it is! The only thing I thought of was—"

"Well there, I knew there must be some kind of a catch. What is it, Althea?"

"I thought that, perhaps, instead of waiting in London to find out where we were going next, Celestino and Lalisse might come here. They'd expect Bertha to order them around—of course, they'd expect you and Hilary and me to order them around, too; but we could be careful not to give contrary orders. Lalisse could save Bertha ever so many steps and Celestino could do the errands, so that Eben wouldn't keep being interrupted when he ought to be helping Harvey around the place. It's just an idea. I haven't even mentioned it to Hilary yet. So, if you don't like it—"

"Why, I don't know," Abner said pensively. "I don't know—I don't know but what I do. That French girl of Hilary's—well, she sure is smart as a steel trap and she's not ill favored, either. Do you happen to know whether she's a widow woman?"

"No, I'm quite sure she isn't."

"I only asked because it wouldn't be handy, once we got her over here, to have a husband turning up from nowhere and wanting to take her away. And if she's a maiden lady, I suppose that, sooner or later, some of my hired help will want to be keeping company with her."

Wisely, Althea made no direct challenge to this supposition. After all, her father-in-law did not seem to expect one. "Perhaps someday, Lalisse and Celestino—" she hazarded.

"Now that would be a solution wouldn't it? Why don't you put the whole thing up to Bertha—that is, if Hilary's agreeable."

So that night, after they were by themselves, Althea "put it up" to Hilary and found that he was, indeed, "agreeable." And the next morning she made one of her rare excursions into the kitchen, where she found Bertha, who was already surrounded by pies, in the act of popping two more into the oven.

"Why, Bertha!" she exclaimed in surprise. "Are we going to have company?"

"I presume so. Most generally we do, for Thanksgiving."

Althea had been told about Thanksgiving in principle, but this was the first time she had seen concrete evidence of how it was actually interpreted, in the way of preparation.

"How much company?"

"I suppose that would depend partly on what you want this year. You and Hilary've been asked out quite a lot. I thought maybe you'd be wanting to pay back some of your obligations, even where he wasn't related. Besides, we've always done like most other families around here does; we've invited in some that didn't have any other place to go: the minister, if he was unmarried; the schoolteachers that live too far away to get home; one or two whose families have moved away and are all alone; and, of course, some woman who's seen better days, but doesn't have a good provider any more."

Bertha briskly rolled out more dough, placed it carefully on top of a waiting pie dish, already filled with some luscious-looking substance and, after pressing it down around the edges, trimmed them carefully with a floury knife. Althea sat watching her with fascination, meanwhile carefully considering what she had said. It was true that the bridal couple had been most hospitably received. This hospitality had, for the most part, taken the form of excellent home-cooked suppers, with or without bridge afterward; Althea had been amazed at the number of astonishingly good cardplayers, available to get up a game at almost any time. She and Hilary had also been invited to some of the famous resort hotels in the near-by mountains, many of which now remained open the entire year. She had been asked to address the Women's Club and, though appalled at the prospect, had found the experience less trying than she expected; and she had not shared the general embarrassment when she had been urged to join the local chapter of the Daughters of the American Revolution before someone had tardily remembered that, as a Britisher, she was, to say the least, ineligible! It had then been agreed that she could go to meetings anyway, as a guest, and rather coyly suggested that her daughters *would* be eligible, through Hilary, since his great-great-grandfather had been outstanding among Ethan Allen's celebrated Green Mountain boys. Hilary had addressed the Rotary and Kiwanis clubs, quite impartially, and had consented, time permitting, to go to affiliated clubs in the larger centers; but the greatest number of their joint social activities seemed to stem from their association with the Congregational church. Althea had undergone one of her few moments of instinctive recoil when she discovered that not only Abner and Hilary, but most of their relatives and friends, were "nonconformists," but these pangs, like other brief periods of maladjustment, had been of short duration. The church building, with its sturdy steeple and snowy white portico, exemplified a type of New England architecture as charming as it was chaste—an architecture wholly in keeping with the spacious four-square houses; some white clapboarded, some made of locally quarried stone or locally kilned brick. The services were conducted with dignity and distinction; the correlative activities in the vestry—church suppers, meetings of the Ladies' Aid and so on—brought different groups together in a way that was as genial as it was beneficent; and no one seemed to think it was in the least illogical that these same groups should go to movies and square dances together. It had entered Althea's mind that she and Hilary should, indeed, be returning some of the courtesies so wholeheartedly offered, not because she felt especially "obligated," but because she wanted to reward friendliness with friendliness. However, she had been so completely contented without company that she had not put the idea into movement until Bertha suggested it.

"Why, I'd like to have a party on Thanksgiving," she agreed readily. "How many people do you think I ought to ask?"

"I've seen the day when there wasn't never less than thirty sitting down to table," Bertha replied, removing the pies which were already brown from the oven, and putting in some which she had just carefully pricked in the center with a fork. "These last few years it's seldom ever been more than twenty. And the ovens they make nowadays!" Bertha cast a withering glance in the direction of the gleaming electric range which supplemented, though it had never been allowed to supplant, the huge coal-burning cast-iron stove. "Why, those ovens wouldn't hardly take care of a medium-sized turkey—I mean to say, one over twenty pounds. I'm thankful to say I've never been dependent on 'em. But no one eats pie, the way they used to."

"But you've got dozens of pies!"

"I've got apple and mince and squash and pumpkin," Bertha admitted. "That ain't bad for a start. But I ain't even begun the cranberry or the lemon meringue or the coconut-custard or the ginger rhubarb. I'll get to those this afternoon, unless you want something extra for supper. All I got lined up now is venison steak and creamed potatoes and buttered beets and coleslaw and floating island and currant jelly tarts. But I don't need to do anything about the chicken pie until tomorrow."

"The *chicken* pie!"

"Yes, for breakfast. You don't mean to tell me you don't have chicken pie for breakfast on Thanksgiving Day in England?"

"Why, Bertha, we don't even have Thanksgiving!" Althea exclaimed.

When Hilary came in for noon dinner, Althea was still in the kitchen and the fate of Celestino and Lalisse had been amicably settled. Indeed, the only aspect of the case which had caused discussion was the probable brevity of their stay. Bertha thought it was a sin and a shame that when they were coming to Vermont anyhow, they shouldn't still be there for sugaring off and corn roasts at least, and that would mean not only staying through March, but through August.

"I didn't know there was so much wonderful food in the world," Althea told Hilary as they left Bertha to her preparations for what she called a plain meal and went off to find Abner.

"It's just a small part of that wonderful world you didn't know about until you saw the silver mists and the golden trees," he answered laughingly.

"I know . . . . Do we really have to leave it, Hilary?"

He put his hand lightly under her elbow and steered her, not in the direction of the sitting room, but in the direction of the library. After they had entered it, he carefully closed the door.

"Would you honestly like to stay here?" he asked.

"Would I–oh, Hilary, can we?"

"Of course we can. I can resign from the State Department almost at the drop of a hat. They're getting rid of men so fast down there in Washington that there's no telling where the ax will fall next–in fact, I shouldn't be at all surprised if it fell on me. Of course, they all know I wasn't in any way to blame for poor Castle's death, or even connected with it; but all the same, the fact that he was at my house the night it happened is just as good a pretext as any when they're reducing numbers. I could do unto the other fellow as he would like to do unto me and do it first and nothing would please me better than to stay here. Besides, I know I'm needed—at the nursery and the mine both. Not that my old man's losing his grip. But the business has grown so . . . . He wouldn't say a word to hold me, of course. And I never supposed that after growing up in London, and with the chance that I wouldn't be sent to Patagonia or Tibet, as Dad's always suggesting, but to Rome or Quebec or some other charming place, you'd really want. . . . I still thought it was just because you were in love with me and . . . . However. . . ."

The last few halting words of his speech fell on the empty air of the library. Althea had already darted into the sitting room and, rushing across the floor to Abner's rocker, had flung her arms around his neck.

"Father," she cried, "we *are* going to stay here quite a length of time. I mean for good! I'm so happy about it I can hardly breathe. Aren't you glad, too?"

Abner did not attempt to disengage himself from her embrace, but neither did he immediately return it. For a minute or two, he sat very still. Then he raised one hand and began to stroke Althea's hair, looking lovingly down at her. When Hilary entered the room, Abner glanced up at his son and cleared his throat.

"Why, yes," he said. "I'd just as lieve you did as not."

VI

AHANI

THE ARISTANIAN AMBASSADOR to the United States of America was giving a reception in honor of the Sultan's birthday.

It followed the usual pattern of such functions, frequent in the nation's capital. A long succession of limousines, bearing the number plates of privileged American officials and members of the Diplomatic Corps, came rolling slowly up to the porte-cochere of the Embassy, where a tall-hatted doorman tore numbered tickets into halves before the chauffeurs were assigned to parking places by the police. When the guests went inside, the sexes were briefly separated, while a maid relieved the ladies of their ermine or mink coats in the dressing room at the right, and a manservant relieved the gentlemen of their Chesterfields and Homburgs and white silk mufflers in the dressing room at the left. Then husbands and wives, fathers and daughters, and various other persons whose relationship was not quite so close, rejoined each other and went up the vast red-carpeted stairway, glowing against the dazzling whiteness of its surrounding marble, to the entrance of a great apartment where a liveried functionary stood waiting to announce them.

"The Secretary of State and Mrs. Deckers! The Ambassador of Great Britian and Lady Fairchild! Senator and Mrs. Whiting! The Chargé d'Affaires of Sweden and Madame Lindstrom! Admiral and Mrs. Needham! The Chief Justice and Mrs. Holloway! General and Mrs. Daingerfield!"

On and on went the roster of dignitaries. Immediately inside the entrance to the great ballroom, the Aristanian Ambassador and Madame Ahani were waiting to receive them. When Ahani had been promoted to Washington, he had insisted that his wife should abandon the conservative customs imposed upon her by her mother, who was no longer in evidence. Zeina was now always to be seen with him. And none of the women whose ermine and mink had been shed to reveal satin and velvet, diamonds and emeralds, could compare with her in opulence and costliness of attire and adornment. Her dress, designed on purpose for her by Balenciaga, had been flown over from Paris expressly for this occasion; jewels encircled her neck and wrists and sparkled on her bosom and in her ears. Correspondingly, no other ambassador was wearing as many orders and decorations as Ahani. He, too, was resplendent.

Though the greetings given the guests were appropriately cordial, they were necessarily brief; there was barely time to extend and acknowledge congratulations on the Sultan's birthday from one dignitary before another was crowding on his heels; so the first, perforce, pressed forward, to greet still other dignitaries who already formed part of the throng that overflowed both the ballroom and the great reception room into the state dining room beyond. Here, under a series of crystal chandeliers, a mammoth buffet was spread. At one end, double magnums of champagne were being opened, in swift succession, by two butlers, while two others mixed cocktails and two more served highballs. Beyond the lavish bar, the smoked turkeys and clove-spiked hams went almost unnoticed amid the platters of salmon, the bowls of caviar, the galantines of pheasant. The ices were placed apart, molded into fantastic shapes and mysteriously lighted by multicolored bulbs. The accompanying cakes had been frosted with designs representing the crossed flags of the United States and Aristan or erected to look like miniature buildings—the White House, the royal palace at Kirfahan. As fast as one was demolished, another took its place.

"Ahani's certainly living high, wide and handsome these days," Senator Whiting observed in an undertone to the Chief Justice. There was really not much reason why he should lower his voice; the hubbub was now so great that most of the guests were screaming in the attempt to make each other hear at all.

The Chief Justice shrugged his shoulders without answering. General Daingerfield, who had joined the other two just as the Senator spoke and, by some miracle, caught most of his words, answered instead.

"Why not? He's the Sultan's white-headed boy these days."

"And Needham, whom we sent to Aristan in place of poor old Castle, has really turned out to be the right man in the right place," chimed in the Undersecretary of State, joining the group and, in his turn, catching some of the latest remarks. "No interference to offend anyone, no extreme measures. We're very much pleased with him in the department . . . . Oh, how are you Edson?"

"Could I speak with you a minute, sir? I mean, privately. I'm sorry to intrude, but something urgent has come up."

The Undersecretary looked at the newcomer with unconcealed displeasure. Edson was a career man, still young, who had forged ahead fast and who had been put in charge of the Division of Middle Eastern Affairs in spite of his, the Undersecretary's, preference for another man. He had never ceased to resent the selection, and at this moment he resented it more than ever; but under the circumstances there was nothing to do but excuse himself. With Edson beside him, he threaded his way through the crowd, graciously stopping to acknowledge greetings when this seemed advisable or, at least, inevitable, despite Edson's unseemly display of haste. When they finally reached a small deserted apartment, evidently a disused breakfast room, the Undersecretary spoke coldly.

"Couldn't this urgent matter that has come up have waited a quarter of an hour or so? Perhaps you didn't recognize them, but I was talking with–"

"Yes, sir, I recognized them. But no matter with whom you were talking, I'd have thought I ought to interrupt. The news has just come over the wire: Izzet's been assassinated."

"What!"

"Yes. We've known in our division for several days that trouble was brewing. But we didn't expect it to come to a head quite so soon–that's why we didn't bother you about it before. However, the situation looks very bad–from an international standpoint and from the standpoint of our host."

"What do you mean, for our host?"

"Just that the ringleader of this revolution happens to be his brother-in-law Toufik Mikhardi. We've reason to believe that he's tried, for a long time, to get Ahani to go along with him, and that it looked for a while as if Ahani would be willing to play ball. I'm not sure he didn't try—without success. So then he decided that the Sultan was his best bet after all. The Sultan's rewarded him accordingly and Mikhardi's never forgiven him. Now the Sultan's dead and Mikhardi will have his revenge."

"Does Ahani know yet?"

"I saw his aide edging toward him just as I came to you. So perhaps he does. But, if I'm not mistaken, he'll see this show—his last—through to the end. Meanwhile, with your permission, I'll hurry back to my desk. And if you'll excuse me for saying so, sir, the sooner you could return to the department yourself—"

He bowed and walked rapidly toward the door of the breakfast room. On the threshold, he paused.

"Isn't it sad to think, sir, that if an experienced man like Castle had only been there, this probably wouldn't have happened?"

VII

JANICE AND HUGO

"THE DRIVE SHOULD be beautiful, darling. I've heard you say that autumn in New England might be more brilliant, but that autumn in Old England held more peace and more promise."

"That was when there was something promising in my life, and some peace to look forward to."

"Janice, there is still. Even the critics say you're better and better all the time. You're not quite in the Duse-Bernhardt class yet, but you will be. Isn't that promise? And isn't there peace, at least, in our life together? Was Evan all that ever really mattered to you? Evan and—his father?"

It was very seldom that Hugo's voice betrayed bitterness. This was not strange, for there was very little of it in his nature. But his voice was bitter now. Janice looked at him in sorrowful surprise.

"Of course they weren't the only ones that mattered. You've given me more–much, much more–than either of them ever did or ever could."

"I'm not talking about what I've given you or, at any rate, tried to give you. I'm talking about what it's meant to you."

"It's meant everything. Well, almost everything. Not quite. I know you don't want me to lie to you, Hugo. I know you want the truth. The truth is you've meant everything to me that any man could after–after what happened when I was very young. More than I dared expect or even hope for. More, much more than I deserved. Yes, there is peace in our life together–I shouldn't have said what I did about that. But promise . . . . I'll go on telling the truth. I don't seem to care, any more, about being in the same class with Bernhardt and Duse, even if I could. I don't seem to care about anything. So what's the promise worth?"

"Worth keeping. You weren't ever the kind that broke promises, Janice. It's just as important to keep one you've made to yourself as one you've made to anyone else. And you promised yourself you were going to the top. You promised me, too. But let's forget about that, if you'd rather. Let's just remember the promise you made yourself. However, we mustn't keep on talking like this now. It doesn't prove anything, and if we put off starting much longer, we'll be too late for visitors' hours. Come along, darling."

He picked up the sable stole that lay on the chair beside her and wrapped it around her, managing to make a caress of the simple service. Then they left the suite and went silently down the long carpeted corridor to the lift. In a quiet way they acknowledged the operator's courteous greeting, and the salutations of the top-hatted doorman and their uniformed chauffeur. But they did not speak to each other again until their car, in its swift and even progress, took them past the locked and damaged gateway of wrought iron, surmounted by a battered coat of arms, which had once opened on the noble avenue leading to Haverford House.

"Lady Laura is coming to the play tonight," Hugo said casually. "Evidently a royal command. At all events, she's in the Princess' party. She certainly has staged a comeback, hasn't she?"

"Yes–thanks to another rich American. Perhaps now she'll stop blaming the first one she knew for all her misfortunes and damning them as a race. If she had an ounce of real feeling in her make-up, she'd never come to one of my plays again, no matter who commanded her. But I understand the Princess got very chummy with Althea after the engagement was announced. Of course, that was more on account of the generally cordial relations with the American Embassy than anything the Whitfords had to offer. But Lady Laura wouldn't ever think of that."

This time it was Janice's voice which was bitter and Hugo did not answer. The car swung into the dreary High Street of Hammersmith and on toward Chiswick. Janice spoke again, more naturally.

"Do you know who's living in Jacques's house now?" she asked. "Of course, it really wasn't ever Jacques's house at all, but somehow I still feel as if it were–the garden, even more than the house. I do hope it hasn't gone to seed again, the way it did during the war, before Jacques took it over."

"I understand that the owners are back there again and that they're very keen on gardening themselves. So probably they're keeping it up. It must have been a real grief to them, when they had to let it run down–a beautiful place like that, in the same family for generations. We could easily ask to go there, if you'd be interested. I'm sure they'd be glad to see you."

"No, I'm not interested, thank you. I'll always associate the place with Jacques."

"You don't need to. Architecturally, the house is a gem–that's the right expression, isn't it? At least, so they tell me. Someone was saying just the other day that Barbara Villiers, a torso-tosser who got to be no less than the Duchess of Cleveland, most probably lived there for a while. At least, nobody really knows whether she did or she didn't, but they say she had a son who paid what they call the tithes on it when the old gal was sick for a long spell. And she's buried in the parish church right close by the place. And anyway, the house dates from King Charles the Second. Get me! History right from the feedbox. Some stuff, eh?"

"Professor Hugo Alban is today's lecturer, boys and girls," Janice said unsmilingly, "How did you come to know all this?"

"I've been waiting for you to ask me. A writer told me. He's working on a play about the old gal, and I think his piece has got what it takes—for the public and, most of all, for you."

"For me?"

"You could lay 'em in the aisles as the Duchess."

"Thanks. I don't care about impersonating a prodigal king's favorite."

Silence fell between them again. The day had been bleak to begin with; now a drizzle of rain was falling, and the drab suburbs through which they were passing were even more dismal and depressing in their effect than usual. But after the bottleneck of Staines had been passed, the rain slackened and then ceased. Where the road began to wind through the lovely hills and dales near Bagshot, a fine mist appeared, with the sun shining through it, at first hesitantly and then more boldly. Gradually the sun prevailed, gilding the tinted trees of the forest and the fallen leaves that formed a yellow carpet beneath them, and sending beams of light into woodland roads that curved away to dim mysterious distances. As the car swung around a bend, a waterfall came suddenly into sight; the sound that it made, cascading over smooth stones, was like pleasant music; so were the glad voices of the boys and girls, clustering in little groups to shake the chestnut trees and gather the tumbling nuts into small baskets. Farther on, a still pool in which the foliage was reflected doubled not only its expanse but its glory: the red of beeches, the yellow of maples, the rich rust of wild service; under all, the royal purple of dogwood, beyond and above all, the deep green of pointed firs.

The people walking and sitting near the pool were older and quieter than the gay young nut gatherers; they were resting, not rollicking, their mood obviously one of tranquillity rather than merriment. But both moods seemed to harmonize with the day.

Alban glanced at Janice. She had always been sensitive to beauty in its every form and quick to catch a state of feeling and respond to it. But this time she said nothing and showed nothing until, as if disturbed by his scrutiny, she turned her head away from his and looked steadily out of the car window. This motionless impassivity continued as they went by the imposing grounds of Sandhurst; but as they turned off the highway from the pretty little village of Crowthorne into the steep narrow road leading to Broadmoor, he realized that she was trembling, as she always did when the monumental red brick pile, towering above its forbidding walls, loomed into sight.

"Don't," Hugo said involuntarily. "Don't, darling. It doesn't make things easier for anyone for you to suffer so."

"I know. But I do suffer and sometimes I can't help showing it. To think of all that charm—all that talent—trapped in an asylum for the criminally insane! And you were talking about promise! Did any actor ever show more promise than Evan?"

"It was reluctant promise—almost forced promise. That's different from a promise given of your own free will."

"And it was our fault that he was reluctant, that he was forced. We are the ones that ought to be paying for his crime. It was our crime, really. And we're free, we're successful and he—"

"Hush, lover, we're there. You must try not to give way like this. You don't want the medical superintendent to see that you're unstrung—or Evan—"

The car had come to a stop by the formidable main entrance and the chauffeur stepped out of the car and touched the bell by the Gothic doorway. The door was opened immediately by a uniformed attendant and the manner in which the visitors were greeted was apathetically courteous.

"Good afternoon, sir. Good afternoon, madam. Mr. Alban and Miss Lester, isn't it? Yes, you are expected. Won't you step into Dr. Goring's office? He's coming to have a word with you right away."

The medical supeintendent was already awaiting them–a small, bearded man with keen but kindly eyes –in his quarters at the end of a long light corridor. He shook hands with them quietly, and came to the point of his remarks without preamble.

"I asked to see you myself, before sending your son to you, because I wished to prepare you for a change in him." Dr. Goring paused briefly. "A change, I am sure you will agree, that is very much for the better."

Janice drew a deep breath. With her eyes fixed on the superintendent's face, she waited excitedly for him to go on.

"I am not sure whether you know that from time to time we have theatricals at Broadmoor. We have other types of entertainment, too, of course–lectures, concerts, that sort of thing. But theatricals are the most popular of all among our patients. I am sure you will understand that, under all the circumstances, I was not certain how your son would respond to a suggestion that he might take some part in these. Indeed, I was so doubtful that I hesitated for some time to suggest it. Eventually, the suggestion came from him."

Again Janice took a deep breath, and this time she glanced quickly from the superintendent to Hugo, who nodded reassuringly and smiled in response.

"He said he would be glad to do anything he could to be useful," Dr. Goring continued. "The offer could not have been made in a pleasanter way nor, as it happens, could it possibly have been more opportune. We did not seem to have as much talent available as we generally do, and there was not as much widespread enthusiasm as usual for undertaking a play. From the moment your son took charge, all that was changed. He quickly assembled a cast from what seemed very unpromising material, and rehearsals are now proceeding in a most satisfactory manner–indeed, I have never known rehearsals at Broadmoor to go so well. I must say the play–your son chose that, too–is very thrilling–very moving. The actors and actresses could hardly do otherwise than throw themselves wholeheartedly into their parts."

"What is the name of the play?" Janice asked, speaking for the first time.

"It is not a new one," said Dr. Goring, speaking rather apologetically. "But, of course, we have to consider the question of royalties. A recent hit would be far too expensive for us. However, I understand this was a great success when it was produced in New York about twenty-five years ago. It was first used as a starring vehicle for the well-known actress Maryse Verlaine, who later married a French nobleman. The name of the play is *Dusk in December.*"

It was Janice herself who suggested that they should go back to London by a different route.

"Not that the way we came wasn't lovely," she told Hugo. "But somehow Ascot always seems festive, even when the paddocks and the racecourse are empty. And then, there's Virginia Water–we might get out there and walk around a little while ourselves. There'll still be time before it gets dark."

The sun was getting close to the horizon, but it was brighter than ever as they went down the hill from Broadmoor and swung into the main road again at Crowthorne. Along a lane leading to an isolated farmhouse, the double rows of poplars had staged a paper chase of their foliage, for the leaves, with no apparent reason, had fallen white side uppermost. From the slender birch trees beside the high road, a shower of golden leaves, shaken by the wind, laid a trail which the hazels, checkered in their turn with yellow, were sweeping into the forest. In an earlier rain, the wild cherry had been robbed of its most vivid carmine and primrose tints, but enough still remained to give a rosy tinge to the woodland's edge.

"Beautiful," Janice said, slipping her hand into Hugo's, "beautiful, isn't it, lover?" It was a long time since she had called him that–so long that he could not remember when she had last done so. It had been the term of endearment most precious to him, but apparently it had not meant as much to her. She pressed his hand. "I never expected to see Evan looking so well, did you?" she asked. "Such fresh, healthful color! And he must have gained just the right amount of weight–enough to take away that hollow-faced, caved-in look he had before, and yet not enough to put an ounce of superfluous flesh on anywhere. It's wonderfully becoming."

"He does look well," Hugo agreed ungrudgingly, returning the pressure of his wife's hand.

"Well and–and happy," Janice went on excitedly. "Why, he didn't talk about anything except that play he's producing! He even joked about it–about the foundling! Said they'd *have* to use a doll this time! And there wasn't a trace of sarcasm or reproach or anything like that in his voice when he said it. Just enthusiasm and joy."

"You're right," Hugo answered, agreeing again.

"He–he might be a great actor after all. He might be let out, after a while, and go back on the stage. Mightn't he, Hugo?"

"I suppose it's possible." Hugo spoke more guardedly this time. "But don't let's begin thinking about that just yet. Let's just think that–well, that when things were looking their darkest for him, and he couldn't see any escape from his prison and the consciousness of his sin, it was the theater that gave him the lift he needed. He knows now in his own heart that he is an actor, that there isn't any question this is what he was meant to be. He isn't in an uproar any more with you and me for helping to develop a talent God Almighty gave him; he isn't imagining that he'd have done better in–in some other line." Hugo continued to choose his words carefully, but he could see that he had made no mistake so far, that Janice was reassured and comforted by what he said, and the realization gave him courage to continue. "I wouldn't be surprised if he felt freer than he ever did before in his life. He practically told you so, didn't he, when we were saying good-by? I see he still goes in for quotations. Well, that's not a bad sign, either —shows he's not trying to forget anything he's learned. Just how is it those lines go?"

"You mean, 'Stone walls do not a prison make, nor iron bars a cage'?"

"That's it. And he meant it, Janice. He looks well because he is well. He looks happy because he is happy. It's a strange thing, but it's true."

"You don't think his happiness is—just part of his mental derangement? A new twist?"

"Could be, of course. There's no use kidding ourselves. It's anybody's guess what 'new twists' there'll be in cases like this. Just the same, I don't believe so."

"Neither do I."

"Good . . . . Look, Janice, I'm afraid we can't get out at Virginia Water after all. I've been trying to figure where we were—saying to myself I didn't remember any tunnels along this road and still we seemed to be in one every time I looked ahead."

"Of course there aren't any tunnels. But the fog's coming in again, and the way it closes down, above the overhanging branches of those trees, gives the effect of a vaulted passage."

"Pretty, too, with the lights shining underneath the white mist. But I think we'd better go straight on to London, don't you?"

"Yes, I do. The fog might get worse and of course we mustn't risk being late. And after all, we can talk about the new play just as well in the car as in the woods."

"What new play?"

"Why, the one you were telling me about—the one you want me to act in—*The King's Favorite.*" She let go his hand, but only to put her arm around his neck and press her cheek against his. "The part in which I'm going to outshine Bernhardt and Duse both—don't you remember?"